Arnold Arnold has developed ~~described in this book over the p,~~ and in the United States, he be~~ industrial designer. He specialize~~ play and learning materials, exhi~~ York's Museum of Modern Art.~~ Brothers (the manufacturers of Monopoly, whose trademark he also designed), among other game and learning materials producers, writing several books, and a syndicated newspaper column about education that appeared in more than 120 papers in the United States, Canada and Britain. He became involved in systems analysis and cybernetics as a result of his interest in game and learning theory. Arnold was Director of New York's Workshop School, has served as a Fellow of Boston University and was a Leverhulme Fellow. He lives in London, is currently a consultant systems analyst, and is involved in independent research on the findings disclosed in this book.

ARNOLD ARNOLD

Winners

PALADIN
GRAFTON BOOKS
A Division of the Collins Publishing Group

LONDON GLASGOW
TORONTO SYDNEY AUCKLAND

Paladin
Grafton Books
A Division of the Collins Publishing Group
8 Grafton Street, London W1X 3LA

A Paladin Paperback Original 1989

ISBN 0-586-08760-5

Printed and bound in Great Britain by
Collins, Glasgow

Set in Baskerville

to Alison,
my only love

Contents

Acknowledgements

I wish to thank all authors whose works I have quoted. As I stress throughout this book, making value judgements and learning from my own and other people's mistakes are part of the evolutionary development of ideas, of individuals as much as of the species. I have tried very hard to discover and correct whatever errors I could find in this book and enjoyed valuable help from friendly critics who read it while it was in progress. I take full responsibility for mistakes that may have escaped their and my notice.

It remains to thank those who have helped in allowing me to complete this work. The late Grey Walter must be acknowledged for his encouragement, without which I might have abandoned this project at a critical moment. I might have perished in a German concentration camp had it not been for the foresight of my maternal grandfather, Julius Lahnstein. I am grateful to Bedales, J. H. Badley, and GeeGee Mayo, who gave me visions of possibilities reflected in this book.

I owe special thanks to Alison Pilpel who helped me through the years in every possible way as a loyal friend and in her professional editorial capacity; to Geoffrey Kolbe who also went through this MS with a fine-tooth comb; to Audrey Adams, another discerning reader; to Martin Lewis who read the sports chapter; and to Ian Paten, my editor, without whose sympathetic help this book might never have seen the light of day – all contributed valuable critiques or checked facts, for which I will always be grateful.

I owe acknowledgement for co-operation when I needed it most from Victor D'Amico, Abe Versh, Ed Kalbough, Nigel Primrose, Dina Katz, Mohammed Matador, Marco Leonardi, Howard Smith, Douglas Tanner, Bill Antonee, Peter Matthews, Beulah Ballard, Maurice Goldsmith, Richard Pickard, Peter Paul Schreiber, Leigh and Gail Middleton, Sarah Lewis, Hassan el Banna, Cedric Conterno and many others. I apologize to anyone to whom I am indebted but whom I may have overlooked.

The Leverhulme Trust supported the development of some of the ideas expressed in this book relative to learning, by means of a Fellowship granted for the year 1984.

I am also mindful of those who hoped to win and make me lose, who did all in their power to prevent the realization of this work, these visions of the future and my happiness. Their names are best forgotten.

Introduction

As a result of various experiences, intuitions and work, I have come to certain conclusions that I wish to share; perhaps the best reason for writing this book. Others will become clear to the critical reader, especially when referring to the last chapters, the conclusion and the Appendices.

It is not my intention to change the world. Some readers may feel tempted to jump to the wrong conclusion that I am an idealist. Quite the contrary; I am a realist. I like to win, like everyone else, with one difference. Everyone can win when I play games, and no one need ever be a loser. However, before expressing views and presenting facts to back them up that some people may find disturbing, I ask that the following be taken into consideration.

The ideals and principles to which societies (or individuals) subscribe are reflected in their practices. It is therefore necessary not only to listen to what they say, but also to watch what they do. It is unlikely that any ideal can ever be reached except in a limited way, because the possibilities of error increase in proportion to complexity, no matter how hard we may try to achieve perfection. To use the game analogy, it is possible to achieve a draw (i.e. perfection and an agreement to agree) in noughts and crosses every time, but in chess there are so many options that not all games between equals may end as draws. For that reason alone whatever utopia we seek may always elude us because, at best, it is a quality of mind.

What is not usually realized is that whatever ideal or principle is chosen determines the quality of life. It can be to win – the ideal of a competitive society; to draw and achieve parity and agreement between equals in error-free excellence – that of a co-operative one; one in which both exist side by side in varying proportions; or one in which opposing views stalemate one another, as is largely happening today in most countries of the world.

For example, the American ideal of perpetual competition is reached in that country, if imperfectly, in most walks of life. The consequences are inevitable, even when they are not foreseen or faced: an alliance of the State and private vested interests that wins in competition against the individual who loses, despite lip-service to the contrary.

In actual fact, and if we look closely at election results in the US, Britain and in most 'democratic' countries during the post-war years (with some exceptions due to large numbers of voters staying away from the polls), and even in diplomatic intercourse between nations and clashing interests, today's world seems locked into a near-perpetual stalemate. This can be observed in many temporary phenomena such as the cold war, the nuclear stalemate, the wars between Israel and the Arab states, that in Afghanistan, or that between Iran and Iraq, all winding down to an uneasy peace. Those who subscribe to the left are counterbalanced by those who subscribe to the right, while the remainder, locked into a middle that is inclined sometimes to the right, at others to the left, often provides the only means for a so-called 'tie-break'.

The reason for these political stalemates (and many intelligent voters' refusal to vote) is really quite simple. Today's elections to office in most countries are popularity contests and gambles, seldom decided on the issues. The very electoral process (i.e. competition between two or more candidates) assures this outcome and makes it easy for vested interests to put up 'their' man who is most likely to 'appeal' to the voters. A look at elected world leaders in capitalist countries confirms this. Unfortunately for the voters and everyone other than those who finance the candidates, these leaders do not represent their interests. If the public interest were at issue most would never get into office. Much the same is true in socialist countries.

Co-operation is the expressed Soviet ideal. None the less, as in the United States, the individual is subservient to the State and the State's interest is in perpetual conflict with individuals as well as with other socialist and capitalist states. In such a society it is believed that, as in animal species, the individual counts for relatively little. But the State is an artificial idea and there should be a co-operative relationship between it and the individual. In practice the bureaucracy should be the servant of the individual because the individual pays for it. But in capitalist and communist countries alike it is the other way around (see the late President Kennedy's inaugural speech quoted later). The similarities between America and the Soviet Union are therefore greater than their differences. Those differences that do exist are predominantly quantitative rather than qualitative, despite appearances. The carrot and the stick prevail in both societies to varying degrees.

Clearly a co-operative society should have different ideals and goals, and work on different principles than a competitive one, yet both the American (competitive) and the Soviet (co-operative) societies are alike, even when they clash. The trouble is that competitors tend to call co-operators 'idealists' and 'unrealistic' because their 'ideals' differ and are supposedly unattainable, just like their own (i.e. no one can win everything or for ever, as history teaches us). Co-operators tend to call competitors 'unprincipled' because, they insist, they have none. Both are idealists; both act on principles of one kind or another.

The difference between them lies in the fact that the ideals and principles of competitors are selfish, based on error, short-term profit and are ultimately self-destructive, whereas those of co-operators are supposedly guided by enlightened self-interest, long-term survival and equality of opportunity to share the world's wealth on the basis of effort, qualitatively superior performance and a striving for perfection. Neither of these sets of 'ideals' are necessarily realized by either group, although only those of the co-operators can come close to realization in the short- as much as in the long-run, depending on evolutionary change, learning and behaviour. Common sense dictates that long-term survival depends on the right kind of co-operation. Perpetual competition of the wrong sort must lead to inevitable destruction.

In practice, individuals and societies depend on a mixture of various kinds of co-operation and competition, but, as we shall see, only one kind is ideal. It is an ideal that allows maximum tolerance of differences and aims for a minimization of conflict between individuals, groups and nations. However, the world's future well-being does not depend on uniformity. Just as we benefit collectively and individually from the diversity in the world's gene pool, so can we learn from cultural differences and the different games people play for fun or profit. These suggest a variety of approaches to solving problems that beset all mankind. However, a very few principles underlie the best and worst solutions, but only the best and most appropriate ones allow us the widest tolerances in their application, as we shall see.

The ideas that I discuss have been proposed in the past, but because they were misunderstood or misrepresented they remained articles more of faith than of practical value. For example, the advice to 'do unto others as you would have them do unto you' is a very dangerous one. It is an invitation to disaster. Instead, this rule should read 'do more of the same unto others as they have done to you'. If everyone followed that advice we would do nothing but nice things for one another.

The penetration of what used to be called the 'game enigma' is shown to provide the clues to the mainsprings of human nature and to much else in terms of a redefinition of a metaphor that was used incorrectly in the past and one that anyone can understand. That understanding can open up a future that most men and women have considered practically impossible in the past (and only very young children intuit), despite the fact that the most creative individuals and societies have applied these principles to whatever extent was possible to them at different times in history. This book presents an optimistic alternative for our future. How soon and how quickly it might be realized depends on learning and on individual and collective appropriate behaviour.

1 Play The Game

A quitter never wins; a winner never quits.

They ask not how you played the game, but whether you won or lost.

Show me a good loser and I'll show you a loser.

It's not the size of the dog in the fight, but the size of the fight in the dog.

When the going gets tough the tough get going.

American aphorisms[1]

Ten Commandments of the English Public School Boy:

1. There is only one God and the captain of football is His prophet.
2. My school is the best in the world.
3. Without big muscles, strong will, and proper collars, there is no salvation.
4. I must wash much, and in accordance with tradition.
5. I must speak the truth even to a master, if he believes everything I tell him.
6. I must play games with all my heart, with all my soul, and with all my strength.
7. To work outside class-hours is indecent.
8. Enthusiasm, except for games, is in bad taste.
9. I must look up to the older fellows, and pour contempt on newcomers.
10. I must show no emotion, and not kiss my mother in public.

H. B. Grey in *The Public Schools and the Empire*, 1913[2]

People play games for all sorts of reasons. They play out of boredom; for fun and to pass the time; to be sociable; because they think it is fashionable; to escape reality; because they enjoy taking risks; to win medals, glory, money and the esteem of others; to go for the jugular, to kill and make others lose; to be 'cool' and show that losing money or anything else means nothing to them; because they do not know what they are doing; because they are addicted to game playing or gambling; because they are insecure; because they are superstitious and believe that the outcome of a game reveals the future; because they are willing victims; because they want to get even with or be one-up on fellow players; because they are masochists; because they are sadists; because it is a 'macho' thing to do; because it provides an outlet for 'bitchiness'; because they are paranoid; because they are schizoid; because they suffer from schizoid paranoia; because they are drunk, criminal or insane . . . in other words, for all the reasons that people do anything whatsoever.

Each of the reasons for playing games, or doing anything else, is a variation on one of four themes, which can be summed up as follows: people play games because they want to win by making others lose; because they enjoy being victimized and sacrificial; because it is a satisfying, co-operative social activity; or because they do not know what they are doing.

Internal and external struggles for domination and supremacy are exemplified by the games people play and how they play them, by competition between commercial, national, ideological and religious groups, the political dogma of the right, left and centre, and special interests of every kind. Historically, an obsessive preoccupation with winning is reflected in most societies. Sagas in every culture, the Old and New Testaments, the Koran and the *Ramayana*, among others, deal with battles between man and his inner self, of man against man, nature, God and among the gods themselves – a never-ending round of conflict, winning and losing. Life can therefore be viewed in the context of such a game metaphor. That is why game playing seems analogous to existence and human behaviour.

There are some people who claim that they do not like to play games for fun or profit. They cannot see the point of playing with or against others; they fear that they may reveal the strategies of the games they play in real life; they cannot stand losing; they lack a sense of humour; they do not like to compete or do not understand that every game, including so-called competitive games, can be played co-operatively. They lack insight into themselves and others and are therefore perpetually puzzled by their own and other people's behaviour. A new understanding of the game metaphor can be an eye-opener for them.

Scholars have considered competitive behaviours in every conceivable setting, but no philosopher of consequence has considered the implications of the relationship between competition and co-operation in game or any other terms. Economists from Adam Smith to Milton Friedman have concentrated on competition. To them, to writers on war, such as von Clausewitz, and to von Neumann and Morgenstern, whose ideas on game theory have been applied to economics,[3] the only acceptable form of co-operation consists of a temporary banding together of vested interests for the purpose of defeating competitors; a coalition to be dissolved as soon as convenient.

These and specialists in many other fields believe that competitiveness is embedded in our genes to a greater degree than any other innate behaviour; that co-operation only serves the purposes of more effective competition against others; and that the only mediating behaviour – altruism, seen as an act of charity – is not innate but must be taught, yet reserved for special occasions, unless you want to be a saint.

Despite the fact that most people are convinced that winning is what life is about, many feel a nagging sense of unease and suspect that there is something wrong with a point of view that suggests that we are constantly embattled. The preponderance of advice from experts of every kind deals with 'how' to succeed and win. Yet few have explored 'why' winners win and losers lose; why some games end as draws or stalemates; and what all of this means, not only in the context of the games we play, but also in real-life situations.

One of the interesting aspects of the game analogy is that it is universal. For example, it is commonly applied in biology: the concept of the survival of the fittest. Here the strongest are said to survive at the expense of the weak; 'survival' is the name of the game, and the winner takes all. Play can therefore be considered a rehearsal for survival. All species play – it is their means of learning – some even play games. But most people believe that games must be played competitively; that there is no other way to play; and that we must play *against* rather than *with* one another.

It is true that those individuals and species most fit to survive are likely to do so. In animal species, this is usually a question of relative health and strength. But for human beings this is not necessarily so: survival often transcends mere existence. We are perhaps the only species for which fitness to survive can mean many different things, depending, for example, on the creation of language or an appropriate technology. The ability to think, discover, communicate our discoveries, make tools and exercise craft and art is often more important than muscle. It could therefore be said that fitness to survive is a purely relative concept that depends on the species, the environment in which it exists and the options it can exercise.

Winning in games is often compared to survival. But winning in competitive games, whether played for fun or profit, is not a sign of 'fitness', as we shall see, except in a very limited context. The question that must then be asked is: which human characteristics are adaptive and which are not? The game metaphor seems to provide many of the answers.

It can be dangerous to stretch any analogy too far, but it is equally hazardous not to stretch it far enough. To see a game or game-like relationship solely in terms of winning and losing, as most game theorists, psychologists and game players do, is to miss the point of the game and of what it means to be human. To insist that the game analogy is inappropriate because of life's complexities, or that its general application is a simplistic form of reductionism, can only be due to a lack of understanding of the causes of complexity, of the principles of diversity and the multiplicity of options, of games, and of the fact that simple solutions are often the best.

All aspects of existence have become tinged with values borrowed directly from game playing. Every relationship within and between the sexes and species has been compared to it. Business, education and even religion are regarded as competitive enterprises. These perceptions range from 'Onward Christian soldiers, marching as to war' to 'All is fair in love and war'. The same is true of the language we use to describe various aspects of our lives. We 'win' the affection of those we love. We compete for success in every enterprise. Wittgenstein attempted to treat language as a game and, although he never succeeded, sought to find a common ground between the rules of grammar, syntax and meaning and those that obtain for games. A competitive orientation seems reflected in the games we play as much as in the lives we lead.

As David Miller, a theologian, writes:

... once the game and play metaphors begin to take hold, they change man's way of viewing not only situations and events *outside* himself; but they also affect *his own way of viewing his viewing* of those outside things. The metaphors change him. He now has a new criterion for his insatiable quest for meaning . . .[4]

The Dutch historian Johan Huizinga believed that all culture is first played in the form of a game. Anthropologists like Malinowski and Ruth Benedict had come to the same conclusion somewhat earlier, although they differed with Huizinga's belief that competition is the mainspring of human creativity.

Game playing involves value judgements. We must decide whether we want to play to win, lose, draw or achieve a stalemate and which of these outcomes has a greater or lesser value. In life we tend to substitute the word 'success' for 'winning'. That is a value judgement, although it is not necessarily the correct one (see Appendix C). Once we accept that making value judgements is essential before we can play any game or do anything successfully, then we must concede that the ability or willingness to make such judgements is one of the essentials of being human. The ability to make existential value judgements, provided we make the correct ones (to decide, for example, that winning may not be the best way to succeed and that a draw outcome is one that is actually error-free), is one criterion of intelligence – a crucial test of what it means to be human.

Obvious differences exist between games and the real world. Even the most complex games, like chess or go, are far simpler than daily life. Besides, the consequences of winning and losing in games are usually harmless, whereas real-life situations involving questions of physical or economic survival can be critical. Yet because of their relative simplicity – keeping in mind that the universe would probably come to an end before all possible chess games could be played – games would seem to be an ideal miniature model on which to try out the various strategies and tactics that apply in situations that matter.

The game metaphor has affected the prevailing outlook of individuals and whole societies in as many ways as there are games to play and ways to play them. Every game encapsulates deep meanings that are often misunderstood. Our belief systems seem to depend on perceiving life and existence as either random games of chance or as purely strategic ones, without any awareness of what turns a game into one or the other.[5] Far more than the artefacts – cards, dice, spinners, or chess pieces – or even the complexity of the game, the players' attitudes, intentions and attention determine whether the outcome is predictable or a matter of chance. These and other criteria are defined and illustrated in following chapters.

When we regard one another and nature as rivals to be defeated, we turn every enterprise, relationship or game into a gamble, including those that we believe to be purely strategic. This may be seen in every classroom and on any playing field. Competition and conflict are seen as the driving forces that stimulate success in commerce and creativity in the arts, science and technology. We seem to be engaged in a never-ending gamble that is renewed in every generation.

Karl Marx insisted that co-operation must replace competition within the State. Yet he preached perpetual competition between the system he espoused and all others. Marx and Engels were both avid readers of von Clausewitz, author of one of the best known books on war.[6] Von Clausewitz believed that war is simply an extension of diplomatic and economic competition in times of so-called peace – thus we are perpetually engaged in war at one level or another; this certainly seems to be true today. War-games played by all nations owe their origins to von Clausewitz who equated business competition with warfare. In this world view co-operation is only considered as far as it temporarily serves the cause of victory.

We hold these ideas to be true not only for ourselves, but also for all other species. They are reflected in our social beliefs, literature and the sciences. For example, Malthus declared about 200 years ago that the earth's resources were limited and that reproductive rates, were they to remain unchecked, would lead to the domination of our planet by one or a few species, and eventual standing room only for the winners. This led to the supposition that ruthless competition was the most effective brake on over-population; a belief that has infected virtually every field of human endeavour and rules our perceptions about the processes of nature.

Darwin's principle of 'natural selection' was re-interpreted by Spencer as 'the survival of the fittest' without defining what 'fitness' meant in this context, relative to differing survival needs of species in a wide variety of environments. Nature was anthropomorphized to favour winners, in keeping with the competitive prejudices of the nineteenth and twentieth centuries. But those fittest to survive in the urban jungle may not be best suited for survival on a polar ice cap. Fitness to survive is therefore a conditional, rather than an absolute, term.

Even today, Richard Dawkins, a British biologist, and Edward O. Wilson, an American zoologist who coined the term 'sociobiology', suggest seriously that our very genes predispose us to be competitors, except when we join forces and co-operate in order to compete against others or are 'taught' to be altruistic. In Dawkins's world, genes and spermatozoa appear to be competitive, 'the fittest' of the latter elbowing less competitive ones out of the way to be the first to reach and impregnate the ovum, thereby 'improving' the species. '. . . Unlike both of them [Ashley Montagu and Konrad Lorenz], I think "nature red in tooth and claw" sums up our modern understanding of natural selection admirably.'[7] Dawkins also believes that computers could already be or will become 'artificially intelligent' because to him they seem capable of competing with human beings, defeating them in chess, noughts and crosses and other competitive games.

Despite Dawkins's disavowal of Lorenz's point of view, both agree on fundamentals. Konrad Lorenz believes that human violence is the ruling, innate trigger of behaviour, and that it can only be discharged harmlessly by, for example, vigorous football games. The idea that an innate aggressive need to win requires some sort of catharsis dates back to Aristotle and has been used more recently to excuse the proliferation of violence and the celebration of conflict in the media.[8] The study of animal behaviour – ethology – has given birth to conflicting ideas about intra- and inter-species competition and how the various species acquire and defend territory. The theories of Lorenz, Tinbergen, Eibl-Eibesfeld, Storr, Ardrey and Morris are directly related to their understanding or misunderstanding of what constitutes survival, winning and losing, and the game metaphor in its widest sense.

Ruth Benedict, the American comparative anthropologist who studied different human cultures, understood the difference between zero-sum (competitive) and non-zero-sum (co-operative) gaming. She wrote the following on the subject of the relation between nature and nurture, what is biologically and genetically innate and what is culturally conditioned:

Cultural interpretations of behaviour need never deny that a physiological element is also involved ... Biology does not deny chemistry, though chemistry is inadequate to explain biological phenomena ... In every field of science it is necessary to stress the laws and sequences that most adequately explain the situations under observation and nevertheless to insist that other elements are present, though they can be shown not to have had crucial importance in the final result. To point out, therefore, that the biological bases of cultural behaviour in mankind are for the most part irrelevant is not to deny that they are present.[9]

Isaac Asimov, who writes about science as well as science fiction, shows just how deeply our understanding of games has affected modern attitudes:

Even scientific research can be viewed as a game of man against Nature, and game theory has been helpful in selecting the optimal strategy of research, assuming that Nature stacks the cards in the way that will hamper man most.[10]

The physicist Werner Heisenberg proposed, to put it simply, that uncertainty and indeterminacy rule in the universe as they do in games of chance. Einstein disagreed, believing that 'God does not play dice with the Universe'. Mathematics as a tool of science owes much to our perception and misconceptions of what chance and randomness actually mean, and of the strategies and tactics that tend to achieve success in any of the games we play.

The question of whether we live in a deterministic or probabilistic universe, whether existence is governed by relative certainties or chance, and whether any of these can be calculated mathematically, was first discussed seriously in the seventeenth century by the mathematician Blaise Pascal in his correspondence with Pierre Fermat. They used gambling games as their models and essentially established the methods of statistical analysis used today in science and every kind of enterprise. Statistics became the mechanism for the analysis and prediction of events in which chance was said to be operative. But later in this book we shall see that a new examination of how chance works in games demands a reconsideration of random processes in physics and biology as well as in the social sciences.

Operational research and the study of systems apply game theory to determine which strategies (plans) and tactics (the execution of the plans) lead to successful analyses of how systems work and how to improve them. Simulation techniques derived from game theory attempt to predict winning and losing, success and failure in peace and war, in government and business management and on stock and commodities exchanges. They are used in fields as diverse as investment and space programmes, nuclear energy production and military studies which seek to discover whether first-strike capability offers an advantage in war.

Business games are used for instruction at America's Harvard and Wharton Schools of Business and at the London School of Economics in Britain, to name but three. They have become a way of life in corporations, government departments and political election campaigns. The term 'competition' runs through the literature on economics and politics and is directly related to game playing and definitions of 'rational behaviour' as expressed by von Neumann and Morgenstern in *The Theory of Games and Economic Behaviour*.[11]

Freud overlooked the game-playing aspects of the human psyche and assumed that competitive behaviours, as epitomized by the 'Oedipus complex' (competition by the child for the affection of the parent of the opposite sex), was an innate, rather than an acquired, human characteristic. The game analogy did not in fact become part of psychiatric folklore until the publication of Eric Berne's *Games People Play*.

Berne's conception of game playing became an integral part of transactional psychiatry. He felt that the winning and losing cycle is characteristic of a psychological flaw, but never got much beyond that realization. Berne expressed the need for a reorientation – one that lies outside the game analogy – as essential to end, or at least mediate, the addiction to the internal and external conflicts from which individuals, couples, families and social groups seem to suffer in modern cultures.

For certain fortunate people there is something which transcends all classifications of behaviour, and that is awareness; something which rises above the programming of the past, and that is spontaneity; and something that is more rewarding than games, and that is intimacy . . .[12]

Although the game analogy, as conventionally interpreted, has been applied to every human endeavour, it has been found to be somehow incomplete and unsatisfactory. Winning in the conventional sense implies that nature sides with the strong against the weak; that it rewards the haves and discriminates against the have-nots – ideas that have served as justifications for some of the worst forms of exploitation. If God were on the side of the big battalions He would seem to be biased in favour of the most atrocious crimes in history – a problem that has fuelled religious debates for centuries.

Game theory – the mathematical and scientific study of game-derived principles – distinguishes between two main game families: the zero-sum (winning and losing) and the non-zero-sum (co-operative). Game theorists have never managed to define the meanings of either correctly, with one exception – Anatol Rapoport – about whom more is said later (see Chapters 2 and 9). According to Shubik, a Rand Corporation game theorist and a leading figure in game simulation and operational research:

There is no truly dominant solution of the n-person general sum game [i.e. any number can play], for which there exists a sufficient body of experiment or knowledge or observation to give a clear dominance over all concepts of solution in all instances.[13]

Braithwaite, the British moral philosopher and mathematician, stated the problem more precisely: 'Though the theory of the wholly competitive game theory is pretty conclusively explored, the theory of the general case of collaboration is almost virgin forest.'[14]

As we shall see, Braithwaite not only put his finger on the problem that lies at the core of the game enigma, but also on the flaw in the human psyche to which Berne referred without being able to name it. It is largely a semantic question – a question of meaning – and one that this book explores as far as game and real-world behaviours are concerned.

It almost seems as if those who profess the greatest interest in games and human behaviour don't really want to discover answers to the questions they pose. Most are conditioned to subscribe to erroneous beliefs and therefore cannot learn. Others appear to have a vested interest in not wanting to know and not finding out, possibly because they fear what von Neumann erroneously believed to be true: '. . . if the theory of chess were known there would be nothing left to play'.[15]

But von Neumann, brilliant as he was in other respects, was wrong about this as he was about most aspects of games and economics. He and his co-author, Morgenstern, never understood what is really involved in winning, losing, achieving a draw or a stalemate; how these various end states of games of strategy and chance come about and what they mean. None the less the game analogy is valuable because the causal, consequential and operational processes involved in winning, losing and achieving a draw or a stalemate are extremely complex in real life, and are virtually impossible to untangle unless they are examined first in the simplified context of actual games.

The intentions of individuals and groups, what they do perfectly or relatively so, how and why they err, and the behavioural characteristics of these and other conditions, can be laid bare by a true understanding of the games we play for fun and profit. The behaviour of John McEnroe on the tennis court, Bobby Fischer at Reykjavik, Richard Nixon and Ronald Reagan in the White House, Margaret Thatcher at 10 Downing Street, Colonel North before Congressional committees, of members of our own families, neighbours, friends and business acquaintances, become comprehensible and relatively predictable when considered in terms of the real-life games they play, and how and with what purpose in mind they play them.

Psychologists have described human intentions as 'invisible black box behaviours' because on the one hand they seem to have no physiological basis, and could not be modelled on the other. The workings of such behavioural mechanisms seem as mysterious to psychologists as would those of a car's engine, hidden under the bonnet, to a visitor from another planet where combustion engines had not been invented. The game analogy is useful in taking the lid off that 'black box', thus exposing the hidden and sometimes unconscious behaviours of winners, losers and of those who refuse to play, or who play for a draw. It works when the behaviours of people in real life are compared to corresponding ones in related game situations. But then it is not enough to consider only those games that are won and lost. All possible outcomes and how they are achieved must be taken into consideration. The true meaning of each different outcome, how it was achieved, and its consequences must be analysed and related to actual events and circumstances, as I have tried to do in this book. Thus a full understanding of the game metaphor can enable us to read one another's minds.

It is generally acknowledged that game theory is incomplete. There are a number of reasons for this. One is that no distinction was ever made between qualitative and quantitative success. Another is that the 'draw' is believed not to count and is dismissed. But an unprejudiced analysis shows that games are only won and lost by default and as a result of errors committed by winners and losers alike, and not, as is generally assumed, by any 'superior' strategy, tactics, performance or intellect. The subjective, qualitative and co-operative draw principle – and not winning in the relatively objective, competitive sense – turns out to be the *primum mobile* in nature (see Chapters 6 and 8). It is the only outcome that is actually or virtually error-free and superior, subject to certain conditions.

'Subjective' competition means an aggressive striving for individual or collective perfection, one of the definitions of the draw – an agreement to agree to a truly superior outcome from which everyone benefits. Brilliant and creative performances in life, in the arts, crafts, sciences, sports, games or anything else lead to a raising of standards. But relatively objective, quantitative competition – treating the rest of the world as objects, opponents and enemies to be defeated – is the cause of conflicts, wars and human misery.

Playing to win rather than for a draw lies at the root of the world's corruption. Societies east and west, north and south, do not work as well as they might because most people have been conditioned to operate on the wrong game-derived principles. They believe that winning is all that matters. The conditioning to be a winner begins in the cradle and is one of the best examples of the pernicious effect of what is known today as operant conditioning with reinforcement (i.e. carrot and stick training).

The relationship between the relatively objective (winning, losing and stalemate) and the subjective (draw) outcomes in games must first be understood before we can understand ourselves and each other. Only then can we begin to penetrate the supposedly black box of the human psyche.

This book consists of three interwoven parts. The first deals with explanations of how game-derived ideas have affected human cultures and perceptions. The second analyses exemplary games and their behavioural meanings, from the 2 × 2 game known as prisoner's dilemma to chess, from simple children's games to football, from tossing coins to roulette. The third part suggests what we can do about some of the problems that affect us most, given the world as it is.

The meaning of human intelligence and of intentional and unintentional behaviours can be demonstrated in any number of ways within the context of games of strategy and chance. When we play to win, even the simplest game of strategy becomes a matter of randomness and chance, won by what in real life is nothing less than deception, taking advantage of other people's spontaneous or induced errors, or by strategic or psychological randomization. We tend to put the result down to 'luck', 'superior performance', or intelligence, but, as this book shows, all of these are superstitious or prejudicial value judgements.

To attribute the winning of games or success in life to luck is an abrogation of responsibility. The pretence that winning anything in the conventional sense is due to superior intelligence is a result of arrogance, greed or operant conditioning. These beliefs are complementary. However, winning is merely a short-term phenomenon. In the medium term all would-be winners except the 'house' (i.e. the casino) turn into losers. In the long run winners and losers must eventually achieve a draw, an outcome most insist does not count. A minority of life's players play for a draw from the start. Others learn later, and some never learn. But those who play for a draw use their intelligence in the most rewarding manner possible, and as it is meant to be used.

2 A Brief History of Games

To hell with the Queen of Marksberry.

Pierre 'Butch' Bouchard, 1973 Canadian
ice-hockey star, on being told that
'butting' was against the Marquess of
Queensberry rules.[1]

We can only speculate about the prehistoric origins of game playing. But the conceptual evolution of games can perhaps be reconstructed on the basis of an understanding of games related to human behaviour – the game metaphor.

Early man was enslaved by superstition. For as long as he believed that the success of the hunt depended on the favour of the gods, chance did not exist in his world. However appeasement of the gods through ritual (co-operation) and sacrifice (altruism) was a tacit admission that human behaviour affected the future and that not everything was predestined. Eventually man must have concluded that chance played a role in any game that is played to be won. No matter how carefully the hunting ritual was conducted or the hunt itself organized, his prey could escape because one beater was inattentive or some unexpected event interfered with the best laid plans. This realization may have inspired games in which a random element was introduced in order to discover strategies that might reveal a means to limit chance.

Man therefore probably invented strategic games in an attempt to limit or even eliminate chance. He was no longer just a plaything of chance because some of life's contingencies could be anticipated, even if their outcomes often depended on people and events that could not always be trusted. Trust in one's fellow man and in the processes of nature therefore became an important component of planning for the hunt, of the hunt itself, the limitation of chance, the organization of human society and the evolution of predictive science and culture.

By scratching a game plan into the sand early man may have instructed himself and his fellows in rudimentary tactics. He may also have realized that the same stratagems that served him when hunting with traps and by deception were more advantageous than brute force for defending himself against animal predators. Some human beings must have begun gradually to conceptualize and recognize the patterns of nature and of human nature itself. The hunt was miniaturized and symbols – twigs or pebbles – began to stand for things, people and game, the forerunners, perhaps, of images (as in the caves at Altamira and elsewhere), ideographs, runes and written language.

Eventually, a few individuals must have awakened to the fact that game-derived patterns of behaviour could be used for aggression; to pillage and murder and enrich themselves at the expense of others. They co-operated with a few criminally inclined followers who helped them to appropriate territory and crops, and dominate and enslave their fellows, ruling over them against their wishes. They discovered that they could extort tribute, taxes and exorbitant profits and exploit their victims in a variety of ways by the same means they used to trap game. The 'game' was pre-empted by arrogant and corrupt kings, dictators, landowners, aristocrats, priests, bureaucrats, traders, industrialists and, eventually, elected officials. Some of these co-operated periodically among themselves in order to compete more effectively against everyone else.

The game analogy is symbolic of economic and political warfare conducted by the unscrupulous who victimize members of their own species and society. Some of their victims tolerate this because they hope to share in the spoils and become winners in turn; others fail to pay attention, become apathetic or collude in their own degradation. They are willing victims and perpetual losers. A few unwilling victims rebel now and then, and some even manage to dethrone rulers who abuse their powers. But more often than not those who successfully defeat such oppressors fail to protect themselves from counter-attacks (e.g. Spartacus), or become corrupt winners in turn (the French Revolution is a typical example). The arrogance of new-found power usually deludes the winners of such contests into believing that they have won because they are innately superior and more intelligent than those they have defeated, or because God is on their side. That way those who win for a while must eventually become losers.

In many cultures the idea became institutionalized that nature admits no options other than perpetual conflict, winning and losing, and that competitive winning represents all that is best in human and all other aspects of nature. Games, as a microcosm of life, appeared to reflect these values.

The history of actual games is difficult to trace because similar ones are found in different cultures in widely separated places. Some undoubtedly share a common origin and have migrated, whereas others seem to have developed spontaneously in different parts of the world. The work of Murray[2] and Culin,[3] both historians of games, permit the mapping of which games were played where and when, although in many cases their true origins are shrouded in mystery. However, the types of games found and how they are played in any one time and place reveal a great deal about prevailing value systems.

There is a considerable difference of opinion among historians about the origin of games. Culin ascribes it to divination, magic and ritual. More credibly, Groos writes that:

... primitive races ... naturally take to marking on the sand and hence figures [i.e. game or strategic diagrams] might arise. If the leader of one of the more intelligent peoples wished to instruct them concerning some part of future combat, it would be a simple method of illustrating his meaning to draw an outline on the ground and represent the position of the hostile forces by small stones or similar objects, whose movements would symbolize the manoeuvres of the forces ... This would, no doubt, be exceedingly interesting to those conducting it and might easily be repeated for the sake of the amusement afforded ...[4]

But I suggest that earliest populations must have been sparse and family groups or tribes widely spaced. There could, therefore, have been little cause for territorial competition – the only plausible reason for warfare at that time, unless you subscribe to the view that man's innately ill-willed, competitive nature makes warfare inevitable even in non-competitive situations. As stated earlier, strategic diagrams scratched into the sand were more likely to have been made in preparation for the hunt or to work out a defence against wild animals, rather than for warfare against fellow human beings.

Johan Huizinga, who took a keen interest in the game metaphor, wrote:[5]

Modern games have so nearly lost their original meaning that even with the light afforded by history it is practically impossible to trace their origin . . .

Based upon certain fundamental conceptions of the universe, they are characterized by a certain sameness, if not identity, throughout the world . . . [they] are of the highest value from the wide applications which may be made of the principles which they illustrate.

Now in myth and ritual the great instinctive forces of civilized life have their origin; law and order, commerce and profit, craft and art, poetry, wisdom and science. All are rooted in the primeval soil of play.

Like most people, Huizinga never fully understood the difference between play and antagonistic games, or what is involved in winning and losing:

Closely connected with play is the idea of winning . . . Winning means showing oneself superior in the outcome of a game. Nevertheless, the evidence of this superiority tends to confer upon the winner a semblance of superiority in general. He has won esteem, obtained honour . . .

Huizinga was correct about the origin of play, but the origin of games arises from human characteristics and behaviours that differ radically from what he suggested. His understanding of the relationship between play and games was hardly different from that of Plato who, inspired by Spartan influences, also urged players to win.

Life must be lived as play, playing certain games, making sacrifices, singing and dancing, and then a man will be able to propitiate the gods, and defend himself against his enemies, and win in the contest.[6]

The psychological aspects of actual and symbolic contests and their ultimate resolution became prototypes for myth and folklore, for helping explain what seemed sacred and mysterious, divining the future, appeasing the gods and discovering what Jung, Freud's one-time colleague, called 'archetypal truths'. For example, the natives of Madagascar used to play a variation of alquerque – a game related to noughts and crosses and nine-men's-morris – before going forth to battle, the outcome of the game always predicting that of the life and death contest. The warriors went to war with confidence and won when the end of the game foretold success. If not, they became afraid, inevitably made mistakes, and were defeated.

The variety of games people invent and play fall into a few, easily identified categories and families. This alone says something about the fundamental aspects of game playing as part of culture-free, evolutionary human behaviour. The three game categories are: games of strategy; games of chance; and games that combine both characteristics. These categories can be divided into families, each of which reveals the players' intentions, attention and methods of play.

Strategic games that have survived through the centuries can be sub-divided into games of the hunt (e.g. fox and geese, coyote and chicken), those of war and territory (noughts and crosses, chess and go), and those of systematically 'seeding' and picking up stones from holes in the ground (i.e. mancala) to see who can collect most – presumably an agricultural analogy.

Games of chance range from the Egyptian race game of senet, the seventeenth-century European royal game of goose, and modern snakes and ladders to lotteries and games that involve dice, spinners or shuffled cards. Sports, aside from their primary classification into athletics (i.e. individual performances) and team games, can be classified into similar families.

Artefacts used to play games have been discovered by archaeologists in all parts of the world. Ancient strategic games did not need anything other than shells, pebbles or seeds in addition to the game diagrams themselves, none of which survived or, if they did, provide no clue to the purposes they had served. None the less logic suggests that strategic games predated gambling ones despite the fact that the oldest finds consist of gambling paraphernalia.

The most ancient games on record were found in Egypt and Mesopotamia. Gambling was popular among the Egyptians, if dice found in a 5,000-year-old tomb are any indication. Astralagi – sheep's knuckle-bones, the precursors of dice – have been found in the Middle East dating back to about 3,600 B.C. An early version of backgammon existed there around 3,000 B.C. (modern rules were first drawn up in 1743 and modified as recently as 1925). Gaming diagrams are engraved in the steps leading to the Acropolis in Athens. Playing cards existed in China in the tenth century A.D. but did not become popular in Europe until the fourteenth century.

The 'seeding' game mancala appears to have originated in Africa. Different games spread from Egypt to Assyria, Sumer, Palestine and to Greece, Sicily, Rome, the Byzantine Empire and southern Russia. From Rome they reached Britain, all parts of Europe and Scandinavia. An eastern route of dispersion can be traced via Arab and Moorish cultures to Europe and central Africa. A third ancient path of transmission originated in the Far East.

From China, wei-ch'i (originally called 'i' according to Joseph Needham[7]), a forerunner of chess said to date back to early Taoist times well before the birth of Christ, found its way to Japan, Burma, ancient Malaya, Indonesia and India and from there to the West. In Northern India boardgames go back to about 500 B.C.; from there they spread to Kashmir, Persia and westward to Europe. This migration of games continues even today. Pachisi was brought to Britain from India only about a hundred years ago. European colonists introduced a variety of games to South America and Africa where they blended, and can be found side-by-side with indigenous ones.

Games were known in the most primitive cultures before the arrival of colonists and invaders. Australian and New Guinean aborigines, although they did not possess boardgames, played others they invented spontaneously. European explorers and traders discovered games of strategy and chance among American Indians and Eskimo similar to those played elsewhere in the world.

Gambling games and lotteries seem to have constituted an early form of taxation in many parts of the world. At certain times they were forbidden or regulated by law. Fan t'an, a popular Chinese gambling game, was invented to defray the military costs of a siege:

This game is an old establishment, and was first introduced by Chéung téung of the Great Han Dynasty. When the city was hard pressed [as a result of a siege], and provisions were beginning to fail, they [the military leaders] were anxious to increase the contributions, and to exhort people to subscribe more for the army, but were unable to do so. Hence they established a game of chance (to guess characters) by which they hoped to tempt the people to hazard their property . . . They had only opened the game for about ten days, when they had accumulated more than a thousand pieces of silver; and after a few more decades their wealth was boundless."

Lotteries were known to the Romans, and became a means for disposing of merchandise in Italy during the Middle Ages. By the sixteenth century lotteries were run in all European countries, many in lieu of taxation.

The earliest British lottery was drawn in 1569 at the west door of St Paul's Cathedral during the reign of Queen Elizabeth I. It was used to raise money for public works and the building of harbours. The next, for a prize of 'marvellous rich and beautiful armour', was held in 1586. In 1630, under licence from King Charles I, a lottery was held, the proceeds of which were to pay for a new aqueduct to bring water into London from Hertfordshire. During the reign of Charles II, lotteries were customarily drawn at London theatres and goods of all sorts, including books, were offered as prizes. Over the next few centuries gambling infected everyone, with tickets available for as little as a penny. Greed and a spreading gambling fever contributed to a soaring increase in public gullibility, instability and insane speculation among rich and poor alike, no different from the stock-market speculation of today. Life insurance and horse-racing – both gambles – originated in England in the sixteenth century.

The gambling craze was responsible for the South Sea Bubble (wild speculation in Britain and France concerning non-existent, supposedly wealth-bringing colonial plantations in the Pacific) in the early eighteenth century, as it was some years earlier for Tulipomania in Holland (speculative investment in hybrid tulips). Both these frauds eventually bankrupted virtually all investors except the few who, having made their fortune, pulled out early. Similar forms of lunacy born of greed (simply another word for the concept of winning at the expense of others) infected most other European countries in the eighteenth century. Huge amounts of money were made and lost, and property changed hands, often as a result of absurd wagers. The stock-market was born in that time, although for a while (but not for long) it provided some of the seed capital for exploiting the wave of inventions that made the industrial age possible. But dealing in stocks soon turned into a gambling game in which prices were artificially manipulated out of all proportion to the value of products, manufacturing and distribution efficiency and legitimate profit.

By the second half of the eighteenth century gambling had become a chronic affliction among Britons of all classes. Estates were lost on the turn of a card at London's famous clubs, which had evolved from the less exclusive coffee-houses. Hogarth's *The Rake's Progress* is a fair comment on the times. The wives of the gentry were equally addicted and sold their favours to recoup their losses. The lower orders were restricted to betting on public sporting events like bear-baiting and, of course, lotteries, run by and on behalf of the government. The gambling fever had reached such a pitch that reformers claimed: '. . . it is a scandal to the government thus to excite people to practice the vice of gaming, for the purpose of drawing a revenue from their ruin . . .'[9]

The public lottery was ended temporarily by an Act of Parliament on 18 October 1826, but not before a final draw took place, advertised in a typical manner by the Crown's chief London ticketseller, one Bish of 4 Cornhill and 9 Charing Cross:

> Run, Neighbours, run, the LOTTERY'S expiring,
> When FORTUNE'S merry wheel, it will never turn more;
> She now supplies all Numbers, you're desiring
> ALL PRIZES, NO BLANKS, and TWENTY THOUSAND FOUR.

> Haste, Neighbours, haste, the Chance will never come again,
> When, without pain, for little *Cash* – you'll all be rich;
> Prizes a plenty of – and such a certain source of gain,
> That young and old, and all the world, it must bewitch.[10]

Bish fought the proposed ending of the State lottery to the very end, protesting that:

. . . To stake patrimonial estates at hazard or écarté in the purlieus of St James's is merely amusement, but to purchase a ticket in the Lottery, by means of which a man may gain an estate at a trifling risk, is – immoral! nay, within a few hours of the time I write, were not many of our nobility and senators, some of whom, I dare say, voted against Lotteries, assembled betting thousands upon a horse-race?[11]

Bish had made a fortune, trading in league with the government of the day on the gullibility of the poor while professing to be their champion. Having failed to stop the end of the public lottery at that time, he entered a different kind of lottery. He got himself elected to Parliament. Eventually the British lottery was restored, although on a one-time basis, in which buying whole blocks of tickets with a particular number series did not increase the chances of winning, as it had, at least marginally, before 1826.

Governments, the Church and the military banned all forms of game playing from time to time according to Joseph Strutt, the early nineteenth-century chronicler of *The Sports and Pastimes of the People of England*:

[Certain games] ... were not forbidden from any particular evil in themselves, but because they engrossed too much of the leisure and attention of the populace, and diverted their minds from the pursuits of a more martial nature [e.g. archery practice].[12]

This shows how innocent or ignorant governments and kings of former times were, for the competitive games they forbade their subjects to play were those that might have made better and more willing soldiers out of them for the interminable and stupid wars they fought among themselves.

Towards the close of the twelfth century, we meet with a very curious edict relative to gaming ... This edict was established for the regulation of the Christian army under the command of Richard I [the Lionheart] of England and Philip of France, during the crusade of 1190. It prohibits any person in the army beneath the degree of a knight from playing at any sort of game for money: knights and clergymen might play for money, but no one of them was permitted to lose more than twenty shillings in one whole day and night, under the penalty of one hundred shillings, to be paid to the archbishops in the army; the two monarchs had the privilege of playing for what they pleased; but their attendants were limited to the sum of twenty shillings; and if they exceeded, they were to be whipped naked through the army for three days.[13]

King Henry III prohibited the clergy from playing chess and gambling with dice. During the reign of Richard II dicing was generally forbidden. Henry VII banned card-games, especially among apprentices, except during the Christmas holidays 'and then only in their masters' houses' under the penalty of six shillings and eightpence for every offence. Edward III proclaimed an edict against all forms of gambling, including sports, games and pastimes like handball, football, club-ball (an early version of golf), bull-baiting and cock-fighting.

James I considered game playing, gambling and sports favourably within limits, but banned tumblers, 'comoedians and balladines' from his court.

> . . . from this court I debarre all rough and violent exercises; as the football, meeter for lameing, than making able, the users thereof . . . [and he advised his son to] Beware in making your sporters your councellors . . .[14]

Henry VIII forbade bowling, tennis, dice, card- and boardgames, including backgammon. And in 1801 London magistrates made a law against the playing of dutch-pins, nine-pins and other bowling games that were commonly played in the streets, presumably because they interfered with traffic. But because only those named in the edict were unlawful, the game of nine-holes was revived under the name of 'Bubble the Justice'. As in all games, the law was defeated by default.

But after periods of prohibition during which lotteries, gambling and other games were temporarily forced underground, they became respectable once more. Roulette and poker were invented round the turn of the nineteenth century; the former in France and the latter in the Louisiana Territory of America, a French possession at that time. Craps, bingo, keeno and bridge are all late-nineteenth and early twentieth-century inventions.

Gaming-rooms in bordellos and elsewhere were well known in eighteenth-century London, most clustered in and around the Strand and Jermyn Street. But the more elaborate casinos go back less than two centuries in Europe. Most were located in France and Germany, but since the Great Depression of 1929 they have blossomed in many Western countries. France today ranks first as the nation with most casinos, Britain comes next with well over a hundred; Germany, Austria, Belgium, Italy, Holland and Malta follow in that order.

Las Vegas and Atlantic City may be the most notorious gambling cities in the world, but the most fashionable and best-known casino was built in Monte Carlo by Francois Blanc in 1861. He was nearly bankrupted by Charles Bonaparte who wagered larger sums than the house could afford. Thereafter Blanc and all other casino managements set limits on what could be wagered, although these can be exceeded at the discretion of the house. In 1978 a group of Middle-Eastern punters won $2.5 million in one sitting in Monte Carlo, but lost it – plus $1.4 million more – two hours later. This is the stuff of which gaming legends are made.

The Monte Carlo Casino has been the source of many dramatic tales of gamblers and gambling systems that were claimed to have succeeded, others that failed, and tragic suicides. Prince Rainier is said to have a 65 per cent interest – in an annual income estimated a few years ago as amounting to $80 million from the gaming tables, and a further F40 million from one-arm bandits installed since the Second World War.[15] Prior to the influx of American gamblers, the Côte d'Azur casinos would not allow one-arm bandits and slot-machines in their crystal chandelier-lit premises. But since then, and with a democratization of gambling, the profits of the Casino de Monte Carlo are greater than ever.

Sports have a history of their own that runs parallel to games of strategy and chance. Wrestling is perhaps the oldest form of sporting combat, recorded on Assyrian frescos, Minoan and Greek vases and Mexican artefacts. It has been a favourite in Japan for centuries where sumo consists of a ritualized wrestling contest. The original Greek Olympics are believed to have represented the ideal of sportsmanship, but they also seem to have served a political purpose, more bloody, but not too different in spirit, from today's elections in democratic countries:

. . . the Olympic contest was a means of determining who should be king of the district and champion of the local tree-Zeus. The holder of such an office defended it until he was defeated and superseded by a successful combatant. Agonistic combat (with death as the outcome) decided who had the power, and therefore the right, to intercede with the gods in assuring the regeneration of the year in the fertility rites. Deciphering the myths, which contain elements of both combat (survival of the fittest) and contest (defeat without death of the agonist-challenger) and adducing pertinent historical comment assists in the disentanglement of social events reflective of normative life applicable to and predating the Olympic games prior to 776 B.C.[16]

Such 'games' eventually led to the lethal contests in Roman circuses where quarter was seldom given, except by special dispensation from the Emperor. Conditioned by these games, compassion for others virtually ceased to exist in the population, to which Cicero testified when he wrote: 'We hate those weak and suppliant gladiators who, hands outstretched, beseech us to live' – a sentiment reminiscent of Nazi ideology.

Don Atyeo, in his book *Blood and Guts*, catalogues the outrages that passed for sport through the centuries. Strutt cites others. Boxing, introduced to the Olympics in 688 B.C., remained a neglected sport until it became popular once again in Britain in the late eighteenth century. Ball games in general and football in particular have a violent history concerning both players and spectators. In the middle of the eighteenth century it was difficult to tell the players from the spectators.

In 1740, for example, it was recorded [in Britain] that 'a Mach of Futtball was Cried at Kettering of five hundred men of a side, but the design was to Pull Down Lady Betsy Jesmaine's Mills.'[17]

Hence football hooliganism, while often thought to be a modern phenomenon, is as old as the game itself. Polo is believed to have originated among Iranian tribes in the sixth century B.C. Afghan tribesmen on horseback still play buzkashi, one form of the game, using a sheep's head instead of a puck. The head is captured and wrested from whoever possesses it in encounters that can be fatal to horses and riders.

Even more bloodthirsty [than the Afghan game of buzkashi] was peloya, a game popular with Mexican tribes around 800 B.C. Players were equipped with wide leather belts, leather aprons, chest protectors and thick leather gauntlets to protect themselves from the solid rubber ball which hurled round the court like a bullet ... [An eyewitness reported that] 'Many players were carried off the field dead when the ball had hit them in the stomach or over the heart, knocking the breath out of them so that they fell down dead'.[18]

This was one version of a game portrayed in the 1960s film *Rollerball*, which attempted to call attention to the current American and British infatuation with sports competition. While not meant to be taken literally, this film turned out to be a fairly accurate prediction of what is happening today on a global scale.

Hunting and shooting, once a survival necessity in many parts of the world, changed in character with the invention of the rifle and its use in hunting 'for sport'. The mindless killing of hundreds of thousands of buffalo on the prairies of America in the middle of the last century dramatizes the shift in values from hunting for survival to doing so 'for fun'. These excesses were witnessed by George Catlin, a painter and chronicler of Indian life. The killings had nothing to do with meat for the pot, or hides for clothing and shelter. Hunters simply rode into the vast buffalo herds shooting, reloading and shooting until the prairie was littered with spent cartridges and carcasses left to rot.[19]

There is little difference between those buffalo hunts and today's game farms where wild animals bred and domesticated in captivity are driven before 'sportsmen' who 'hunt' from the comfort of four-wheel-drive vehicles. These are simply the most recent manifestations of 'hunting for sport', once the prerogative of royalty, the aristocracy, Indian maharajas, German *Junkers*, the British raj, and those able to afford African safaris – all perversions of man's original and legitimate hunt for meat and hides.

As I suggested earlier, the first games are most likely to have evolved from a recognition of the need for stealth and deviousness as the most effective means of trapping game, as well as in self-defence against animal predators. The historical record, such as it is and despite unsubstantiated claims for early man's innate 'killer instinct', suggests that the first games were born of such necessities, rather than for aggressive territorial or sexual reasons. For example, the capture or rape of a neighbouring tribe's women must have been highly unlikely in earliest days, although this certainly happened in the more recent past and still happens today, because then the female of the species was probably just as tough and able to defend herself as any male. In fact, some of the remaining artefacts of prehistoric societies in places like Malta indicate convincingly that many were matriarchal and female-dominated (e.g. their priests were females and their temples were built in the shape of pregnant women).

It was only when the 'game', instead of being used for aggressive defence against animal predators or for aggressive hunting, was converted into an instrument of aggressive offence, that other men and women along with their property began to be regarded as objects (i.e. relatively objectively). At that point in human culture the theft of resources, the rape of women and the enslavement of adults of both sexes and of children began. The leaders of the tribe even came to look on their own troops as expendable 'things'.

Eventually, mankind, alone among all species and with sufficient self-conditioning, became used to regarding itself and indeed all of nature as potential 'adversaries' to tame, to dominate and over which to rule, rather than seeing itself and nature as partners. At this point sports and hunting turned into apprenticeships for war. Perhaps it was then that women became increasingly tied to the hearth; they could not be counted on as warriors since in their younger days they were probably pregnant much of the time, given prevailing infant mortality rates, and the need for food gathering and gardening while the men were absent on the hunt or at war. This was debilitating and probably turned them into the 'weaker sex' physically, given evolutionary and cultural changes over long periods of time. It was only then that rape, one of the most terrible forms of aggression, became a possibility among human beings – yet remained an impossibility among any other animal species. All human activity turned into the war of all against all.

The sports which began life as war-games – boxing, hunting, wrestling, football and so on – we have continued as war-games, playing them in exactly the same manner as we fight our wars – to win by any means at our disposal, including tooth-and-nail violence. After continuing centuries of playing-field Armageddons, the line dividing sports and war has never been so blurred.[20]

While the competitive spirit is rampant in the US, it waxes and wanes elsewhere in the world, including Britain.

In the literature of the public school, by far the most popular moralistic exhortation was 'play the game'. It was a refrain taken up again and again ... Learning to 'play the game' on green and pleasant playing fields would appear to have been a universal feature of the English public school for many generations ... In the adult world the public school admonition to 'play the game' reverberated through the pages of journals in which secular and clerical missionaries either sought to set the world to rights, or strove to maintain its rightness, through the simple expedient of propagating the public school ethic of 'playing the game' ... The practical virtue of 'playing the game' was extended beyond the national welfare, economics and politics to imperial administration which owed its integrity ... to those from Britain to whom 'It isn't cricket; it's not playing the game' was a moral axiom dictating colonial action.[21]

While this is perfectly true, 'playing the game' was also a preparation for war, as was chess, at one time said to have been used to train Chinese warriors and Indian maharajas in the art or science of war. Yet the principles of chess, as von Neumann and Morgenstern admitted, were never understood. Andrew Wilson [22] and Thomas B. Allen [23] trace the history of war-games from their early beginnings up to today. They are played seriously in the Pentagon, in Britain's Ministry of Defence and in every war college throughout the world. Wilson chronicles the effect of war-gaming on military thought up to the war in Vietnam. He estimated that in 1968, at the height of that war, between 15,000 and 30,000 US officers, civilians, computer scientists and game theoreticians participated in Pentagon-funded computer war-games. Wilson writes:

To see modern war-games in perspective it is necessary to observe earlier games, and the disasters to which they occasionally led. Again, one cannot describe the military use of war-games without touching on the use of similar games for academic research; in international relations and social science, as well as in business and for economic studies. Finally, computer games are used not merely to seek answers about today's and tomorrow's weapons systems, but also to generate 'scenarios' about the possible shape of the world in general in ten, fifteen and twenty years' time. [24]

A summary of the history of war-gaming is given in Chapter 12, the most significant feature of which is that war-games, as conducted by the military, continue to this day and are based on the wrong game theoretical principles. These false premises and conclusions persist despite the fact that the lessons of history should have taught military strategists and game theoreticians that what occurs on the battlefield could only be compared to the games they play with or without computers if they understood the principles of game playing itself.

The inspiration for war-games was a search for the 'true principles' of war. Such principles can be viewed in pure strategic and tactical terms, seen as offensive instruments for domination, subjugation and territorial and economic aggrandizement; or for defence against any unprovoked attack and to restore peace at the earliest moment with a minimum of damage to life and property. The most recent findings in game theory show that whoever strikes the first blow in war suffers severe disadvantages in winning terms, except in so far as he can take advantage of an opponent's errors one turn earlier.

Anatol Rapoport, a psychologist and game theoretician, took exception to the majority view of the war-game players and military experts. His objections went unheeded because they were based on ethical and philosophical principles that differed from those that prevail in the Pentagon and throughout the United States. Rapoport attempted in *Strategy and Conscience*[25] to define principles of co-operation and peace founded on agreement rather than on conventional game theoretical and mathematical grounds. As could be expected, Herman Kahn of the Hudson Institute, Schelling at Harvard, and other US war-games experts ridiculed Rapoport's views. But the new game theory and Rapoport's 1978 Tit-for-Tat prisoner's dilemma solution (see Chapter 9) demonstrate that classical game theoretical perceptions applied in any field – and especially in warfare – are mistaken in assumptions and conclusions for practical, mathematically and scientifically demonstrable reasons, rather than for purely philosophical or moralistic ones.

Until the sixteenth century people played games on and off the battlefield, depending largely on 'luck' to win or lose, except in contests involving sheer brute force, superiority in numbers or, in rare instances, on commanders who intuitively understood the operations underlying winning, losing, draws, stalemates and chance. However, in the early 1500s an Italian gambler, Girolamo Cardano, began to keep track of his winnings and losses, in an attempt to discover a mathematical method whereby he might predict and assure future successes in games of chance. His book of notes and observations was not published until 1653,[26] just a few years before the French mathematician Pascal's correspondence on this subject with the geometer Fermat. In 1658 Pascal made a famous wager by which he sought to prove the existence of God. At about the same time (in 1657) Huygens, a Dutch mathematician, published *Calculating in Games of Chance* in which he also tried to explain methods for calculating expectations and probabilities. Yet another mathematician, a member of the famous Bernoulli family, published *Ars Conjectandi* in 1713, a work that established game theory as an academic discipline.

Leibnitz and Newton, through their discovery of the differential calculus, provided the mechanisms that helped make modern physics, genetics, game theory and the social sciences possible. Newton, who modestly attributed his successes to the fact that 'we all stand on the heads of famous men', was succeeded by scientists and intellectuals in the following centuries who stood on his head in turn and developed the mathematical tools he had provided in many different applications and in a wide variety of fields.

By the twentieth century, and with the advent of modern science – and the behavioural sciences especially – game theory and an exclusive preoccupation with competitive processes helped establish statistical mathematical procedures for general problem solving and forecasting that are seldom questioned. In 1928 von Neumann and Morgenstern developed their game theory which has since influenced thought in every academic and practical aspect of decision making, and in what was believed to constitute 'rational' behaviour.[27] Their 'min/max' theory (minimizing losses while maximizing winnings), the open-ended decision-tree model, and probabilistic processes for predicting conflict resolution of every kind, became undisputed standards.

Despite the fact that von Clausewitz and social Darwinists had long equated business and biological evolution with war-like competition, the twentieth century provided the incentives and opportunities (two world wars and increasing economic competition) for game theory to become the serious concern of economists and mathematicians. The mathematical analyses of winning and losing, directly related to actual games on which modern economics are based, can be traced to von Neumann and Morgenstern.

Like Pavlov and other academicians, von Neumann and Morgenstern provided a formal 'scientific' rationale for what had been practised for a very long time. They made reprehensible economic practices respectable by cloaking them in a mantle of mathematical and pseudo-scientific jargon. The interest aroused in game-related economics led to a wide use of economic and management games based on the theories of von Neumann and Morgenstern. The American Management Association's (AMA) *Top Management Decision Game* and *Future*, designed by two Rand Corporation game theoreticians and used as a public relations tool by Kaiser Aluminum Corporation,[28] is a typical early example. The history of and perceptions in game theory are therefore important components of the way we view and judge 'rational' human behaviour in war, economics and in any other enterprise.

By 1957, when a comprehensive bibliography was compiled on game theory,[29] more than 1,000 papers and books had been published, solely devoted to trying to figure out the most effective ways of winning (a number that has since more than quadrupled). As pointed out earlier, only Anatol Rapoport tried to run counter to this mainstream of thought.

The availability of computers since the Second World War should have called into question statistical methods of game analysis. Computers operate on linear and binary whole number principles – the antithesis of statistical and probabilistic fractional methods. Instead, probabilistic techniques were made to override the momentarily finite and conditionally deterministic processes shared by computers, games of pure strategy and the human central nervous system. Rather than taking advantage of new opportunities for a reconsideration of dubious principles, the computer was used to confirm and reassert them in a manner that seemed superficially convincing.

In Appendices A and B, I demonstrate how an infinitely expandable, but finite geometric modelling technique and linear, combinatorial processes provide a very simple, but powerful and precise analytic tool that is ideally suited to binary mathematics and computers. It also lends itself to a new penetration of the game enigma. Anyone can understand it and even those who are uninterested in mathematics can apply the conclusions derived from it intuitively and without recourse to numbers. It is a method that enables us to consider the sum of all combinatorial possibilities and then to select – and understand the meanings of – those that interest us most. Game theorists, mathematicians, systems analysts and philosophers (with the exception of Leibnitz) have overlooked or avoided this method, although it has existed in part since pre-Christian times. It is currently being revived in the guise of 'neural-networks' – another false lead in the search for artificial intelligence.

The concepts of chance, winning and losing as the dominant features of our universe, and the idea that draws and stalemates do not count, have become entrenched in all Western cultures and in those they influence. Few question this outlook on life and existence, and those who do are deemed religious or philosophical fanatics.

The latter offer nothing but a reserved place in heaven to whoever forswears all forms of materialistic competition. As a result, and despite hypocritical denunciations of materialism, the winning and losing concept (but not that of chance) is a cornerstone of many religions. They insist that only believers can win God's favour, while the heathen are condemned to lose, roasting in an everlasting hell. Other versions of this materialist/spiritual creed offer a variety of recipes for winning. To quote Oral Roberts, the American evangelist: 'God is like a bank. The more money you put in, the more you get out.'

Game theoretical methods and models are applied today in just about every enterprise. They are used in economic modelling, forecasting of every kind, technological research and development and in all branches of science. They are also the models on which our social and political organizations are based. For example, in the US there is a constant and bitter conflict of interests (i.e. a competitive game) between the executive, legislative and judicial branches of government. This conflict is exacerbated by lobbyists for competing commercial, industrial, union, consumer and military interests who use every dirty trick including distortion of the facts and corruption to assure that some special interests win at the expense of the others.

There can be no national or international co-operation, consensus or peace when the only way to achieve a result is for one conflicting interest to try to win at the expense of the others or, indeed, when society is perceived as consisting (or actually consists) of special interest groups, each of which attempts to dominate and exploit many of the others. That way every individual, special interest group, the society and indeed the whole world is perpetually at physical, psychological or economic war and is therefore involved in a needless gamble. Of course none of this is ever admitted, but these are the lessons taught by the game theoreticians who wield great influence in shaping the economic and political strategies of governments. Games are used as the models for successful management and supposedly rational behaviour in most parts of the world.

The socialist countries of Eastern Europe and the Orient are as infected with the madness of perpetual competition as the capitalist ones. Winning at chess is a national mania in Russia, as table-tennis is in the People's Republic of China. These countries' leaderships are in perpetual conflict internally, with one another, and with much of the rest of the world. The manner in which games are played by the Russians and modern Chinese symbolizes the essentially competitive spirit of societies that are supposedly dedicated to co-operation. It can only be hoped that it is the intention of Gorbachev and of the new leadership in the People's Republic of China to reverse characteristics that have always eventually defeated the principles on which their ideologies, as well as capitalist ones, are supposedly based.

Socialist views on co-operation and competition have turned out to be as self-contradictory and hypocritical as those of the capitalist world. For example, a *Dictionary of Cybernetics* written by East German scientists recites the conventional von Neumann and Morgenstern game liturgy side by side with the Communist dialectic without any awareness of the contradictions. Winning – the zero-sum game – is all that counts. The authors write: 'A satisfactory theory for the non-zero-sum [i.e. the co-operative] game does not exist at present.'[30]

Such a theory may not exist in the minds of many, but in practice the co-operative principle has existed since time immemorial. Without it, babies could only be conceived as a result of rape.

3 Meanings

> I'm not ashamed of leaving a trail of fractures
> among the opposition – a finger, a thumb, a whole
> right hand and one foot on the latest count. After
> all, that's what I'm there for. Not to inflict
> deliberate injury, but to rough up a batsman,
> make them apprehensive and destroy their
> confidence . . .
>
> John Snow, England Test fast bowler[1]

Our understanding of what is actually happening in the world
depends on our interpretation of the meanings of words like *play*,
winning, *losing*, *draw*, *stalemate*, *competition*, *co-operation*, *altruism* and
chance. The definition of meaning is therefore of fundamental importance. The words we use in any one language are arbitrary conventions of long standing that can change in time. But there must be a
general agreement as to their meanings at any given moment. An
understanding of factually-based ideas therefore depends on what
we agree to be the meanings of the words we use to express them.

There is a fundamental difference between understanding and
agreement, although one depends on the other. We can agree to
anything – even to a misunderstanding, prejudice or dogma. For
example, people agreed for a very long time that the world was flat,
which was understandable in the absence of proof to the contrary.
Once the flat earth idea was shown to be false, anyone who persisted
in believing it was clearly dogmatic or insane. That the earth is a
globe was known long before it was proven by Columbus. None the
less, some people preferred the flat earth idea even after its fallacy
had been demonstrated practically.

However, we must make a clear distinction between two forms of
expression even within one and the same language. All of us use

two tongues, irrespective of the language we speak. One is literary and poetic and its meanings are entirely subjective and depend on individual interpretation. There is no 'right' or 'wrong' way to interpret poetry, for example. It is largely a matter of feeling and taste. The other form of language is purely informational and is used to describe matters of fact. This is the form and the meanings that concern us here.

Factually-based meanings are culture free or else translation from one language to any other would be impossible. Unfortunately many of the informational meanings of words and ideas we use are garbled, remain untested or are factually inaccurate and that is why misunderstandings occur, even among people who speak the same language.

Count Korzybski, founder of the School of General Semantics, characterized people who are unable to define the meanings of fundamental concepts as psychologically disturbed or insane.[2] He also implied that the meaning of any word, term or idea can be extracted by an analysis of causes, consequences and the operations that bring both about within any given context. Chuang Tzu, a Tao philosopher who lived around 350 B.C., said much the same thing when he wrote: 'Speech is not mere breath. It is differentiated by meanings. Take away that and you cannot say whether it is speech or not. Can you even distinguish it from the chirping of birds?'[3]

Ask different people what is meant by some of the words redefined here and in Appendix C, or to look them up in different dictionaries: you will often get contradictory answers, or the meanings they give will conflict with factual analyses of the states they describe.

Why this should be so within one and the same language is anyone's guess. Mine is that few people ever question the assigned meanings of words once they enter common usage and a dictionary definition is established. A prejudicial value judgement founded on nothing but belief has become institutionalized until someone blows a whistle, and even then most people will defend wrong conventional definitions to the death. Having taken a stand, they will not reconsider because they have a vested interest in proving themselves right no matter how wrong they may be. Rather than learning from their mistakes they persist in them. The years – indeed centuries – it took for the global earth idea to be accepted is typical of this intransigence. There are still some 'flat earth' people around. All of us are guilty of this sort of self-deception and dogmatism at one time or another.

Questions concerning meanings – semantics – become critical when it comes to translations from one language into any other. Today attempts are being made to achieve automatic machine translation by computer. This is possible up to a point for informational language, although considerable editing by hand is still required. But literary language cannot ever be efficiently translated by machine, because most of it depends on feelings, ambiguities and idiomatic understanding, rather than on a knowledge of facts. No computer could ever decide autonomously what is meant by 'fruit flies like an apple'.

There is a further difficulty in extracting the exact meaning of informational words and phrases: every transactional word has a relatively objective and subjective meaning even within one and the same informational context. Arnold Toynbee, the historian, understood the need for such a dual, relatively objective and subjective definition of meanings very well:

... Ideally, any definition that we make of anything whatsoever ought to be made in this dual form, considering the duality of subject and object, and the problem of what the true relation between them is, are inherent in all thinking.[4]

For example, playing to win and competing in the conventional sense in games or any other enterprise is a *relatively objective* process. I use the qualifier *relatively* because *total objectivity* must include *subjectivity* also. The winner views his confederates, troops or playing pieces and those of the opponent as 'objects' to be manipulated, defeated or destroyed in order to serve his purposes. The *subjective* feelings of his own and the enemy forces do not matter. A would-be winner – a player whose intention is to win and make others lose – attributes *subjective* feelings only to himself.

Subjectivity does not consist of turning the other cheek – that is how you get a broken jaw. It also does not consist of complaining and claiming to be more sensitive than anyone else. These are the subjective feelings of losers and would-be winners alike. An overview of the game metaphor that includes the relatively objective and subjective vectors of choice defines total objectivity (i.e. a value judgement made from a vantage point outside a system, environment or universe of discourse) and that is what is lacking today in most definitions of ideas, concepts and the words used to articulate them. No dictionary with which I am familiar distinguishes between relatively objective and subjective meanings for transactional words or phrases (I will deal with the 'subjective' aspects of game playing later).

Margaret Mead [5] described a situation that defines the difference between relatively objective and subjective meanings in a related context. She notes that there is a difference between tribeswomen competing to make the best mats for the marriage of a chief's daughter, and their competing as to who can turn out the largest number in the shortest period of time. In the first instance the *competition* is *qualitative* and *subjective*, whereas in the second it is *quantitative* and *relatively objective*. (The meanings of *relative subjectivity* are discussed in greater detail in the context of play – see below – and a 'stalemate' in game playing – see Chapter 9.) In trying to make the very best mats the individual is in competition only with herself and co-operates with others for the benefit of her craft, the quality of the product and the bride. She has no trade secrets and her companions can learn from her. Everyone wins in proportion to effort and accomplishment, and no one loses.

These are *subjective*, co-operative and qualitatively competitive aims and outcomes. But in trying to be the first to manufacture the largest quantity in the shortest period of time, a tribeswoman pits herself against everyone else. She is competing only quantitatively, and hopes to win by trading on the lesser co-ordination, speed and skill of others. She will keep to herself whatever technical knowledge or advantage she enjoys. The benefit is minimal and the quality is likely to suffer at everyone's expense, especially that of the product and the maker's own craftsmanship.

One of the problems with defining words and phrases is that it is often attempted to extract meanings from the context – syntax – in which they are found. Context, while pointing us in the right direction, cannot reveal a word's actual informational content. A causal-consequential-operational analysis in a given context is needed in order to extract the meaning. For the same word can mean the same or a different thing in a variety of different contexts. Or the same idea expressed by one word in one frame of reference may be expressed by a different one in another. This last problem is resolved by establishing how and where the same ideas recur even when different words are used to define them, and what they really mean in various frames of reference.

For example, the word 'drawing' can mean one thing when we are talking about game playing, another when we are looking at or creating pictures, a third when it comes to getting water from a well or money out of a bank. But 'winning' always means the same thing whether we are talking about conventional 'success' at chess, on a football field, on the stock-market, in getting a scholarship, or a bride. As we shall see, the words 'drawing' and 'winning' are incorrectly defined in most dictionaries and languages when it comes to game playing. The context in which these words are used does not provide the slightest clue as to what they mean, which states they describe or how these states come about. The only way to establish such meanings is by applying a causal/consequential analysis of what takes place at the very beginning, during and after play on a game board, table or playing field.

Throughout this book terms are given definitions that often differ from those found in standard dictionaries. These words have been redefined on the basis of global, causal/consequential analyses in the context of game playing. In Appendix C I provide a small glossary of additional defined words, although I do not go into as much detail as I do here. It is important to bear in mind that these same definitions hold true in many other frames of reference, even when different words are used. For example, *success* can mean *winning* in a context other than game playing, as mentioned earlier. None the less, success of a higher and creative order is defined by the draw: actual or near error-free, perfect achievement in any relationship or field of performance.

A causal/consequential analysis means that a train of events is traced from original causes to the eventual consequences or outcome via the various operations that bring both about. This is called *induction* in logic. The same object can be achieved by tracing the chain of events backwards from consequences to causes by means of *deduction*. In the real world it is difficult to establish original causes because each cause usually leads backwards to a previous one in what appears to be an infinite regression. When it comes to games, however, the original cause and consequences are easily established.

The operations that bring about the consequences are less well understood, for most people really do not know how and why they win when they do. Many persuade themselves that this is due to superiority of some kind, but that is untrue.

An *intention* is always the original cause in game playing. People *want* to play a particular game to *win*, to *defeat* another player or team, to *succeed* and to reach a well-defined *objective*. The consequence can only be a *victory* or a *defeat*, a *draw*, *stalemate* or an interrupted game. No other outcome is possible. The operations that bring these outcomes about are usually only vaguely defined. They consist of strategies, tactics, turns, moves, doing things correctly or incorrectly according to given rules. But just what these strategies and tactics are or the meaning of doing things correctly or perfectly, while supposedly and implicitly leading to victory, is somehow never spelled out. Yet all these states and conditions are amenable to step-by-step analyses, from which their meanings can be extracted precisely. Typical questions to be asked and tested along these lines could be:

What does *play* mean?
What is the meaning of the word *game*?
What is the nature of *rules*?
How do you *win*, *lose*, *draw* or achieve a *stalemate*?
What roles do *intentions* play in games?
What is a *perfect* strategy?
What is an *error*?
What does *winning* mean?
. . . and so on

Let us begin by defining play and games.

Play is a thing done for the sake of the thing itself: learning, love of life and the sheer joy of survival. It should never be done just for money, power or glory. It is a means for discovering the meanings of rules, rather than by following 'orders' blindly. Play, then, is the highest form of *subjective* experience. It is related to games when we play them for fun and for the exercise, rather than to win by making others lose. A game, as conventionally understood, defines a relationship in which something is won or lost; in which a player is victorious or defeated; and successful or unsuccessful as a result of particular strategies and tactics, according to given rules. But the actual criteria for deciding what is actually achieved are never clearly defined. One of the objects of this book is to define them.

This brings us to a definition of rules, one that appears to have given the philosopher Ludwig Wittgenstein a great deal of difficulty. Without ever defining language or games, Wittgenstein maintained that language is a kind of game. His writings dwell at length on rules, but he never defined the real causes, consequences and operations that bring these about.

Wittgenstein believed that rules are something to be obeyed, agreed to or interpreted.[6] While perfectly true as far as it goes, his statements tell us nothing about the nature of rules themselves. All Wittgenstein stated was what we must do and how we should behave, relative to rules, but that is not a definition. It is an order. The game metaphor provides us with demonstrations of how man-made and natural laws come about and can be defined causally, consequentially and operationally under any conditions.

The rules for the game of noughts and crosses are useful examples. It is played on a field of nine squares and involves nine factors. The sum of all possibilities for this or any other game can be calculated in a number of ways. One of the smaller of such sums is purely *permutational*. It is one that is commonly used, but it is totally misleading and inadequate (see Appendix A). The *combinatorial* sum of all possibilities for this game is about 618 thousand million and it includes the *intentions* of the players. Any such sum is a finite limit, relative to the number of factors that are involved.

Noughts and crosses is played by each of two players taking alternate turns with the objective of occupying three spaces in a row with his or her symbols. The hoped-for result is an XXX or an OOO horizontally, vertically or diagonally. Other outcomes do not count as victories. The arbitrary, alternate turn, three-in-a-row, man-made rules severely limit the sum of all possibilities. Combinations like OXO, XOX, XOO, OXX, XXO, OOX do not count. Externally created psychological disturbances that might cause a player to make mistakes are implicitly – but not explicitly – forbidden. Rules are therefore binding limitations placed on the sum of all possibilities by agreement between the players. Playing any game would be impossible without these limitations and agreements.

Let us consider the consequences of a game that lacks limiting rules. This and the confusion of meanings as it applies to games is demonstrated by what happened to me in the mid-1960s in New York.

A group of students from the Massachusetts Institute of Technology had asked me for my opinion of a new game they had invented. It consisted of a large game board, handsomely designed, and plastic discs on which astrological, cabalistic and other metaphysical symbols were inscribed. When asked what the rules were, the students replied that there were none. Every player could do whatever he liked. The point made was that this was a 'total freedom' game, an idea that was popular in the sixties. This might be confused with a 'draw' but, as we shall see, it is nothing of the kind. The inventors were taken aback when I pointed out that 'no rules allowed' was itself a rule. They clearly had no idea what the concept of 'rules' meant.

When I asked how the first turn was determined they explained that anyone could have a turn whenever they liked – another rule to play the no-rule game. I elected to go last. Finally I wanted to know how the game was won and who would be the losers. They told me that in this game everyone could win, that no one need ever be a loser and that, in any event, each player decided these questions for him- or herself at the end of the game, depending on how he or she felt. Before beginning to play I predicted that in accordance with this spate of rules made to play a 'no-rule' game, I would win and make everyone else lose, and that is exactly what happened.

When my turn came I simply folded up the board, collected all the playing pieces and stuck them in my pocket. The MIT students were shocked a second time by this unexpected turn of events. I had demonstrated that any anarchic game without explicit limits (i.e. rules) can always be won by one player. He ends up as the all-time, only winner and all other players become permanent losers. But he is also a loser, for he has no one with whom to play in the future. The maharajas' chess tournament (see Chapter 9) is a variation on this principle. The students had unwittingly created a conventional winning and losing situation in which no draw was possible, and one in which even the winner would ultimately be stalemated.

They had allowed themselves to be seduced by the clichés of their time and culture. They believed that all meanings are arbitrary and matters of opinion. I showed them that informational meanings are demonstrable matters of fact, derived from analyses of causes, consequences and the operations that bring both about within any given context. That, as I stated earlier, is how the meanings of any 'informational' word, phrase or concept can be discovered. The self-limiting rules for the correct definition of informational meanings are therefore essential because they furnish a yardstick for analysing behaviour, provide deep insights, and delve beneath superficial beliefs to show what is really happening.

Play is impossible, life chaotic and anarchy reigns when we pretend that we can do without rules or laws. When that happens one winner most likely walks off with the spoils in the short term, but even he loses in the long term as illustrated by the example of the MIT students' game. This principle seems to hold true for games and for every manifestation of existence.

Intentionality in games is causal, as stated earlier. It is clearly the intention of the player to achieve something as a result of his or her activities. In addition to the definition of game playing given above, the word *game* defines a relationship between two more or less equally matched individuals or teams (or between a contestant and himself, as in the game of solitaire) in which each side does its *best* or its *worst*. If they are not equally matched then this can be a learning situation, but then if the more experienced or co-ordinated player plays to win he is simply taking unfair advantage of the other and doing his worst. It does not matter whether this is done over a game board, on a playing field, in the classroom, in business, politics, diplomacy or in bed. The same criteria apply in all cases, provided we do not limit ourselves to winning and losing, but include possible draws and stalemates and what all of these different game endings mean causally, consequentially and in terms of the operations that bring them about.

According to conventional game and sports lore, *draws* and *stalemates* do not count. They are considered worthless outcomes in all the games we play. Von Neumann and Morgenstern, the leading game theoreticians of our time, insisted that draws and stalemates are inconclusive *ties*. But before we can examine the meanings of these two terms, it is useful to examine *winning* and *losing* in a causal/consequential manner.

If both sides play to *win*, each must do its *worst* to defeat the other by inducing and taking advantage of every error. Both are in the hands of *chance* if they play to win (because errors are unpredictable) or if they do not know what they are doing. The intentions of the players and how they define their objectives – even when they have none – therefore play crucial and causal roles in the outcomes, whether they occur in game playing or in any other relationship involving individuals or groups.

The causes and operations that bring about *winning* in any game that involves *competition* between individual players or teams are not any superior strategy on the part of the winner, but errors committed by the loser. That is true whether the game is one of strategy, chance, sport, or involves social, political or economic relationships. It is true in love and in war. The errors may be induced or made spontaneously, but to lead to a victory they must be taken advantage of. We have therefore established that all victories between equals are achieved by chance and by default.

In other words the winner does not win because of superior skill, co-ordination or intelligence, even when he possesses or exercises any of these. Instead he wins because the loser made fatal mistakes spontaneously or his mistakes were induced by tactical or psychological ploys on the part of the would-be winner. In either case, and to put it bluntly, the winner is simply the bigger bastard. The quote that heads this chapter is testimony to this fact and it applies to all relatively objective, competitive situations. This is what I meant when I stated earlier that each side must do its *worst* in order to win.

It is generally held that, while perhaps true for some games, this is not true for winning at chess. Chess is 'believed' to be a game requiring high intellect and foresight. But victories in any game or game-like situation are only won by deception and by taking advantage of the resulting errors. Foresight, if any, is minimal. Consider tennis where a good deal of physical skill and co-ordination are involved in any game between equally matched partners – yet some highly competitive champions, like McEnroe, employ tantrums and other ploys to destroy the concentration of closely matched opponents and intimidate umpires as part of a winning strategy. It does not always work and that is when such players lose.

It remains to examine the causes and operations that bring about draws and stalemates. They are not understood any better than winning and losing in today's world. Games invariably end as draws when both players are equally skilled and play as hard as they can; when no mistakes are made by either side (or an equal number cancel each other out); when a learner's mistakes are forgiven; and when the scoring rules are not deliberately biased in favour of winning (e.g. 'the best of three games'). The achievement of a draw, unlike a victory, does demand great skill, foresight and intelligence. In playing to achieve a *draw*, each side must do its *best* to co-operate in playing an error-free game with the object of achieving parity and maintaining absolute equality.

Whereas *winning* is the *relatively objective* game outcome (as we saw earlier), the *draw* is the *co-operative, subjective* one. When modelled analytically, winning and losing and achieving certain kinds of stalemates represent concluded outcomes and relationships. Draws, when properly understood and applied, lead to perpetual feedback in an ever-expanding environment, as does one kind of stalemate. But a stalemate can lead to one of three wrong conclusions (see page 60), unless it consists of a draw played out to the last or last-but-one turn. In all except this last outcome, a stalemate is *relatively subjective*. Like winning in the classical sense, stalemates of the wrong sort lead to perpetual repetition. Only playing for a draw leads to subjective learning, creative, skill and cultural development (see Appendix C for definitions).

There is no rule in any game that states that it can *only* be won and lost. There is no law that states that you cannot play for a draw if that is what you prefer. It is one of the permitted possibilities. Whichever goal a player intends to reach is a decision that each is allowed to make for him- or herself.

In games of strategy like noughts and crosses, chess, go, nim, nine-men's-morris, alquerque or any others of that type, a draw occurs when both players or sides agree that, given the current state of play, it is unlikely that either side will make a future mistake and that the game will end with both sides having achieved perfection – a draw played to the last or last-but-one turn or achieved in an even number of successive games. The true meaning of the draw is therefore an agreement-to-agree that error-free or relatively error-free play, perfection and absolute equality are in sight and can eventually be reached by both players – a predictive, conditionally deterministic outcome that applies equally in situations other than games.

This definition of a draw can be tested in all the ways there are and is true without exception. Yet many people will argue about it. They have been conditioned to believe that draws and stalemates do not count and that winning in the conventional sense is the only goal worth playing for. But you cannot be more intelligent or skilled than to strive for actual or relative perfection in any situation or field. You and your partner cannot be more successful than to play without error or fault and to co-operate flawlessly. Nor can anyone do better than to predict success and then to achieve it – something that is only possible when playing for a draw with a like-minded partner. Our perceptions of success and achievement (i.e. competitive winning in the conventional sense) are therefore based on false value judgements. Some people suspect this, but seem unable to demonstrate it convincingly.

One of the problems concerning an understanding of the draw concept is that it is frequently considered passive, boring and non-productive. Winning is believed to be stimulating and exciting because it sets the adrenalin flowing. But that is true of any aggressive pursuit of goals, including benign, creative and peaceful ones, like playing for a draw in company with others. It all depends on where we invest our value judgements and these determine the results and what excites us most. None the less, I venture to state that there is a qualitative difference between the passionate pursuit of peace and hysterical engagement in combat, the composition of a symphony and dropping napalm on an 'enemy'.

The error in the belief that the draw is passive whereas victory is active is inadvertently illustrated by the games played at Twin Oaks, the American commune that has tried to create 'Walden II', based on the psychologist B. F. Skinner's supposed utopia[7]. Skinner is the prophet of 'behaviourism', 'operant conditioning' and the 'teaching machine' (carrot and stick training) in the US, and claims to 'believe' in non-aggression. I visited Twin Oaks in Virginia a number of times and observed its members at work and play. They showed little passion or skill in either of these activities. The spirit in which they approached their work matched their attitudes in play. Further, while the 'commune' itself had 'survived' for a number of years, the period of residency for individuals was quite short. Most stayed no longer than a year, and only a few up to a maximum of a year and a half, at the time I visited Twin Oaks. Therefore 'survival' can be interpreted in a number of ways, depending on what is considered.

Handball at Twin Oaks is played by teams of players who line up facing one another on both sides of a net and pass the ball lethargically back and forth between them. No effort is required for such a 'non-game'. All players are losers because they develop no skills. The Gahuku-Gama version of football, described in Chapter 5, is an example of how genuine draws are achieved that require an aggressive, co-operative pursuit of goals in what are ordinarily regarded as competitive games. This also points to the need to redefine *aggression*, a concept that has been persistently misinterpreted in game playing, evolutionary biology, ethology and sociology.

But first the *stalemate* needs redefinition, despite the fact that it, like the draw, is said 'not to count'. Stalemates have several different meanings, irrespective of context. A stalemate can be an agreement to disagree when the best possible outcome between equals – a draw – has been achieved on the last or last-but-one turn. Alternatively, it can mean that due to a misunderstanding on one or both sides, the draw principle cannot be extended to any larger universe of discourse. Either kind of stalemate can occur when both players reach such an outcome without understanding its meanings, but keep playing the same game over and over in the hope that one or the other will win. A third kind of stalemate takes place when both sides have exhausted their means and cannot continue the conflict. These, as pointed out earlier, are all *relatively subjective* states. Only when a stalemate is recognized as a draw played out to the last or last-but-one turn, and when this outcome is understood as a predictable, co-operative outcome that can be achieved in any larger universe of discourse, can it be said to be truly subjective. (See Appendix A.)

However, a stalemate is conventionally misinterpreted to mean that the game has come to a standstill or ended without a winner due to error, and that for this reason this outcome is valueless and does not count. One or both sides usually insist that if a mistake had not been made, one or the other would have won. That is an absurdity, considering the fact that, looked at totally objectively, such an outcome is perfect or relatively so, or the result of a perfectly balanced exhaustion of means. Because of this chronic misunderstanding of the stalemate, like that which prevailed during the First World War, or in more recent coal-miners' strikes in Britain, a renewal of hostilities at the earliest opportunity is inevitable because, as a result of their conditioning, one or both sides feel cheated out of victory and will try to compete again as soon as they can. In this context it is worth pointing out that it is possible to condition oneself in all the wrong ways as easily as in all the right ones.

Transferring these precise definitions to real life from the universe of games suggests the need for a reconsideration of our relationships to one another and to the world at large. In games and in the real world, trying to win in the conventional, competitive sense means to treat others as enemies to be defeated; to take advantage of their every error or to help matters along by inducing errors that can then be taken advantage of. The latter is the common practice in the courts, in government, elections, business, in union/management disputes, among academics, in sports, war, and in many personal relationships.

The consequences of a growing predisposition to win can be seen in the increasingly large number of breakdowns in the relationships between husbands and wives, lovers, parents, teachers and children. Enmity and lack of consideration for others is on the increase in the world at large. Pretensions of friendliness (e.g. 'have a nice day') are merely cosmetic devices that hide true feelings (i.e. not giving a damn or resentment). Thus even in peacetime we could be said to be at perpetual war, as hostility escalates within and between nations, groups, families and individuals. That is why ours is a zero-sum (winning and losing, competitive) society. One individual or group gains what is lost by others. If you subtract the winnings from the losses the outcome is exactly zero.

A preference for such game outcomes is by no means universal. Some societies and individuals have entirely different goals and use different criteria for success. They are non-zero-sum (co-operative and subjective) cultures in which players consciously play for a draw. This means that there is a net gain to all individuals and groups as a result of playing. For example, the profit and benefits of

Michelangelo's painting of the Sistine Chapel or Mozart's symphonies viewed culturally, historically, subjectively and even in terms of expenditure of effort, far outweigh their actual costs. Their achievement was worth almost any cost and they are priceless. Generations of viewers, listeners and performers have benefited from them and will benefit for an unforeseeable length of time. They are the products of a non-zero-sum game played by all who had a hand in their original creation, including the sponsors.

Regrettably, particularly when they happen to live in highly competitive times, creators of such rank are often momentary or even life-long losers (e.g. Mozart and Van Gogh who, like many great men, spent much of their lives begging or working for a pittance). But even they are usually 'rewarded' posthumously by having their original scores, paintings or manuscripts auctioned at Sotheby's for exorbitant prices. Of course this does not do them or the society much good for it only encourages the worst kind of 'creators' who turn out high-priced 'fashionable' merchandise by the yard at the expense of genuine creation, or scientists who do 'fashionable' research supported by academic and government establishments, while those who do independent work are derided and seldom rewarded even after they have succeeded. None the less, the hacks and opportunists are soon forgotten while the work of genuine creators lives after them.

But the definition of the non-zero-sum game is not restricted to relatively rare and extraordinary achievements. Every human being can reach one or another level of perfection in whatever he or she does – educating children, baking bread or playing noughts and crosses. It is important, however, to remember that willing partners are required for any of these games to be played to a draw. Such an outcome cannot be achieved even by a perfect player, playing with someone hell-bent on trying to win. Such an opponent is bound to be a loser. It is therefore worth dwelling on the assignment of informational meanings to some of the most common transactional words used in different languages to express essential concepts in game playing.

Given that words like winning, losing, draw and stalemate are generally misunderstood, it is easy to see why their interpretation in any one language reflects the value system of the culture that speaks it. *Winning* at any cost is prized above everything else in a *competitive* society. Ruthless competition is considered the height of achievement, intelligence and a supposed superiority. Those who fail to win by making others lose are believed to be unintelligent, genetically or socially inferior or are disqualified due to age or ill health. They are despised as *losers*. Such cultures also worship youth, a stage at which *winning* and *getting ahead* in competitive events (in sports as much as in the classroom, office or factory) is often prized ahead of any other accomplishment. The US youth cult is a typical example.

In any of these cultures those who play for a *draw* are believed to be weak, non-competitive, or effete. A draw is thought of as a form of submission and inadequacy. Co-operation is limited to short-term alliances made to defeat others and dissolved as soon as this is convenient. (That is perhaps the main reason why divorce rates increase in competitive societies.) Drawn games and stalemates are said not to count, to be inconclusive dead ends, brought about as a result of error. Such values predominate in a zero-sum (conflict of interest, winner and loser, relatively objective and competitive) culture.

People encode in language those ideas and things that are most important to them. That is what makes an analysis of words associated with game playing in different languages interesting. I have discovered that in some languages it is impossible to articulate the concept of the 'drawn game' because no word or phrase exists to express it.

In French *remis* (or no value), *null* (the game ends in nothing), or *impasse* (impossible to go on) and *pat* (standing pat) all define a stalemate. There is simply no equivalent word for a *draw*. The same is true in German. *Unentschieden* (undecided), *das Patt* and *der Stillstand* (standing pat), as well as *Remis* (valueless) describe a *stalemate* more or less correctly, but no word for a *draw* situation exists. No word for a *draw* can be found in Spanish: *empate* (dead heat – tie) and *tablas* (tie, stalemate, deadlock) are words used to describe a *stalemate*, but no word defines a *draw* as far as game outcomes are concerned. Words for *equality, perfection, flawless* and *fault free* exist in all these languages, but none are used in the context of games, sports, contests or conflicts.

But in Italian *la partita finì in parità* (the game ends in equality), *pareggio* (the game ends in balance), or *punteggio pari* (to score equally) define both draw and stalemate outcomes; words, phrases and definitions applied to games that are not found in many other languages.

Mandarin has several words that stand for a drawn game – *pinshou* as a general term and *heqi* for chess. Sanskrit, Hindi, Hebrew, Zulu and Vietnamese are also among those languages that distinguish between winning and losing on the one hand and drawn games on the other. These examples reflect prevailing cultural value systems. In Germany and France the traditional objective of success is to win competitively. Failure to win means defeat and inferiority. Draws and stalemates do not count and are both meaningless and without value in such cultures.

The existence of words like *draw* and *stalemate* in a language does not guarantee that their informational meanings are understood. For example, despite the fact that the word 'draw' is as much part of the American as of the English language, competitive winning is the only outcome that counts in America. American presidents are usually dedicated followers of football, poker or other highly competitive games, and their political styles and fortunes parallel how victory is achieved in their favourite sport or recreation. Richard Nixon was an American football devotee.

Regrettably there has been a noticeable reversal in the British value system as this country becomes increasingly competitive in its orientation, despite a long tradition of 'playing for a draw' during its most successful and creative periods as a nation (e.g. during the first Elizabethan era when a stalemated chess game – i.e. a draw played out to the last turn – was considered the best possible outcome). Chapters 5 and 9 show how these valuations of winning, losing, achieving a draw or a stalemate are reflected in the social life and psychological orientation of individuals, groups and whole cultures.

It is obviously impossible to redefine more than a representative selection of words in this book. The causal/consequential analysis of informational words and concepts and their division into relatively objective and subjective categories can be a never-ending task, but one that will have to start if informational machine translation is ever to be more than a gimmick for research-grant-hungry computer scientists and linguists. However, it is worth applying the causal/consequential analysis of meanings to a few additional words to show how general such an application can be.

For example, the first turn move in a game played to be won can be considered the first and unprovoked strike, blow or attack in any contest, conflict or battle. That is *aggression* pure and simple in relatively objective terms. Aggression of this kind excludes all 'subjective judgements'. Everyone – your own soldiers and those of the enemy – is a pawn to be moved or sacrificed without regard to suffering or death if winning is all that matters.

The second moving player is obviously the defender. That requires a subjective orientation and means following the aggressor's lead. An appropriate response to unprovoked aggression is thus essential for any defender who has no place to hide or who cannot run away. A proper defence, therefore, requires even more aggressive behaviour than that of the attacker if it is to succeed in stalemating or defeating him. Such survival-oriented aggressiveness can take many forms. It can be an attempt to escape, to neutralize an attack, deflect it or find the shortest path to a re-establishment of peace and an agreement to agree (i.e. a draw). Or, if the attacker refuses to arrive at a peaceful solution and persists in his attacks it may be necessary to defeat him. Different defensive strategies apply, depending on circumstances. But all these efforts require greater and more aggressive and single-minded evasion or pursuit of the aggressor or else they are bound to fail.

In warfare or conflicts of any kind, the aggressor is the side that strikes the first blow; the defender responds. He can capitulate, run away or defend himself by the available and most appropriate means. But even successful running away requires an aggressive pursuit of a goal. The runner must run faster and more aggressively than the most aggressive pursuer. While it is generally appreciated that an aggressor attacks aggressively, it does not always seem to be understood that it is incumbent upon a successful defender to protect himself even more aggressively, or he loses. Here then we have a *subjective* definition of *aggression* – a vigorous defence against a provocative aggressor. In this context that means an *aggressive* pursuit of creative, constructive and survival-oriented goals.

Obviously the attacking aggressor has staked out a goal for himself (i.e. winning), and therefore what counts is not having a goal *per se*, but whether that goal is benign or malign. The value judgement that applies even in hunting or fishing for food is whether only one side benefits or whether all benefit, if not equally, then in proportion to the effort spent in reaching the common goal and preserving a balanced ecology. The first is a winning and losing proposition and the second a draw. The latter is directly related to other subjective meanings for the word *aggression*, all of which are benign. We *aggressively* pursue worthwhile goals achieved as a result of qualitative excellence from which everyone benefits and from which no one loses. We also have the option of aggressively pursuing worthless goals like trying to win by making others lose.

I will show later (Chapter 12) how Sun Tzu, living about 350 B.C., a Chinese philosopher of war, explained the meaning of the draw in defensive warfare. He detailed how a general leading a defending army can defeat an aggressor and restore peace by the most direct method and succeed in a vigorous (i.e. aggressive) defence, minimizing damage to his own and his enemy's troops and property. On the other hand, fighting for a conventional victory usually means a maximization of destruction.

Konrad Lorenz admits that he did not define the word featured in the English title of his most popular book, *On Aggression*, [8] with sufficient clarity. Anthony Storr [9] attempted to do better, but foundered because he lacked any definite yardstick other than psychiatric theory. These aspects of 'game playing' are elaborated in following chapters in the context of biology, human and animal behaviour, economics, sports and war. The game metaphor provides the means to define *aggression* with relative precision.

The last word I shall discuss here briefly is *chance*. I deal with it in greater detail in Chapters 6 to 9. It plays a vital role in all strategic games played to be won and lost, but not in those played to be drawn. It also defines various aspects of physics (e.g. the random movements of particles in space) and biology (e.g. chance mutations). Chance can be limited severely in so-called games of chance when its causes and operations are fully understood. Chance recedes almost to the vanishing point in the longest run in any subject or context in which it is examined with care. The occurrence and recurrence of so-called chance events in our world is simply a question of sequence, time, human behaviour, and understanding.

Conventionally, chance is associated with words like 'accident', 'coincidence' and 'unpredictability'. What then do we mean by *accident*? According to any causal, consequential and operational analysis, an accident is caused by a *coincidence* of events. The latter is a certainty wherever one or more living organisms are involved. For what appears to be a random convergence is clearly inevitable when it is regarded from a totally objective vantage point outside the system, given the behaviour of the participating individuals. Therefore all accidents involving one or more sentient beings are certainties. The only chance event that is possible under such circumstances is that no accident occurs.

At first glance what I have just written may sound paradoxical, but on closer analysis it will be found to be perfectly logical. Given a little thought and common sense the truth of these definitions becomes obvious. Car accidents and plane crashes are typical examples. To believe that, except in the most rare circumstances (e.g. an unpredicted earthquake), they are caused by anything other than human carelessness is an abrogation of responsibility, because even then such unexpected events are due solely to human ignorance, inattention or an inability to react appropriately, and not to good or bad luck or some universal law of chance.

The meanings of *chance, accident, coincidence, predictability, determinacy, indeterminacy, certainty* and *uncertainty* are explored in greater detail in later chapters and are summarized, together with other definitions, in Appendix C. These concepts and their definitions play vital roles not only in the games we play and how we play them, but also in everyday life, politics, economics, technology, science and the arts.

4 Games People Play

> All games have important and probably decisive
> influences on the destinies of the players ... but
> some offer more opportunities than others ...
> This group may conveniently be called Life
> Games. It includes ... 'Now I've Got You, You
> Son Of A Bitch' ...
>
> Eric Berne[1]

The meaning of anything, and of human behaviour especially, as we have seen depends on an analysis of causes, consequences and the operations that bring them about, relative to time, place, circumstances and the behaviour of others. The qualifiers, of course, define the context within which the games that people play must be evaluated.

The previous chapter showed that it can be difficult to get to the original meaning (of behaviour or anything else) because every cause leads back to an earlier one in what seems like an infinite regression. Besides, our information about actual causes is usually complex, prejudiced or inaccurate so that we may find ourselves guessing. In that case we are likely to be wrong and may point to contributing or extraneous causes as the real triggers of behaviour, often excusing the inexcusable, unless we act on some sort of guiding principle. If we use an appropriate metaphor like game playing that allows us to model real-life behaviours in a microscopic and simplified manner, we have a tool with which we can induce or deduce and understand most of the real causes of behaviour.

For example, we often see people behave in strange and disturbing ways, particularly as regards the seeming rise in crime and violent behaviour. It does not really matter whether this is due to greater publicity in the sensationalizing media or whether there is an actual increase in such events. For instance:

An increase in street and highway shootings here [in southern California] since mid-June [of 1987] has surged to a distressing level . . . 'It's war out there,' said Dr Ange Lobue, a psychiatrist . . . the California Highway Patrol and local police have reported ten roadway shootings since June 18, with a total of four dead and two seriously injured . . . Medical and law enforcement authorities attribute the bloodshed to record traffic on southern California freeways, hot weather and Californians' love of their cars . . .[2]

No matter to what extent the weather, crowding, stress or love of cars may contribute to these bizarre and lethal behaviours, they are simply an expression of the war of 'us' against 'them', a product of cultural conditioning carried to excess, and one more illustration of the end result of an insistence on winning at any cost. The heat and crowding simply bring it to the surface and converge with conditioned competitiveness. In any conflict of interest a red-blooded American is expected to win. Cultural conditioning, aggravated by stress or by what such conditioned individuals consider an extreme provocation, predisposes people in favour of competitive winning.

But it would be wrong to allow any individual to blame his conditioning, for each of us is responsible not only for himself, but for all that goes on around him. We are supposed to be able to resist our wrong conditioning and to decondition ourselves from all ill-informed, prejudiced, inappropriate and damaging habits our culture might impose on us or to which we condition ourselves. The current effort to persuade people to give up smoking, alcohol and habit-forming drugs is an obvious example, but the same principle applies to wrong beliefs as well. At the moment we tend to blame genes, history or society and often punish whoever defends him- or herself from an unwarranted attack.

An article in a British Sunday colour supplement described an annual US 'closet commando' convention in Las Vegas at which 5,000 American males, most of whom have never heard a shot fired anywhere except perhaps at a shooting gallery, pay $2,000 each for a five-day pseudo-killing spree with live ammunition in the Nevada desert, and the privilege of gunning down target figures they love to hate, such as Fidel Castro.[3] They do this with arms provided by the organizers that range from First World War Vickers machine-guns to anti-aircraft guns mounted on jeeps, with the assurance that no one will fire back at them, except 'by accident'. Some participants do get killed, but these murders are believed to be caused by 'chance'. (See Chapter 7 for a discussion of chance.)

The superficial reasons (i.e. the causes) given for this mayhem are patriotism and anti-Communism. But the real reason why people enjoy killing, even if it is only simulated, is the need for some losers to prove to themselves that they can win something, somewhere, without risk to themselves – or so they believe.

Britain's Hungerford mass killer/suicide in 1987 must have been similarly motivated, although his form of expressing a conditioned and frustrated competitive urge was lethal to family and neighbours alike and ultimately to himself.

These examples show how easy it is to get back to a significant cause to which all others are subordinate, once we begin to view behaviour in a game-playing frame of reference. The cause – whether in games played only to make another person lose, or killing a supposed competitor in heavy traffic, at home, next door, in mock-battles in the Nevada desert, or even killing yourself – consists of an intention not only as to which game to play, but also how to play it: for fun and to draw, or to dominate, stalemate or defeat an actual or imagined enemy (including yourself). All games, except the pseudo-wars fought in Las Vegas, call for an appropriate response on the part of the other side that will view game partners as friends or antagonists, depending on intentions. It is thus safe to say that the true intentions of the players (especially when they are hidden, as they often are) are causal in all events in which human behaviour plays a significant role.

The American philosopher John Searle reduces the causation of human behaviour to two principles that are worth quoting. Causality, as reflected in game playing, confirms them:

Principle 1 Actions characteristically consist of two components, a mental component and a physical component.
Principle 2 The mental component is an intention. It has intentionality – it is about something … This form of causation I call 'intentional causation.'[4]

If it is the intention of both players or teams to play for exercise, amusement, sociability, or in order to learn, then this will be a co-operative, friendly relationship in which neither side will try to take advantage of the other. If both players are equal in skill and attention, then this is most likely to turn into a draw, equivalent to a perpetual ping-pong volley. However, if one or both sides mean to win and defeat the other, to stalemate him or exhaust his means (something that should only be allowed in self-defence), then even a purely strategic game of skill, sport or athletic event – or any other relationship – turns into an adversarial and possibly lethal contest in which the outcome depends on chance, no matter what the professed intentions of one or both players might be.

In this case any first moving player who is trying to win (i.e. the aggressor) will usually believe that he has a significant advantage and will try to seize and exploit it tactically and psychologically. He will be wrong from the start, whether or not he plays with someone who understands game playing in general, the particular game that is being played, or how to play it faultlessly. The second moving player has a considerable advantage, but only if he is willing to be more brutal than the first.

The belief in the efficacy of 'first strike capability' is based on an entirely erroneous presumption that the first moving player in any game has an advantage (see Appendix B). There is a great deal of confusion about this question even when it comes to simple games like noughts and crosses or more complex ones like chess. Military experts and game theoreticians still argue about it. First strike advantage is discussed seriously on the basis of ideology, belief (e.g. 'shoot first and ask questions afterwards' or 'the only good Indian is a dead Indian') or misunderstood game theoretical ideas, rather than proven or disproven as a matter of fact. These may be amusing and profitable pastimes for theoreticians and the military, but the rest of the world are the victims of their stupidity, as were millions of people in this century's two great world wars, to say nothing of other smaller-scale ones before and since.

The response of the second moving player (the defender) to any first strike attack demands an even more aggressive posture than that of the first moving aggressor, and a refusal to be disconcerted. He has three choices: he can opt out of the game; counter-attack at the expense of self-protection, thus exposing himself to further attacks and traps set by his opponents; or protect himself perfectly, allowing the attacker to exhaust and defeat himself (this last is the true Tao or Zen way of self-defence).

The successive turns and moves are the operations that bring about one or another of a limited number of inevitable consequences: they can only consist of winning for one and losing for the other, a draw, stalemate or abandonment of the game for various reasons. The achievement of any of these outcomes always depends on the actual intentions of the players and their understanding of what is required to satisfy them. For the best or worst intentions will not be realized if strategies appropriate to the desired outcome are not put into operation. But also, as we have seen, the operations that bring these end states about must be understood or else the players are always guessing and in the hands of chance.

To summarize, you always get what you want if you know what you are doing. If not, you get whatever you get by what may appear to you as chance. But chance is not what it is believed to be (see Chapters 6 and 7). Human behaviour should be purely strategic in situations that matter so that chance seldom enters into it (see Chapter 9 and Appendices A, B and C). Anyone can assume full control of his or her life once its conditions, and your own and other people's intentions, are sufficiently understood.

By examining the various causal, operational and consequential states of games, we can get to the actual meanings of the outcomes and the operations that bring them about, eliminating chance entirely or in part. It is then possible to fulfil one's intentions and arrive at the desired outcome to whatever extent the other players' awareness and learning ability allow. These conditions are the same for the games we play for fun as for those we play in real life which can have serious consequences. Instead of getting bogged down in a morass of detail that merely confuses us, we can concentrate on the true meanings of behaviours that apply in games as in life. If this approach were taken by authors of 'How To' and 'lateral thinking' books (e.g. 'I have done so well, why do I feel so bad?'), then no one need ever be confused.

Eric Berne attempted to analyse behaviour in terms of winning and losing in the bestseller from which the title of this chapter is taken. But he understood game playing only to a limited extent, confusing himself and his readers. For example, he was convinced that the first moving player in any game or real-life situation has an advantage in winning terms – a serious mistake: 'As in most games, White, who makes the first move [in chess], wins either way.'[5] Like most people today, Berne knew only one way to play – to win – although he correctly deplored this as a way of life and defined it as a form of mental illness. To Berne the road to mental health was not to play games, at least in real-life situations. It involved lying on a psychiatrist's couch where a patient discovered this supposed fact.

However, Berne was quite unable to offer any advice on how to change the behaviours he rightfully deplored, or identify those that should replace them, other than by platitudes like 'awareness'. American West Coast cults of consciousness-raising, and group-gropes like the Esalen Institute at Big Sur were based on his principles of transactional awareness. Unfortunately nobody told anyone what they were supposed to be aware of other than 'not to play games', 'not to try to win', to love one another, trust, share and co-operate – all unconditionally and without qualification. Many religious sects and political groups have made similar sugges-tions throughout history. None have changed people's behaviour significantly, except to encourage them to surrender their individual autonomy to priesthoods, psychiatrists, cults, gurus and institutions, and to become willing victims by giving up their autonomous thought processes to the 'will of the leader'.

Berne found ready disciples who prescribed his nostrums without providing the answers that enabled people to solve their problems independently. One of Berne's followers, Thomas A. Harris, also believed that there is only one way to play games, and came to similar wrong conclusions:

Are winning and losing the only options for persons or for nations? Winners and losers have been the only models we have had . . . I believe all games have their origins in the simple childhood game . . .: 'Mine is bigger than yours.'[6]

Ideas like 'Mine is the same size as yours!' or 'What difference does it make?' or 'I've got something different but just as good that complements yours' (useful for co-operation between the sexes) do not seem to have occurred to Harris.

Since, like most people, they do not understand the meanings of any outcome other than winning, transactional psychiatrists give vague advice like 'don't try to win', 'don't be a loser', or 'don't play games'. These are negative and trite suggestions. They know what they are against (winning), but do not know what they are 'for' except whatever can be expressed by other clichés like 'be nice' or 'be good to yourself'. Berne and Harris also never established any connection between the private and public lives of their patients – their identical 'winning' behaviours on the other side of the ranch-type colonial, picture-window world of middle-class America – and that between individuals and groups. But the competitive successes of their patients in offices and factories were the very behaviours that allowed them to afford the high cost of psychiatric massages, drugs or alcohol. The techniques of winning within the family, in bed and among friends are the same as those used in business, politics, the courts, diplomacy, art, sports, science and on California's freeways. It was a significant oversight.

When the 'draw' alternative to winning and losing and what it represents is not understood, then 'altruism' would seem to be the only alternative option for those who wish to be perceived as generous. The concept of altruistic behaviour (especially when this term is interpreted to mean being 'selfless') is convenient because it allows 'giving' which makes you feel 'good' because you are being 'nice' without getting involved in the misery of those you help. Besides, you can always expect altruism from others who can afford it, without ever feeling called upon to give anything yourself. There are all sorts of variations on the 'altruism' game that are not worth exploring here.

Co-operation, according to the usual valuation, is only possible in competition against others, as in any army. Altruism is conventionally equated with generosity and self-sacrifice. But seen in the context of gaming, altruism usually means 'letting those whom we consider inferior or handicapped win once in a while'; in other words making them more dependent than they already are, rather than helping them become as autonomous as possible. Altruism in this sense turns them into permanent losers.

This definition of altruism should not be misinterpreted as advocating neglect of the young, aged, unemployed, ill or disabled, who deserve all the help a society can give them as a matter of right. But altruism (as distinct from social justice – a version of the co-operative draw) can be just another form of classical winning; of turning what should be everyone's due into a manipulative act of charity or paternalism, or a self-serving way of assuaging guilt.

People like Bob Geldof seem to be aware that the object of giving is to help people become autonomous, yet, as I have said before, biologists, social scientists and economists view altruism as the only alternative to competition. To them co-operation means joining forces to defeat others.

Erich Fromm describes how the Eskimo view altruism and their understanding of the meaning of 'charity':

Once Peter Freuchen [the Arctic explorer] was handed some meat by an Eskimo hunter and responded by gratefully thanking him. The hunter was cast down, and Freuchen was quickly corrected by an old man: 'You must not thank for your meat; it is your right to get parts. In this country, nobody wishes to be dependent on others. Therefore, there is nobody who gives or gets gifts, for thereby you become dependent. With gifts you make slaves just as with whips you make dogs.'

The word 'gift' has overtones of charity, not of reciprocity. In no hunting-gathering society is gratitude expressed, and, as a matter of fact, it would be wrong even to praise a man as 'generous' when he shares his game with camp mates. On another occasion he may be said to be generous, but not in response to a particular incident of sharing . . .[7]

It never occurred to Berne and Harris to consider co-operation as an alternative to selfishness and competitiveness. The standards by which the character of a man or woman is judged in an Eskimo culture seem strange to most people reared in our society even when they are generous and wish to help anyone who is in need. To those with a closed mind any form of sharing is seen as an act of altruism or even weakness, rather than as one of co-operation and *noblesse oblige*. Again it is the intention and state of mind more than the act that really counts. There is a vast difference between 'wanting to help' (i.e. to co-operate; a perpetual subjective feed-back state) and 'wanting to give' (a one-way operation that ends in closure – see Appendices A and B).

The American zoologist David Barash, in *Sociobiology and Behaviour*, is as confused about the meanings of competition, co-operation and altruism as were Berne, Harris and others:

Co-operation and altruism are major themes in the evolution of social behaviour. None the less, the unpleasant fact remains that maximization of personal, inclusive fitness often involves asserting one's self at the expense of friends, neighbours, and even relatives . . . if there is enough to go around, then there is no reason for competition . . . To the victor belong the spoils, in contest competition. In scramble competition, the victor is simply that who scrambles for the most spoils.[8]

The differences between a 'scramble' for scarce commodities or territory, and battling for them, or between overtaking other drivers on the freeway or killing them if they block your passage, are obvious. But the excuse given by the would-be winners of scrambles and fights to the finish for scarce resources or the fast lane on the highway is that 'nice guys finish last'. They feel that this somehow vindicates their elbowing out of the way or gunning down those they fear might arrive ahead of them. The possibility of sharing or mutual consideration does not even occur to them.

The following quote from Barash's book shows who is and is not fit to survive on and off the highways of the world, according to sociobiologists, neo-Darwinists, ethologists and other authorities:

Evolutionary theory suggests a simple answer to the question, when should an individual be aggressive? . . . each individual should be aggressive when such behaviour increases the individual's inclusive fitness. In other words, aggression should characterize situations in which contest competition is more efficient than scrambling. This is particularly true when resources are in short supply . . .[9]

The author seems to endorse criminal behaviour if that is his answer to the allocation and distribution of scarce resources or space. Such a conclusion would appear to be warranted for Barash and others who subscribe to an ill-willed view of evolution. As he states towards the end of his book:

For the victor there is very little problem. It [the victorious animal] will enjoy the fruits of victory: enhanced access to mates, food, territories . . . Given the association between gonadal hormones and aggression, psychological castration may be one proximate mechanism whereby subordinates physiologically ensure the peaceful acceptance of their subordinations.[10]

The laws of nature, according to Barash, not only decide that 'nice guys finish last', but also that they are altruistic, voluntary eunuchs, or deserve actual or psychological castration if they let anyone get ahead of them. By these standards those who are most corrupt would win in the 'struggle for survival', perpetuating their unpleasant traits by being the only ones able to reproduce.

Indeed, the suggestion has been made at various times and places (in the American South pertaining to poor Blacks, and in Nazi Germany concerning Jews, gypsies and mental defectives) that certain minority groups thought to be inferior should be forcibly prevented from reproducing by one means or another.[11] On the other hand, voluntary sterilization of or sexual abstinence by such discriminated-against groups could conceivably be construed as an act of altruism (i.e. saving the 'purity' of and providing *Lebensraum* for the dominant race).

Barash quotes a Scottish ecologist in what seems like support of this last contention:

. . . V. C. Wynne-Edwards, wrote a book titled *Animal Dispersion and Its Relation to Social Behaviour*. Its central thesis was startling: animals tend generally to avoid over-exploitation of their habitats, especially with regard to food supply. They accomplish this largely by *altruistic* restraint on the part of individuals who reduce their reproduction, or refrain altogether, thereby avoiding local overpopulation.[12]

While there are certain self-regulatory population controls such as predation, disease and a reduction in the drive to reproduce which prevent overcrowding relative to territory and food supply, it is highly unlikely that animals practise 'altruism' (or forced physical or psychological castration) in this suggested anthropomorphic way. Many species may behave in a manner that seems altruistic to us, but it is instinctive and innate behaviour that serves the long-term self-interest of the group and therefore the individual.

Garrett Hardin, an American biologist and ecologist, demonstrates how a lack of distinction between the *relatively objective* (winning) and *subjective* (draw) definitions of the concept of *competitive* and *co-operative* success can lead to similar wrong conclusions. He writes:

. . . I here refer to the . . . 'competitive exclusion principle' . . . It may be briefly stated thus: *complete competitors cannot coexist* . . . (i) if two noninter-breeding populations 'do the same thing' – that is, occupy precisely the same ecological niche . . . – and (ii) if they occupy the same geographic territory – and (iii) if population A multiplies even the least bit faster than population B, then ultimately A will completely displace B, which will become extinct. This is the 'weak form' of the principle. Always in practice a stronger form is used, based on the removal of the hypothetical character of condition (iii). We do this because we adhere to what may be called the axiom of inequality, which states that no two things or processes, in a real world, are precisely equal.

The contrast between the two disciplines [biology and sociology] appears nowhere sharper than in the treatment of competition. To the biologist, this topic is central to all discussion of group phenomena. The literature of evolution, ecology, and ethology is saturated with discussions of competition. Sociology being (as biologists see it) but a special sub-field of ethology (animal behaviour) one would expect it too to be much concerned with competition. Is it?[13]

Without stretching this analogy too far, Hardin's argument seems to favour the highway shoot-out concept of the distribution of territory. He elaborates his claim that competition is insufficiently discussed in sociology (something which is true for psychology as well) and cites the following excerpt from a sociological textbook in support of his claim. However Hardin has picked the wrong example and for all the wrong reasons, as will become clear later in this chapter. This quote is indeed one of the relatively rare instances in which a sociologist takes cognisance of the tragic effect of quantitative competitive behaviour and of the possibility that 'everyone can win', although he does not seem to know how that can be achieved:

Faith in progress has played an important part in American society generally; faith in education has been an essential ingredient of this larger faith. The virtues enjoined by the latter have been, among others, individual ambition and competitiveness. The American educational system is based on these virtues and in turn fosters them, beginning with nursery school and going on through college. The games that American children play are very largely competitive, indeed are training devices for competition. Essential to this is the win/lose formula. In every game, in the end, somebody wins and somebody loses; the aim, of course, is to be a winner. It is only very young children who sometimes wish, wistfully, that 'everybody should win'; they soon learn that this is 'impossible' – in American society, that is, for there are other societies in which children actually play games in which 'everyone wins'.

The educational system not only fosters competition but (except in some sports) *individual* competition. Each individual competes with all others . . .[14]

Hardin contradicts himself when he objects to these authors' questioning the value of quantitative competition in our culture and dismisses the possible evolution of a qualitatively competitive and essentially co-operative society:

Should we, for fear of hurting the loser's feelings, allow anyone who wants to practise brain surgery? Or choose the winners by lot? Would either system of selection produce a net gain for society?

A sociologist whose actions were consistent with the passage quoted above would refuse to countenance a competitive system that denied anyone the right to become a brain surgeon.[15]

The difference between qualitative (determining who is best qualified) and quantitative competition (getting into med-school because your father has made a large donation towards a new research lab, as happens in the US) – in the first instance everyone wins, and in the second the son wins and society loses – does not seem to have occurred to Hardin.

The principles of the 'survival of the winners in the game of life' and the curtailment of the losers' right to reproduce were articulated in the nineteenth century not only by Spencer, Galton and eventually Darwin himself, but also by Thomas Huxley, Darwin's staunch defender against the reactionary Bishop Wilberforce and his supporters. The sentiments – for they are hardly more than crude, bigoted opinions – sound familiar, for they underlie much of the oratory of today, although dressed up in modern scientific and political jargon and expressed far more subtly than in the past. Huxley had this to say in the 1890s:

The criminal law, in so far as by putting to death, or by subjecting to long periods of imprisonment, those who infringe its provisions, prevents the propagation of hereditary criminal tendencies; and the poor-law, in so far as it separates married couples, whose destitution arises from hereditary defects of character, are doubtless selective agents operating in favour of the non-criminal and the more effective members of society.

... What is often called the struggle for existence in society ... is a contest, not for the means of existence, but for the means of enjoyment. Those who occupy the first place in this practical competitive examination are the rich and the influential; those who fail, more or less, occupy the lower places, down to the squalid obscurity of the pauper and the criminal.

... As ... among primitive men, the weakest and stupidest went to the wall, while the toughest and shrewdest, those best fitted to cope with their circumstances, but not the best in any other sense, survived. Life was a continual free fight and beyond the limited and temporary relations of the family, the Hobbesian war of each against all was the normal state of existence.[16]

We will see later in this and in the next chapter that a society's value system (e.g. who is most fit to survive; who wins and who loses in the tribal or nationalistic war of 'all against all') determines who is sane and who is not. In the previous chapter I indicated that this may depend on whether true or false meanings are assigned to commonly used informational words and phrases. It is usually unsafe to stray very far from the values and meanings institutional-ized in the society in which we happen to live, unless we do not care whether we are branded dangerous dissidents or insane eccentrics.

Those who consider themselves part of the establishment within one culture seem unable to conceive of a game outcome other than that 'their side' should win and that the others should lose. Even when aware of different possibilities, anyone who wants to 'make it' in any competitive job or society should keep his thoughts to himself to make sure of staying on the right side of what is considered sane and normal in his world, otherwise he risks ostracism or being fired. The correct definition of the draw as the superior game ending (i.e. that individualists can flourish best within a proper co-operative framework) did not exist for Berne, any more than it did for Spencer, Darwin, Huxley or Hardin. That is why Berne could not conceive of a better way to play games. This, as we have seen, is not an exclusively American phenomenon. For Berne's psychiatric heritage goes back to Freud who did more to institutionalize and excuse conflict than any man since von Clausewitz.

Freud differed from social Darwinists only in so far as he dealt mostly with inner conflicts. In fact Freud was a great admirer of Darwin for all the wrong reasons. He decreed conflict to be an innate (i.e. genetically programmed) quality of the human psyche. Such conflict was, according to him, a sublimation of something else – usually sexual frustration. This Jewish, severely disturbed, drug-addicted and guilt-ridden man (he was a cocaine addict and had a life-long secret affair with his wife's sister) was the product of an Austro-Hungarian, sexually repressed and highly competitive, pre-First-World-War culture that openly embraced anti-Semitism. None the less he set the stage for rationalizing and defining his time and culture as normal. He was the founding father of the classical psychiatric valuation, which held that everyone who has doubts or is in conflict with the establishment in any one time and place is potentially disturbed or 'mentally ill'. But in fact most sane people should be emotionally disturbed by today's society and the era in which we live.

Freudian philosophy was a means for adjusting dissenters to society's norms, even if it meant that they bankrupted themselves by spending years on a psychiatrist's or psychotherapist's couch. In many cases they might have been better off refusing to adjust. In others, the sought-after cure would have been certain and faster had patients been faced with an immediate causal, consequential and operational analysis of the culture in which they lived, or of their own culturally conditioned, competitive behaviours. True meanings and intentions (their own and those of others) would have become clear to them fairly rapidly, had they ever been faced with the consequences to themselves and to others. Rather than helping them discover the meanings (and ethical consequences) of their time and culture, or of their own public and private behaviours, Freud concentrated on an exhaustive search for original causes that took patients back to their childhood traumas, dreams and sexual fantasies. This form of treatment is a profitable exercise as far as psychiatrists and psychotherapists are concerned, but patients gain little or nothing other than becoming dependent on their mentors.

The meanings of childhood experiences, no matter what they might have been, can always be misinterpreted. Dreams, like tea leaves, can be twisted to mean whatever you want them to mean. They define the state of an individual's mind (e.g. nightmares are a sign of unresolved problems, but do not necessarily reflect them), but that is a rather different matter. Freud often reversed causes and consequences. For example, art, rather than being a sublimation of sexuality as Freud claimed, is a creative act for which sex is often a substitute.

The *death wish* (the supposedly 'innate' wish to die, to be self-destructive, commit suicide or to fail) provided yet another brick on which rested the foundation of Freud's understanding of the human psyche. It is the most discredited of his theories, although it turns out to be one of his best insights. It is obvious that every winner and loser in games of strategy and chance has the equivalent of a death wish. Both try to make a killing and win, but one of them must certainly lose and symbolically commit suicide. That is the eventual fate of even the most successful winners, for hardly anyone can win for ever. The psychologically interesting question should then be asked (and can be easily answered): why should anyone even try to win when it is virtually inevitable that they must lose sooner or later, thus converting both winners and losers into losers from the start? The only rational answer to this must be that winners hope to win perpetually. Some do, but only for as long as there are willing victims. But even if Freud's death wish is interpreted in this way, he was wrong about its supposed innateness. He believed it to be a built-in motivating force of the human psyche, just like Lorenz's idea of the innateness of aggression. Instead, both are environmentally or self-conditioned forms of behaviour, although the potential is innate. But then the same is true for the co-operative draw, the *life wish* that predominates throughout nature and in human nature especially, because we have the power to decide which options to choose, unless we allow our culture to rob us of such autonomy.

The draw principle also stands for ethics, aesthetics, mature conscience and love – a kind of real-life, near-fairy-tale outcome: 'and they all lived more or less happily ever after'. These positive qualitative and creative aspects of human nature never entered the make-believe of the Freudian world: as a result Freud's teachings are profoundly negative and depressing. All he achieved was to label certain categories of behaviour that had seemed puzzling until then, or were categorized under the general heading of lunacy. His disciples – Melanie Klein, his daughter Anna and those who allowed themselves to be conditioned by the Freudian myth – may have believed in him but they never produced any factual evidence of the truth of his inventions which remain purely theoretical and speculative.

One important clue to Freud's personality was that he lacked a sense of humour, a quality that is essential in any context especially when it comes to meanings. Satire shows reality to be what it actually is. Jonathan Swift, Mark Twain, Art Buchwald and Lenny Henry hold up a mirror to a world where absurdities and lunacy are accepted as the norm. Humour at its best strips conventions of hypocrisy and cant. Psychologizing or dissecting it explains nothing and just makes a joke of the diagnostician.

Freud's academic theorizing on humour is unintentionally funny and misses the point entirely. His book *Jokes and their Relation to the Unconscious*[17] provides far greater insight into his thought processes than his other work. With customary seriousness he tried to establish a connection between dreams, sexual frustration and humour. He only succeeded in making himself ridiculous. Freud's perceptions in these matters founder on the rock of semantics – the touchstone of sanity and reality.

The Freudian approach to psychiatry today has much to answer for, according to Thomas Szasz, his chief and lucid critic, himself a psychiatrist:

... today, particularly in the affluent West, all of the difficulties and problems of living are considered psychiatric diseases, and everyone (but the diagnosticians) is considered mentally ill ... Modern psychiatric ideology is an adaptation – to a scientific age – of the traditional ideology of Christian theology. Instead of being born into sin, man is born into sickness ... in the Age of Madness the ideology is medical, the technology clinical, and the expert psychiatric.

... Criminals are surely ill ... say the 'behavioral scientists' and their followers ... Here we catch the ideologist of insanity at his favourite activity – the manufacture of madness.

... The assumption is made that some neurological defect, perhaps a very subtle one, will ultimately be found to explain all the disorders of thinking and behaviour. Many contemporary physicians, psychiatrists and other scientists hold this view, which implies that people's troubles cannot be caused by conflicting personal needs, opinions, social aspirations, values, and so forth. These difficulties – which I think we may simply call *problems in living* – are thus attributed to physiochemical processes that in due time will be discovered (and no doubt corrected) by medical research.[18]

As Szasz suggests, a major flaw in Freudian and much other psychologizing is that it makes the wrong assumptions about what is innate and what is learned – the so-called nature/nurture debate. It is useful to make this distinction provided we include the significant characteristics of each. Obviously aggression, violence and conflict are innate possibilities that may or may not require expression in different situations. Co-operation, peaceful co-existence and sharing are equally innate. But Freudians, like social Darwinists, sociobiologists, some ethologists and most game players have opted for believing that only aggressive violence (i.e. playing to win) is innate, while an aggressive pursuit of co-operative goals (what to them seems like altruism but is actually playing for a co-operative draw) is somehow unnatural and needs to be taught.

Thomas Szasz is not alone in calling attention to the contradictions in modern psychiatry. Erich Fromm comes equally close in stating what should be obvious. He questions the meanings of human aggression attributed to it by Lorenz, Ardrey, Morris and others, as well as the conventional concept of territoriality, at least as far as primates are concerned. He quotes Tinbergen (see Chapter 8) in support of his position and writes:

Defence of territory has the function *of avoiding* the serious fighting that would become necessary if the territory were invaded to an extent as to generate crowding. Actually the threat behaviour in which territorial aggression manifests itself is the instinctively patterned way of upholding spatial equilibrium and peace . . . To be aggressive, in its original meaning of 'aggressing', can be defined as *moving forward towards a goal without undue hesitation, doubt, or fear.*

The thesis that war is caused by innate human destructiveness is plainly absurd for anyone who has even the slightest knowledge of history.[19]

Fromm is equally dismissive of the claim made by certain biological and social scientists that aggression is used by dominant males in other than human species to claw their way to the top of the hierarchy:

For dominance, as far as it exists, the same comment applies which I have made with regard to territorialism. It functions to give peace and coherence to the group and to prevent friction that could lead to serious fighting.[20]

Aggression is usually considered to be a form of violence and to involve brute force, both seen as the dominant and often exclusive characteristics of nature. This is the view shared by Freud (see Chapter 12) and others, and may be true for certain animal species where physical strength is the sole criterion for survival. But in many species, including our own, other strengths are often of equal or greater importance. It seems remarkable that many academicians who lead essentially sedentary and cerebral lives should prize physical aggression above all other qualities when it comes to survival. In our case an aggressive pursuit of goals can involve language and symbology, art and science, adaptation to environments that range from the tropical to the arctic and extend into space or deep into the oceans, tool-making, and an ability to laugh at ourselves, as well as physical fitness and speed.

Yet most psychologists, ethologists and biologists, all classing themselves as intellectuals, see human territoriality only in muscle-bound terms. They regard territoriality among our species as determined by a genetic endowment that provides males with 'superior' brute strength which they can direct against others of their kind to claim the most desirable space needed for their personal physical survival and reproduction – a kind of genetically determined Wild West shoot-out. They conclude on the basis of their prejudices that innate heritage, crowding and scarce resources are the reasons for human violence, aggression and war.

However, and certainly today, rather than scarcity in the West, we have a glut of foodstuffs and a capacity for over-production caused by gratuitous subsidies that result in grain and butter mountains, wine and milk lakes and moth-balled ships. Meanwhile the Third World goes hungry largely as a result of maldistribution and artificially-induced poverty; and yet competitiveness is on the increase everywhere. The real competition seems to be between nations and multi-national corporations who already have more than they need, to see who can get the most out of those who have less or practically nothing.

None the less some human beings manage to get along with one another under crowded conditions for long periods of time – in an igloo or a space capsule for example – provided they have a common purpose. Clearly, human 'territory' is not simply a matter of physical space unless each wants more than is available, does not want to share, keep out of the way of others, or becomes hostile when inadvertently jostled.

Territories demand aggressive attitudes if claims are to be staked and defended. In our species that may require a subjective (i.e. a draw and qualitative) form of competition that demands high concentration and co-operation with the self and with others; or it may involve a struggle to learn and perfect oneself for a particular purpose. None the less, human goals can be reached by chance and as a result of ruthless competition *against* others, but for these successes the winners pay a heavy price – a loss of inner peace, though they may not care about or even appreciate this. Why then do they pay psychiatrists to listen to their inner conflicts? Those who do not unburden themselves eventually suffer even greater depression because no one can repress his conscience for ever.

Crick and Watson's 'territory' – their discovery of the double helix – is a first-rate example of how great a role chance can play when science is viewed as a competitive and rather nasty game – played 'against' rather than 'with' others. It is also a sad commentary on the character of people who, as Watson discloses about himself and his partner in *The Double Helix*,[21] played innumerable dirty tricks on fellow scientists and friends in order to win by default and make them lose.

Winning by playing 'against' others is clearly anti-social and often caused by the fact that aggression 'for' something – i.e. an aggressive pursuit of goals – is not perceived by, or is denied to individuals or groups. Those who win by less than laudable means have simply anaesthetized their conscience, creative skills, energy and talent. They are third-raters and flawed individuals who only win once in a while and by chance, and because they have taken advantage of others. Their successes last only for as long as their victims are willing, and they take a chance on suffering a rude awakening of conscience at inconvenient times.

The difference between human and animal territoriality is therefore often misunderstood by most who write about it. Territory acquired by a male may make him attractive to the female of his species, but in human societies territory and pecking order are not just questions of muscle, land, trees or food supply. There territory is often more symbolic than real. A top-notch craftsman – male or female – in farming, art, science, business or any other field of expertise – will have his or her pick of options ahead of those who are less capable.

Males who lack territory and unattached females in the higher animal species become a surplus bachelor population. They are the first to be eaten by predators – one form of population control that Jonathan Swift suggested in jest for the human species. Social and economic cannibalism does exist, even among ourselves, yet males and females in our modern world may be territorially successful, and remain single and stay alive; a non-violent form of voluntary (but not altruistic) population control. Further, we no longer need fear predators other than members of our own species: we are our own worst enemies.

Today it is often believed that human males are more aggressive than females. The only difference between the sexes in these respects is the form that aggression takes. Male aggression is more often physical because men are usually stronger than women. But female competitiveness and violence can be as vicious as that of the male, although it tends to be psychological. Physical violence may leave visible scars, but the invisible psychological ones can be far more damaging and lasting. It is fairly easy to get over a broken leg, but not a broken spirit.

The potential for aggression, violence and the will to win and defeat an opponent, as much as the potential for co-operation, are equally innate in males and females. But what triggers such behaviours – or when – depends on strength, conditioning, environment and the behaviour of others, as we saw in the case of California's highway slaughter. But – and this is important, for it is often overlooked today – violence may be needed as a legitimate defence against an unprovoked physical or psychological assault or neglect unless you wish to be the attacker's willing victim.

Violent or aggressive behaviours are misinterpreted by psychiatrists like Anthony Storr who devotes a chapter to 'Aggression in Childhood Development' in one of his books [22] in which he quotes (and disagrees with) Melanie Klein. She believed that aggressive behaviour in newborn infants is proof of its genetic innateness and a preview of adult human nature.

But it is absurd to attribute violent, malicious, competitive behaviour to infants. Their tantrums are aggressively defensive and indicate a need or discomfort that they cannot express in any other way or alleviate for themselves. They are wholly dependent, relatively immobile and unable to communicate effectively except to show distress, especially when they are neglected. Aggressive protest and anger are survival mechanisms. Expressions of infantile 'ferocity' cannot be compared to mature behaviours which are outwardly similar but very different as far as intentions, contributing causal triggers or consequences are concerned.

There is no such thing as a 'violent' or 'competitive' baby who seeks to win by making its parents lose. An adult should be able to control his or her rages; a baby cannot do so. To consider this a form of aggressive violence is to render our language meaningless.

Storr himself suffers from semantic confusion when it comes to behaviour that is aggressive but not necessarily violent, although it can lead to violence.

Disagreement, controversy, and even competitive striving have a positive function in human existence. For how can a man know who he is, and what he thinks and believes, unless there are others who think and believe differently?[23]

This is, of course, an extraordinary, if common, stance. There is much to be learned from *discussion* with other individuals. It is one – but only one – of the ways of learning. But there is nothing to be gained from *competitive striving*, *arguments* and *debates*, except victory by default as in all games of strategy and chance. If we are sufficiently mature we can look at any problem from another person's point of view by means of questioning and discussion. If he or she is factually correct and you are wrong, you can go on from there if you accept your error. If you are correct, then the other can admit his or her mistake and the discussion ends or is enlarged. Trouble only arises when both are wrong, or whoever is in error refuses to admit his mistake.

But people are often so busy defending mistakes that nothing is learned and nothing is accomplished. No one has ever won or lost a discussion, but arguments and debates are won and lost every day and winning them means exactly the same thing as it does in noughts and crosses, chess, poker or any other game of strategy or chance.

It is only possible to argue about what you do not know. If both sides know whatever facts there are, then there is no point in arguing about them. Both should agree. If one is right and the other wrong, nothing is served by sticking to a wrong, entrenched position. That is how everyone loses, including the individual who is right and wastes his time arguing with a loser. There is also no point in giving in when you know that you are right. The facts of the matter demand agreement, sooner or later, unless the object is to win and make the other lose, as in elections for office, committees, debating societies, among the ignorant, the immature, or those who have allowed themselves to be totally conditioned and therefore can no longer think independently. When people argue or debate they are playing the winning and losing game. They are trying for a draw when they discuss the possibilities in the expectation of reaching an agreement as to what is right. The question of common sense, being committed, making value judgements and admitting mistakes has a great deal to do with learning. Without any of these it is virtually impossible to learn.

Learning and education fall within the purlieus of psychology and are especially affected by prevailing attitudes on how games are meant to be played. Education has been a competitive game for far too long. Winning (i.e. gaining credentials) is one of modern education's primary objectives. With conventional 'game theory' popularized in schools and universities during the 1950s and 1960s, it was natural that education from early grades to university levels should become infected with an escalating competitive winning spirit – one reason for apathy among some of the brightest students.

Clark Abt, a war-games consultant to the Pentagon, and James Coleman, a Johns Hopkins University academic, became spokesmen for the idea that conventional gaming was a useful educational tool. Their 'learning games' became popular educational merchandise widely touted as a panacea to American educators. This approach had its critics, but they were few and went largely unheeded:

The legislative game which Dr Coleman cites by way of illustration exhibits the weakness of his approach. He believes that his game teaches the 'basic structure of representative government', but it does nothing of the sort. Instead, it indoctrinates the player into a number of naïve misconceptions about the nature of the American Congress and American politics.[24]

Coleman and his colleagues were successful in doing just that, as the relatively bland acceptance of Watergate and its repeat performance as Irangate have demonstrated. Winning and losing, ruthless competition and a presumed balance arising out of conflicts of interest, remain the core of the American credo. This approach is embedded in the popular interpretation of the Constitution of the United States. It is believed to be a cornerstone in the administration of adversarial justice and in business in most of the rest of the world. It has corrupted learning and education and turned them into processes of training and operant conditioning for success in purely materialistic terms – the very processes that make people stupid.

One of the factors common to human nature is the potential and ability of the self to form and re-form itself and its behaviours through learning; to grow, change and mature – or to remain locked in immaturity for life. Development or the evolution of a co-operative orientation is a question of will, learning, long-term self-interest, social awareness and recognition of the available options. It is possible to condition or re-condition oneself to be co-operative in appropriate circumstances and to stalemate or defeat an aggressor in self-defence when no evasion or agreements are possible. It is equally possible to become totally habituated to winning, even to the point of enjoying torturing other people. This is the hallmark of a psychopathic personality. No one can help such people. They can only help themselves if they want to. Learning is something that everyone must do for themselves. Methods of thinking for yourself are the only things that can be taught. All else is 'training' (i.e. programming – not thinking for yourself and doing what you are told, even when that is wrong).

Most people go along with the crowd, no matter how wrong it may be. But that 'crowd', society, culture or environment is not to blame. All of us are victims of operant conditioning, which both affects and comes from parents, teachers and the culture in which we live. The difference between individuals who achieve balance and autonomy and those who do not is the difference between willing and unwilling victims; between would-be winners and losers on one side and those who truly understand and live the draw principle on the other; between those who differentiate between games played for fun, love of life and survival and those who play only for money, power or glory; between those who accept an insane norm and those who resist it. These are the differences between peace and war, co-operation and competition, sharing and selfishness, learning and being locked into a closed environment, or between a loving and an antagonistic personality. They are not things that are done to us. We do them to ourselves, depending on the conditions we recognize and impose and the meanings and values we assign to what we say, do and experience.

As I said earlier, the potential for every possible human behaviour is innate and even most involuntary reflexive and instinctive behaviours (e.g. breathing, heartbeat, sucking, eye-blink) are triggered by genetic-, environmental- or self-conditioning. Nature provides us with all the voluntary and involuntary behavioural options there are. We pick the right or the wrong ones from those over which we have a measure of control, depending on our exercise of free will. This was understood by the earliest Taoists. Few of their original writings survive and much of what remains has been adulterated. Yet some of the archetypal truths they discovered have withstood the ravages of misinterpretation. One that survived seemingly intact was articulated by Chuang Tzu: 'Therefore wise rulers and Sages rest therein. Resting therein they reach the unconditioned, from which springs the conditioned; and with the conditioned comes order.'[25] In other words, total objectivity can only be achieved by de-conditioning from the force of habit artificially imposed by culture. Recognition of the pattern structure of the best and superior subjective outcomes and the methods by which they can be achieved provide their own form of conditioning, and with such conditioning comes total objectivity, perfect order and peace. This is simply another way of saying that once all winning, losing, draw and stalemate options are considered in terms of what they actually mean, it becomes obvious that the draw (i.e. subjective co-operation) is the best possible short- and longer-term outcome, achieved by appropriate (i.e. intelligent) and systematic (non-random) human behaviour. It is also the inevitable longest-term outcome of all processes of nature. With that understanding the game of life and the behaviours that cause its possible outcomes assume very different meanings from those that we currently ascribe to them.

Space is insufficient to provide more than a few simple examples of what all of this means in terms of the analysis and 'cure' of real-life behavioural malfunctions regarded in a context of game playing. Culture may act as an arbiter of what is sane or insane, but more reliable universal criteria exist, like those that apply to the mathematical definition of the sum of all combinatorial possibilities. This does not mean that there is an unqualified universal, God-given moral law, for we live in a conditionally deterministic universe, as I have said before. This means, for example, that whatever triggers running amok in the Far East can be very different from what releases gun-toting lunatics on California highways from their normal inhibitions. But the real cause is always the same – a high and unbearable level of frustration felt by weak, authoritarian individuals who are hell-bent on winning by making others lose.

Most share a similar personality profile. They lead stressful lives and repress internal conflicts until something – usually a relatively insignificant or even an imagined event – triggers a total loss of self-control. They are loners; withdrawn, secretive, suspicious and authoritarian individuals who insist on excessive external controls – but who lack self-discipline (very much like the psychological profile of 'militarists' provided by Norman Dixon – see Chapter 12). They tend to collect guns, extremist, war and survival literature, posters and comic books – usually of a hysterical and paranoid kind, dedicated to 'winning' in some form. Their families and neighbours usually know very little about them, but consider them perfectly 'nice' and 'normal'. They are usually like everyone else in their community, only more so.

All forms of extreme, unprovoked, hostile behaviours are related, whether they occur in Britain, the US or the Orient. The game metaphor provides not only analogous explanations for these extremes of human behaviour, but also answers how they can be foreseen, prevented and treated when they occur. Even so, some people cannot be rehabilitated. They are so thoroughly conditioned that they can no longer learn (e.g. Charles Manson), yet even they deserve a chance. This is why capital punishment is a bad idea.

The best a society can do for itself is to give everyone a chance to learn if they want to. For once causes, consequences and the operations that bring them about in a particular context are understood, it is no longer necessary to treat symptoms in the way that psychiatry does today. You can treat the causes and help affected individuals change themselves by facing them again and again with the consequences of what they did until they learn. Failing in that, society has the right to protect itself and its members to whatever extent is possible by forcibly isolating recidivist offenders who refuse to learn.

One representative example of the non-psychiatric, game-oriented, 'learn to play for a draw' treatment of psychological disorders concerns depression, a common affliction in all cultures for which there is currently no cure. Depression is caused by a lack of perceived options that locks the sufferer into a closed and repetitive feedback loop. While the psychiatrist's couch or 'anti-depressant' drugs may seem like an enlargement of options (i.e. playing a more complex game to be won in co-operation with the therapist), it only confines the patient in his or her depressed and isolated state more effectively. Sufferers need concerned and totally objective individuals who point out the consequences of the situation and get them to agree to widen their options by stepping outside the closed feedback loop in which they are temporarily entrapped (in other words achieving a classical draw).

This is not always easy to do, but it can be done with time and patience. There is no need to look into the circumstantial triggers or immediate causes of depression, which are often painful for the individual to think about. Nor does it involve any 'treatment' other than making the sufferer aware of the prison into which he has voluntarily locked himself and from which escape is essential if he is to enjoy life once more. However, there are some people who prefer to remain literally or figuratively institutionalized. They need to be faced with the consequences of their behaviour in ways that are sufficiently dramatic and unpleasant to make them venture forth on their own.

Instead of turning a loser into a would-be winner or vice versa – which is the aim of most psychiatric treatment – the objective should be to turn a momentary winner or loser into one who plays autonomously for agreement within and between his inner and the outer world; for recognizing all the vast number of options that are actually open to anyone who plays for a draw, instead of limiting him- or herself to trying to win or being resigned to losing.

Or let us consider an even simpler problem – enuresis, or bed-wetting, an affliction that several generations of psychiatrists have researched without success. It bears the same relation to more serious psychological problems as does noughts and crosses to chess. It is common among young children and is a nuisance to them and their families. The causes of psychological (not physiological) enuresis are thought to be buried in an individual's past. Hans Eysenck, a champion of IQ testing, spent ten years researching this problem and was stumped. Large amounts of time and money have been spent studying and trying to cure people of what is believed to be equivalent to a disease.

Treatment in the past has centred on the symptoms; spankings and other punishment; rewards; rubber sheets; bells that ring in the night to awaken children and make sure that they use the toilet; anti-micturition pills; and years on a psychiatrist's couch. None of these solve this minor behavioural problem. Children either eventually stop by themselves or, in some cases, continue to wet their beds into ripe old age.

The cure is simple. Parents should make sure that the child's liquid intake stops around three or four hours before bedtime and that he or she regularly goes to the toilet just before going to bed. It is difficult to wet a bed with an empty bladder, but some children manage to hang on to enough fluid to do so despite these precautions. If the child is 7 or 8 years old or older, the parent should insist that he (or she) washes out the sheets next morning (i.e. face him with the consequences). This should put a permanent stop to enuresis within a day or two.

You may well ask why this should ever have been a problem for psychiatrists, parents or children if the answer is really this simple? Unpressurized parents with common sense know the answer and their bed-wetting children are never taken to see psychiatrists. The ones who do may be temporarily too busy or distracted by their own problems, may lack common sense, or fail to pay their children attention and teach them to do things systematically. Those are the causes. The cure we have discussed already. Only pressurized, distracted parents and psychiatrists seeking fees and research grants seem unaware of it.

In game terms we can look at this problem quite simply. The unguided child is playing a game of chance and is trying to win subconsciously. That is why he or she loses. Once taught how to do things systematically (i.e. playing for a draw and reaching an agreement to agree with himself and his parents), the problem stops and everyone wins – child and parent. The child actually does not like to wet his or her bed, but is too lazy to discipline him- or herself. If bed-wetting persists, and if the child is old enough, the washing of the sheets faces him or her with the consequences of his lack of attention. Most children are grateful for this lesson and learn to apply it to other things. The parent has shown the child the proper method – all that can be taught. The child does the learning himself and becomes autonomous. That is what education is or should be about – not behavioural or drug-assisted manipulation which increases dependency, as is the case today.

The last psychological problem with which I shall deal concerns alcoholism – an adult form of misbehaviour that is diagnosed today, like enuresis, as if it were a disease. It is nothing of the kind. It is caused by the same abrogation of responsibility as bed-wetting, drug abuse or any other addictive, self-conditioned behaviour. Most so-called 'cures' and treatments, including Alcoholics Anonymous, drying-out clinics, hospices, psychoanalysis or the suggestion that alcoholism is due to inheritance of faulty genes just allow the alcoholic to swap one excuse or form of dependency for another. It may relieve the situation for the moment, but it cures nothing.

It has become popular to say that genetic factors cause alcoholism and other such 'psychological disturbances', enabling those who are concerned with physical or mental 'health' to treat it as if it were a disease, just as enuresis, depression and various forms of addiction are being treated by many practitioners. The excuse of a physiological or inherited, genetic predisposition to alcoholism reverses the sequence of causes and consequences. If a genuine genetic defect were the cause, physicians could predict susceptibility to alcoholism before any alcohol is ever consumed. No one has scientifically shown this to be possible so far, and it seems unlikely that they ever will despite theoretical claims to the contrary.[26]

Therefore two vital questions need to be asked: 'Why do some people get drunk and not others who drink as much or more than the drunks do?' The other is 'Why do they do it?'

Some people drink to get drunk. It usually does not take very much alcohol to achieve this if that is their intention, for intentions are always causal and count as much here as in all forms of game playing and behaviour. This is an aspect of drinking that is generally not admitted.

Confirmed drunks drink to escape – themselves, life, and the consequences of their past actions which they refuse to face. 'Weakness' is no excuse, for these very actions are what has weakened them. The cause can be something of which they are deeply ashamed or regret. They tend to accuse everyone else of what they themselves are guilty – a typical would-be winner's ploy. Or it could be a personal tragedy with which they refuse to cope. As with depression, it is a matter of failing to perceive or act on the available options. Facing the options would mean autonomy and acting on one's own behalf, becoming self-reliant and independent by making amends or choosing a new goal. Drunks are not prepared to do any of these things. They get drunk again and again and behave badly in order to escape assuming responsibility for themselves. This may sound harsh, but it is a totally objective assessment.

A fully cured alcoholic should be able to leave alcohol alone or to take a drink now and then without ever getting drunk to the point of losing control. But he can only do this after curing himself and facing his inner conflict. For it is inner conflict (i.e. playing a winning and losing game with the self) that causes his psychological disturbance and dependency, escapism, lack of self-discipline and goals, as well as abrogation of responsibility. Any of these are the causes of what is usually diagnosed as 'mental illness' today. Endorsed for a sufficiently long time as a disease by self-serving psychiatrists and a self-indulgent society, such diagnoses can become habit-forming. That is what Thomas Szasz means by 'the manufacture of madness'.

The draw principle is much more complex than it seems on the surface once it is applied to things more difficult than being friendly, considerate, thoughtful and attentive, not getting unpleasantly drunk, teaching young children how not to wet their beds, sharing the highway with other motorists without being in competition with them, or playing games hoping to achieve perfection. The reason is that the draw provides life's players with an infinite variety of choices. The selection of which games to play and how to play them is a human responsibility that would-be winners and losers refuse to shoulder. They prefer to let others choose for them, to be dependent, conform and repeat themselves endlessly. That is why they appear to behave in a purely mechanical fashion much of the time. Indeed their mindlessness stems from the fact that their behaviour, in bed and out, is nearly indistinguishable from that of game-playing machines.

I examine next the behaviour of groups and whole cultures in terms of the game metaphor, having explored it here in a framework of individual behaviours. The difference between them is no greater than that between solitaire games, two-person contests and team sports, all of which are discussed in later chapters.

5 The Savage Mind

> They tell us the world is a scrimmage,
>   And life is a difficult run,
> Where often a brother shall finish
>   A victory that we have begun.
> What matter, we learnt it at Harrow
>   And that was the way that we won.[1]

In the last chapter I examined individual behaviours in a context of game playing; here we will see how whole cultures determine which value judgements are sane and which are not, what is normal and what is abnormal, or indeed whether such value judgements can or need to be made. Many psychiatrists believe that various forms of insanity (other than those caused by physical defect, damage or deterioration) are not states of mind but diseases, or that they are genetically determined; some sociologists have made the same claims for criminals; and still others blame the 'environment' and not the individual. The result is that no one assumes responsibility for anything, least of all for themselves. For today we live in an essentially value-free world; one that is amoral, and not immoral as moralists insist.

Modern societies that subscribe to the wrong form of existentialism do not recognize that ethics are governed not by religious or culturally determined dictates but by natural, culture-free laws of cause and effect. Our societies are less unethical than non-ethical in that they no longer admit to ethics as a fundamental law of behaviour. The Judeo-Christian ethic that once provided a behavioural yardstick (straightjacket might be a better word for it) lacks conditional qualifications (e.g. 'Thou shalt not kill' – unless someone comes at you with a gun and intends to kill you and you have no means of escape or the means to immobilize him).

That is the tragedy of our age. Turning away from the hidebound and hypocritical morality of the past (or remaining stuck in it as are Christian, Muslim and other doctrinaire fundamentalists), we do not face the fact that ethics are practical rules of behaviour, rather than idealistic platitudes reserved for Sunday sermons. For as long as ethics are no more than that, anything goes for the rest of the week; whatever can be done will be done and the consequences are ignored for as long as those values prevail. One of the best analogies for explaining what this means can be found in the group games we play and how we play them.

Lévi-Strauss, the French anthropologist, in a book that bears the same title as this chapter, wrote:

All games are defined by a set of rules which in practice allow the playing of any number of matches. Ritual, which is also 'played', is on the other hand, like a favoured instance of a game, remembered from among the possible ones because it is the only one which results in a particular kind of equilibrium between the two sides. The Gahuku-Gama of New Guinea who have learnt to play football but who will play, several days running, as many matches as are necessary for both sides to reach an equal score. This is treating a game as a ritual.[2]

Clearly Lévi-Strauss did not understand games, rules, rituals, the Gahuku-Gama culture, or our own. For our way of playing is also a ritual, although it is a different one. When our football games reach a draw outcome we insist on alternate kicks at the opposing team's goal so that one side wins and the other loses. This is correctly called a 'sudden death' ending of the game. Our ritual, therefore, is the celebration of perpetual conflict, uncertainty and murderous intent.

The Gahuku-Gama play as hard and passionately as we do, but their ritual is the celebration of co-operation, eventual equality, certainty and peace. What may have been the weaker side at the start of the game learns from the stronger so that absolute parity is reached by the time the game ends. The Gahuku-Gama's method of play represents an intuitive understanding of nature's laws of cause and effect and of learning at its most creative. We are the savages – not they.

Obviously, not all primitive societies operate on co-operative principles. Many are highly competitive. Others encompass both competitive and co-operative behaviours. In some cultures qualitative competition makes for carefully honed skills and high craftsmanship from which the whole society benefits. That is the most profitable form of co-operation. Others, like some of the more esoteric cult societies, co-operate internally, excluding strangers or foreigners. Inevitably they tend to fossilize and become immune to cross-fertilization, resisting even convergent ideas from outside their closed groups. Still others practice co-operation internally just to compete more effectively against what they believe to be their external rivals.

Competitive beliefs are expressed by how each tribe or culture regards its members in relation to outsiders. As the American anthropologist Ruth Benedict showed, the names by which many tribes are known – Inuit, Zūni, Déné, Kiowa, among others – are the words for 'human' or 'man' in their respective languages, whereas outsiders are referred to as 'non-human' and alien. That way many find it much easier to deny to others the humanity they attribute to themselves, the better to be able to kill, enslave or rob without compunction the alien 'others'. Some culture-watchers attribute this to fear, but the real answer lies in a society's relative competitiveness: the alien 'other' is regarded as an enemy to be defeated, an act that supposedly bestows superiority on the winner.

The same primitive attitude to the 'outsider' causes supposedly 'civilized' modern societies to regard as 'inferior' racial, ethnic, religious or national groups other than their own simply because they do not belong to their own particular in-group. This makes it easier to discriminate against them – to win by making them lose. The Germans, during the Second World War, carried this kind of tribal savagery to extremes, as militarist and slave cultures have done in the past. Those whom they wanted to kill or enslave, inside and outside concentration camps, became *Untermenschen* (sub-human) by decree.

Identical symptoms were observable among the youthful protesters of the 1960s. Tribalism of the under-thirties in competition against their elders was their cause; the conformity of the buckskin fringed uniforms proclaimed their pretended 'individualism', while their battle-cry was: 'Make love; not war.' One girl-friend of a particularly antagonistic Haight-Ashbury hippy explained his behaviour to a *New York Times* reporter in 1966 with the hypocrisy typical of her generation: 'He has so much love in him that it comes out in a hostile way.'

One of the characteristics of non-individualistic and conformist protesters against actual or imagined wrongs or injustice is that while they seem to know exactly what they are 'against', they can seldom identify what they are 'for'. They usually make up the majority of every political party (including so-called moderate or centrist ones), claiming to have arrived independently at whatever 'truths' they repeat as slogans and propaganda, while blindly following a leader, their in-group or exponents of the latest scientific fad, theory or opinion. It appears to make little difference whether the leader is a guru, a religious prophet who propounds revealed truths (i.e. those that cannot be demonstrated), a political or economic pundit, a gay, black, or women's liberation spokes-'person', or an academic who claims to have discovered an unprovable theory that dies quietly within a decade or two. They and their followers pretend to individualism and originality when they really only want to win by making someone lose (and these are often colleagues or party members). In these respects (and they are the most significant ones, for their differences are always quite minor) they are all alike, even when they differ passionately in detail. All are part of the war of 'us against them'.

Margaret Mead, in her book *Co-operation and Competition Among Primitive People*[3] believed 'individualism' to be a third and distinct category in the co-operative/competitive equation. It is nothing of the kind. She, like the protesters of the sixties (for whom she was an elderly guru), misunderstood the concept of individualism and for the same reasons. She and they essentially believed that competitiveness and individuality are synonymous when in fact the opposite is true. Competitors are conformists to the same ideal and march in step. Those who play for a draw are the only true individualists because there are so many more ways to achieve this outcome than there are ways to win, and they are the true 'heretics' for they always think for themselves and refuse to be seduced or corrupted by operant conditioning.

There is, therefore, nothing wrong with individualism. However, in most societies we prize the wrong form; that of the victor who claims the spoils. The qualitative winner – the creative and deconditioned individual in any field – is deemed difficult and eccentric.

The quantitative winners are conformists to our society's ideals – greed and bland materialism. The same is true for the losers for they also hope to win by making others lose and they, like most would-be winners, usually fail in the long run.

We tend to attribute individualism to competitors, whether they are winners or losers, ultra-conservatives, middle-of-the-roaders or left-wing extremists. Winning itself is considered an outstanding 'individualistic' feat. That is why we believe that heroism in war is an 'individualistic' act. The frequently bizarre behaviour of winners like Bobby Fischer, the former chess champion, is claimed to be due to 'artistic temperament', to an excess of adrenalin or to a psychological stimulus required to get it flowing. The same, of course, is true for many politicians, businessmen and academics or military leaders.

Such theories – and that is all they are – put consequences before causes, as often happens when excuses are sought for inexcusable behaviour. We seldom ask how winners win, why they behave as they do, or what the genuine connection might be between their behaviour and its consequences. Finally, we fail to appreciate the fact that victories won against equals in tennis, chess or any other relationship viewed as a conflict are temporary affairs, achieved by chance or by default and conformity to a common and unsavoury standard.

In widely differing fields of interest, as I will show throughout this book, the victory of the champion is purely quantitative, temporary and not qualitatively superior. The latter deserves to be celebrated and not the former. The expression of true individuality is only possible when playing for a draw, for which the options are enormously more varied and numerous than when playing to win. These qualitative values are quantified in Appendices A and B.

Conventional would-be champions of the rich, poor, right, left, centre and in any game you can name tend to be conformists, march in step and behave in a more or less uniform manner. But those who would obtain equal rights and opportunities for all are not interested in winning by making others lose. They want agreement as to what is just, right and fair in order to enable as many people as possible to achieve independence and freedom under benign circumstances of their own choosing; an individualistic and not a conformist position.

These then, broadly speaking, are the main differences between competitive and co-operative cultures, or those in which one or the other characteristic predominates. Truly co-operative societies tend to be far more tolerant of individual differences than competitive ones. One cannot accept the arrogation of individuality by members of a competitive group to themselves, any more than one can take their word for it that they are the only human beings in the world, or that draws and stalemates do not count.

Nor is short-term survival a litmus test of a self-proclaimed co-operative society, as we saw when considering the Walden II commune. Often the individual perishes and is needlessly sacrificed or drops out because he or she cannot stand the conditions, even when the institution survives. Some forms of co-operation can be disastrous when it means, for example, banding together in a closed society in order to compete more effectively against outsiders. Societies that foreswear self-defence in the presence of rapacious enemies are equally suicidal. Others are competitive to a degree where paranoia reigns in all relationships within and between neighbouring families and tribes. Ruth Benedict, who understood the difference between zero-sum (winning) and non-zero-sum (playing for a draw) gaming as a cultural metaphor, describes the Dobu, a Melanesian society that is a parody of our own, in her classic book *Patterns of Culture*:

Every man's hand is against every other man ... And this is not because the Dobuan lives in a state of anarchy ... but because the social forms which obtain in Dobu put a premium upon ill-will and treachery and make of them the recognized virtues of their society.

... The largest functioning Dobuan grouping ... is the war unit and is on terms of permanent international hostility with every other similar locality ... Danger is indeed at its height within the locality itself. Those who share the same shore, those who go through the same daily routine together, are the ones who do one another ... actual harm. They play havoc with one's harvest, they bring confusion upon one's economic exchanges ...[4]

Ruth Benedict describes some of the deadly characteristics of this society; their jealousies, suspicions, and the greed with which each member clutches property to him- or herself. Unrelenting competition is their way of life and it expresses itself in all their dealings with family members, neighbours and strangers. This is the classic

Hobbesian, social Darwinist or Spencerian game of all against all. It is also representative of what Lorenz and his followers believe to be the innate driving force of human nature that can only be exorcized by periodic catharsis. On the contrary, and as the Dobu demonstrate, winning by making others lose becomes habitual as a result of cultural conditioning and is reinforced perpetually the more it is practised.

Every dirty trick with which to attack and defeat everyone else is sanctified by the Dobu. Bitter rivalry colours every transaction and relationship, including marriage. Everyone is the enemy and a potential victim of everyone else. The Dobuan's conditioned instinct is to induce and seize upon his fellows' every error and turn it to advantage. Meanwhile he lives in constant dread of being victimized by the very misfortunes he or she visits on everyone else. They guard their plots of land and crops, day and night, rightfully fearing robbery or the black magic that is employed at every opportunity. Ill-will reigns supreme and affects every aspect of Dobuan life, including their religion.

Sharp dealing and perpetual competition against others are the sole motives of all the Dobu. Life is a never-ending battle not only against fellow human beings, but against nature itself. Dobu of both sexes firmly agree and believe that winning in this perpetual war is the highest form of achievement for which prosperity is the just reward. The best man in this venomous game is not only the winner who amasses the greatest amount of property at everyone else's expense, but he who mounts a permanent vigil to keep it from being shared, stolen or destroyed by others.

The Dobuan lives out without repression man's worst nightmares of the ill-will of the universe, and according to his view of life virtue consists in selecting a victim upon whom he can vent the malignancy he attributes alike to human society and to the powers of nature. All existence appears to him as a cut-throat struggle in which deadly antagonists are pitted against one another in a contest for each of the goods of life. Suspicion and cruelty are his trusted weapons in the strife and he gives no mercy, as he asks none.

... In ordinary converse the Dobuan is suave and unctuously polite. 'If we wish to kill a man we approach him, we eat, drink, sleep, work and rest with him, it may be for several moons. We bide our time. We call him friend' ... Behind a show of friendship, behind the evidence of co-operation, in every field of life, the Dobuan believes that he has only treachery to expect. Everyone else's best efforts, according to their institutions, are directed towards bringing his own plans to confusion and ruin.[5]

Jonathan Swift could not have drawn a more incisive caricature of our competitive cultures than what was and may still be enacted daily by these Dobu Brobdingnagians. Our politicians, businessmen, academics, and football coaches have little to learn from them. We and they have refined winning by making others lose: we cherish one-upmanship and gamesmanship, perpetual infighting and the resulting paranoia as a cultural art form. Their divorce rate matches ours and for the same reasons. The Dobu could have been the subject of Machiavelli's *The Prince* had he known about them.

Just as the Dobu are not the only competitive society in the world, so there are different co-operative ones. One can only guess at possible reasons for such diversity. A strong, kindly leader in the past, a pugnacious, autocratic one and similarly motivated successors, or an invader's army that crushed the indigenous population into submission, may have been the causal trigger for the future evolution of a culture. The leader may have intended to force co-operation on the subjugated or conquered subjects of an anticipated world-wide empire. That was what Alexander the Great, Napoleon and even Hitler had in mind. But such conformity is corrupting, no matter what the motive may have been, because it is based on competitive methods that stamp out individuality, variety or dissent, making a virtue of all the vices of man and a vice of all human virtues.

Once institutionalized, the co-operative or competitive characteristics of a culture become the conditioned behaviour of its members, passed from one generation to the next. These characteristics may evolve in one direction or another until their origins are almost unrecognizable, but they will continue to evolve in a variety of forms. The divergence of the original Chinese and Japanese cultures is a typical example: both once shared common roots (Chinese invaders originally crushed the Ainu natives, much as the American Indians and Australian Aborigines were wiped out or driven on to reservations by Europeans). Each basically Chinese group lost contact for many centuries and evolved very differently in isolation.

Even when the past is unrecorded but remembered in myth and legend, it is sometimes possible to decipher the likely character of the individual personalities or dynasties that gave a culture its present-day flavour. We can extrapolate the likely personality of Moses from the Ten Commandments, or that of Joshua from his legendary exploits. Viewed in terms of both the 'draw' and competitive principles, the teachings of Christ, Buddha and Muhammad assume human, rather than supernatural dimensions. Each was a product of his time and culture. But they were also more than that in as much as they articulated archetypal truths. This is what made them appear godly or to speak with God's voice to their followers. Some of these truths became corrupted in time, but such distortions can be peeled away to expose the kernel of natural law within.

In more recent history, and in those portions of the world such as America, Australia and Africa which have been invaded during the past few hundred years, we do not need to look very far for the causal triggers of cultural evolution and motivation. The historical convergences of people and events that caused these cultures to be more or less co-operative or competitive are well documented. To recognize the patterns and understand causes and consequences requires only that we free ourselves from parochialism and look at history honestly and without nationalistic (i.e. competitive) pretensions. Geoffrey Gorer is among the few who seemed able to do this and he analysed some of our mainstream cultures with rare insight. His book *The Americans*[6] cuts to the bone and reveals some of the origins of their dominant traits and characteristics.

Gorer cites the immigrant roots of Americans as a major cause for the competitiveness that runs through the whole culture. Arriving at Ellis Island without a penny and struggling in poverty from the start, the first generation insisted that successive ones must do 'better' than the last. More is better in such a culture and that is the common thread of a society that does not know where or when to stop expanding its economy at the expense of the rest of the world. But this is also a total reversal of the erstwhile European tradition where most children were encouraged to grow up to be 'as good' as their parents. Now European and American parents want 'the best' for their children and a 'better life' than they enjoyed, irrespective of their performance. It is natural for the poor to want to better themselves, but above a certain standard of living such 'betterment' turns into blatant consumerism and selfishness.

What makes primitive societies specially interesting to anthropologists is that many existed for centuries in relative isolation and refined their customs and social structures with little interference from outside their own environment until they were invaded or colonized. Until then they tended to be more or less pure examples of co-operative, competitive or mixed cultures in which the consequences and operations, if not the causes, of their customs could be observed and evaluated critically, first in their original closed states and then in more open, penetrated ones. Few anthropologists today share the insights of Bronislaw Malinowski, Ruth Benedict and Geoffrey Gorer, for they could still study primitive cultures in a relatively undisturbed state. Now that is only possible in very few places. A similar condition exists in a branch of social research – that dealing with media influences on young people's competitive and aggressive attitudes (see Chapter 12). Today there are hardly any children who have never seen films or television and no control groups remain to be tested and compared to those who are addicted, affected or remain immune to such influences.

In the 1920s there was a brief surge of interest in the relationship between competitive and co-operative behaviour which faded quickly because it ran counter to American culture, and has not been revived since. Margaret Mead's early work was evidently stimulated by this trend and especially by a 1927–9 study under the auspices of the American Psychological Association.[7] It concerned itself with co-operative and competitive behaviours and habits. However, this study group became bogged down in a linguistic morass. The members decided to distinguish between ideas like 'competition' and 'rivalry', 'co-operation' and 'helpfulness'.

Such distinctions, while they can be made as far as context is concerned, merely confuse the principles that are involved. Rivalry is one form of competition in a particular context: helpfulness is one form of co-operation in another. But in games, as in any other form of individual or group behaviour, we can ignore such distinctions, especially when it comes to establishing principles.

Far more important than quibbling over such minor details is the avoidance of lumping primitive cultures together under a single heading and extending generalizations to everything on the basis of the observation of a few. Rousseau was guilty of that error when he proposed the idea of the 'noble savage'. The diversity of simple and primitive cultures is perhaps greater than our own because at one time there were more of them and many remained isolated for generations. With relatively little traffic even between neighbouring groups, each developed its own idiosyncrasies and differences, even when it conformed to more or less co-operative or competitive principles.

The only PhD thesis written to my knowledge on the relationship between co-operation and competition in the context of education was also first published in the 1920s, again without any further reconsideration or interest.[8] J. B. Maller, its author, while deploring the effects of competition in the classroom, was simultaneously a victim of the egalitarian and group adjustment myths with which most American educators were infected at that time. He, like many others, confused co-operation and the suppression of the wrong forms of competitiveness with bland sameness, the submergence of individuality and the sacrifice of excellence for the sake of adjustment to group conformity.

As a result, no analyses exist to my knowledge, other than the rare studies mentioned in this chapter (and others of which I may not know), that deal with the juxtaposition of competitive and co-operative group behaviours. In fact the words *co-operation* and *competition* hardly ever appear in the indexes of standard works on anthropology any more than they do in those that concern psychology or sociology.

As mentioned earlier, no two cultures in either category are exactly alike, although the competitive ones are far more similar to each other than those that are predominantly co-operative. This point is of special interest because it matches the mathematical findings in my analysis of games of strategy. There the percentage of possible different victories (analogous to 'winning' behaviours in competitive societies) compared to draws (equivalent to a co-operative orientation) is tiny when the sum of all combinatorial possibilities is considered for any single game. As shown in Appendix A for the game of noughts and crosses, the ratio of draws to victories and the wrong kind of stalemates is of the order of 97%, and no two draws are exactly alike. The variety of drawn games is vast and those that are won and lost quite limited by comparison. In a literal sense, game states mirror life precisely.

In the book that she edited, Margaret Mead gathered evidence of co-operative and competitive behaviours in thirteen different cultures into a single volume.[9] Despite this, and although she was Ruth Benedict's student and friend, she never fully understood what is involved in the definition of differences between co-operative and competitive societies. None the less her work confirms and is totally convergent with the principles elucidated here from the study of games. Wherever the co-operative spirit predominates in internal and external individual and group relations, peaceful coexistence and tolerance prevail. Wherever competitive behaviours are enshrined as cultural norms, and especially when they become habitual over long periods of time, paranoia, hostility and a general nastiness become institutionalized, leading to perpetual strife and a decline in creativity. How could the latter flourish in societies devoted to destruction?

Margaret Mead wrote in the foreword to her book:

To lay a background for the study of the relationship between competitive and co-operative behaviour, and the problem of culture and personality, it is therefore necessary to know not only what the form of the culture is which dictates certain forms of adult behaviour and interdicts others, but also how this adult personality is formed in the long process of building the cultureless infant into the adult.[10]

She realized that economic scarcity does not necessarily make for competition or abundance for co-operation as many economists, biologists and sociologists believe. If abundance were a precondition for co-operation, competition as a national credo would have withered away long ago in the US. This concept is explored in greater depth in Chapter 11.

Scarcity is indeed seen in some cultures as a legitimate excuse for selfishness and competition. In war-torn and largely co-operative Britain, while a black market flourished, most people were happy to share and live on their rations. On the other hand, the Germans encouraged the black market in occupied territories, for it made people compete among themselves and helped corrupt and divide those they had conquered. Such corruption was essential to keep the Nazi war machine functioning. The relative co-operation or competitiveness within a society, therefore, does not depend on scarcity or plenty, any more than it depends on genetic heritage or 'human nature', but it does depend on attitudes that are socially and culturally conditioned.

Even so, co-operation is always misinterpreted when it only exists internally and as a device for more effective external competition. In most societies competition with and hostility to 'outsiders' requires considerable implicit and explicit internal co-operation. That is the kind of limited co-operation practised within the armies of aggressors and among concentration camp guards. It was the moving spirit in Sparta as much as in Napoleonic France. It also works admirably for competitors who belong to the same fraternal, union or restrictive trade organization. It is one reason for what was known as the Japanese economic miracle which is now coming to an end (discussed further in Chapter 11). Such limited co-operation is common to both aggressors and defenders. It consists of temporary alliances for the sake of more efficient competition against others. It cannot be maintained for long because when the external pressure lessens or peace is declared, the conditioned hostility within competitive societies can become internalized so that former comrades-in-arms – and formerly co-operative unions and corporations – band together and turn on each other.

Both sides always lose wars, even when one side claims victory. The kind of internal political or economic competition that takes place after an armistice or after peace is declared can depend on circumstances. This was seen in Germany and in the Allied countries after the First and Second World Wars. Increasing political polarization occurred in some, and resurgent economic competition of the wrong kind (quantitative, rather than qualitative) in others. This appears to be true among former enemies and allies alike, following virtually every war (e.g. the onset of the Cold War after the Second World War) and defeats the restoration and maintenance of peace.

According to Jeannette Mirsky, one of the authors in Mead's book, independence and co-operation were the hallmarks of the Ammassalik Eskimo of Greenland. They were a predominantly co-operative tribe, to such an extent that there was very little sex differentiation in the work that was done. Whoever was best at hunting seal – husband or wife – would assume responsibility for doing so. In some instances both would co-operate and share the work. Since women were tent-bound for part of their pregnancy and their children's early years, curing and softening skins was their prerogative. While selecting a wife was highly competitive (and could lead to murder) and success was largely based on physical strength and endurance on the part of the male (a survival necessity under harsh Arctic conditions), husband and wife enjoyed total equality in most matters, including divorce or changes of partners.

Skill in hunting rituals and drum singing matches (in which neither side sought to win and the draw was the preferred outcome) were rated above all other accomplishments by the Ammassalik. Individual freedom and differences in personal identity were highly regarded. During periods of food shortage in winter, co-operation was the rule within the tribe and even visitors were included in this sharing of scarce resources – very different from the standards in competitive societies where it is each for him- or herself, especially in times of economic stress. Obviously such a co-operative culture stands a far better chance of survival in a harsh environment than a competitive one. Yet many in our competitive societies would insist that selfishness best serves individual survival needs.

According to Mirsky, among this tribe:

There is no social coercion, no judgement is passed, and no man's importance is considered relative to that of another. Within this open field an individual is allowed a latitude few societies could tolerate.[11]

Things have certainly changed among the Eskimo of Greenland and Canada since the time when these observations were made. What was true then no longer exists, or exists in adulterated form. Virtually all cultures, world-wide, have been tarnished by Western competitive influences and value systems. But that is what makes these earlier reports so interesting and valuable.

At the other extreme the Kwakiutl Indians of Vancouver Islands had developed a highly competitive society in which:

Public behaviour ... is dominated by the need of the individual to demonstrate his greatness over and against his rivals ... By the humbling of his rival the individual builds up his own prestige ... the greatest rewards of society in terms of individual glorification go to the man who has conquered with property and by a display of privileges his most powerful rivals.[12]

These are among the tribes who compete with one another by means of 'potlatch' – in which every individual seeks to compete with all others by what he can give away. It is a form of competition that differs from, but is related to, 'keeping up with the Joneses', carried to extremes. It is the object of each to beggar himself and thereby to display greater power than his rival in disposing of his possessions. Competitors do the same in return and by a constant exchange of goods two objectives are achieved: potlatch assures that a balance of means is maintained throughout the society and, at the same time, each individual seeks constantly to increase his wealth so that he can outshine all others by giving it away – a rationale for a competitive economy that does not seem to have occurred to Milton Friedman and other champions of unfettered free enterprise.

Among New Guinean natives a rather different, highly competitive institution – the 'cargo cult' – was founded during the Second World War.[13] It is a naïve and novel form of materialistic competition. Natives, seeing cargo ships and planes arrive from what seemed to them out of the blue, decided that they had been sent by the gods and built imitation docks and landing fields so that they might also receive these blessings. Obviously, and in native eyes, white Europeans and Americans seemed to have a monopoly on receiving 'cargo' thanks to their magic; a perfectly reasonable assumption. Hence they sought to compete by building landing places that might be more pleasing to the gods than those built by their rivals. They were disappointed of course.

The failure of the gods to respond caused serious rioting in parts of New Guinea because it was believed that greedy whites had diverted cargo intended for the natives to their own harbours and airfields. If the cargo cult is regarded symbolically, it is really not very different from worshipping at the shrine of Marks and Spencer, Harrods, Bloomingdale's or Nieman Marcus.

An equally extreme form of competition is described by Ruth Benedict. She tells of Vladimir Bogaras, exiled to the wilds of Siberia during the Tsarist regime, who came across the Chukchee, a vicious local tribe.

Even their routine exchanges of commodities were occasions for knifing. Their language had no word for trading; realistically enough, they called it blood-feuding . . . sons killed their fathers, and brothers their brothers. And with impunity. A strong man was one who could abuse anyone, relative or stranger . . . and was envied. The father's boast when a child was born was: 'Ah! I have created a strong man for times to come, one who will take the property of all those living in the country around us . . .' Nothing was clearer than that the Chukchee knew they were not free. Their word for it was 'doom'. They were, they said 'doomed to anger', 'doomed to death', 'doomed to receiving supernatural power' . . . Anger swept over them like a flood from outside themselves; they showed their teeth, they growled, they lost consciousness of what they were doing.[14]

By way of contrast Ruth Benedict tells of a relatively co-operative American Indian tribe that she had personally studied:

A couple of years ago I lived with the Blackfoot Indians of Canada. They too had been rich and they had been democratic, but in addition they were sure they had been free. Even today they could not understand the meaning of being 'doomed'. They were sure every man had his own personal desires and spent his life realizing them. What else could be a reason for living? Even today, when the buffalo they lived on are gone from their plains, I thought them a people to whom an understanding of liberty was as natural as breathing.[15]

It is the fashion among today's well-intentioned, but historically and culturally innocent or prejudiced liberals, to glorify the 'noble' American Indian without distinction in the tradition of James Fennimore Cooper (who never set foot on Indian territory). George Catlin, who lived among them, distinguished between essentially competitive and warlike, and co-operative and peaceful tribes,[16] as does Ruth Benedict. The more aggressively combative American Indian groups contributed to their own destruction in the long run. For centuries before the advent of Europeans they had hunted down co-operative neighbouring tribes who failed to protect themselves.

Catlin describes the sites of villages and territories that had formerly belonged to such peaceful tribes, laid waste by their hostile neighbours. The warlike Indians were easily defeated by the even more rapacious Europeans who killed them off with their superior weapons and employed identical tactics to those the competitive Indians had used to destroy their peaceful kinsmen and neighbours. One essentially co-operative tribe, the Pueblos of New Mexico, survived because they worked out defensive strategies that enabled them to prosper, surrounded as they were by enemies of their own ethnic grouping as well as by European predators. However in their case, the closure of their society and the peculiarities of their bland systems of co-operation prevented any evolutionary development beyond survival at a given level of culture, as Ruth Benedict points out.

There are open, dynamic co-operative societies that continually evolve and change over periods of time, and those that are closed and stagnant. The latter, like the Walden II community in Virginia described earlier, having achieved a standard of physical comfort and psychological safety for its members, permit all creativity to die out and become lazy and complacent. They tend to celebrate their credo in the exercise of mindless and unvarying ritual and dogma. Their social organization, art, craft and industry settle into unchanging and immutable patterns, irrespective of changes in environmental conditions or influences from without. Such ultra-conservative cultures can be swept aside rapidly due to their conditioned inability to adapt once they come into contact with domineering and destructive outsiders or when environmental conditions change drastically (e.g. persistent droughts, seismic upheavals, etc.). That is exactly what happened to many seemingly idyllic Pacific island and other, older cultures. They lacked the ability to defend their benign, co-operative value system from essentially competitive ones, even in matters of religion, belief, art and craft. It has also happened to cultures that simply disappeared because they were unable to foresee or take steps to avoid or adapt to changing ecological conditions that, whether they were natural or manmade phenomena, turned out to be disastrous for them.

The anthropological examples to which I have referred make it perfectly plain that psychological stability, social and economic well-being, peace, equality between the sexes, equal opportunity for all, conditional freedom and survival in perpetually changing circumstances depend on a consciously correct interpretation of the meanings of co-operation and competition in every conceivable context. An understanding of these principles offers variety and freedom within whatever limits are needed to guarantee their responsible expression. For freedom without limit (i.e. the ruleless game) leads to total conditioning and restraint by the shortest route, as I showed earlier in the case of the MIT students' 'no rule' game and demonstrate again later in a different context for the maharajas' chess tournament.

All successful, and by that I mean perpetually evolving, essentially co-operative, peaceful, but defensively aggressive cultures share common characteristics. They enjoy a hierarchical structure built on respect for qualitative achievement from which everyone benefits. There is a division of labour based on who does what best in a co-operative sense. Everyone eats; strawberries and cream you get yourself. In other words children, the aged, or those who are ill or disabled are looked after as a matter of course. Those who are unemployed through no fault of their own, or who may want or need further- or re-education, are publicly supported if they lack the means to support themselves.

Even those who wish to opt out and refuse to do anything are provided with minimal subsistence, housing and care by virtue of the fact that they have been born. But if they want anything above subsistence they must work for it, like everyone else. Such a society is governed by a minimum of laws and restraints, but the conditions of freedom are well defined. They consist of a concern for the self and for others. The purpose of administration is even-handed justice and not that of law; restitution and not vindictiveness; rehabilitation, self-protection and restitution, rather than punishment.

There is plenty of scope for differences in organizing a society based on these non-competitive principles, leaving unlimited room for cultural diversity, individual variety in achievement and qualitative excellence. The only limitations are whatever hurts, draws blood, requires the agreement of those who may be affected and the ability and willingness to assume responsibility for one's own actions. Such a society is governed by uncompromising rules that assure freedom within socially responsible, defined limits which are, none the less, variable and subject to change as the conditions change.

An essentially co-operative society is a tolerant one that encourages 'different', dissident or eccentric behaviour, provided it does not threaten others. Its rituals are a celebration of the co-operative principle, not of conflict or war. It invites discussion but deprecates debate or argument. It supports authority based on creative achievement, but deplores authoritarian controls. It does not teach anything but method, and allows everyone to learn for themselves according to individual preference and style. Neither life nor death are feared in such a society. It is fully at one with itself and with nature. It can exist under the most primitive conditions, re-emerge with its principles intact when things change for the better, and flourish in urban, industrialized communities as readily as in rural ones.

Such a society is not utopian, but as close to ideal as circumstances permit (see the introduction to this book for a definition of 'ideals'). The value judgements that give this society meaning justify its institutions and work for everyone in proportion to what they contribute. To that extent Marx was certainly correct (i.e. to each according to his needs and to each according to his labour) and all societies would benefit if management and labour heeded such standards.

Perhaps the most important lesson to be learned from anthropological studies is the variety of possible cultures that can be found, sometimes existing side-by-side. No matter how different they may be and even when both competitive and co-operative aspects of human nature are mixed in various proportions in any one society, these main classifications of behaviour give every culture its character and flavour and provide our world with diversity.

The values to which any society subscribes decide the psychological orientation, personalities and intentions of its members. There used to be far greater cultural diversity than there is today because at least some portions of the globe were less competitive than now. With the domination of the world by relatively few highly competitive societies – and excessive materialism – this variety has shrunk at considerable cost to human creativity, individuality and quality. Like diversity in the gene pool, individual and cultural differences leaven our global, human tribe, despite some maladaptations.

As Konrad Lorenz said: 'Any culture may do anything analogous to mutation. Just as you have a lethal mutation, you may develop a lethal culture.'[17] Unfortunately, having been reared in the conformist and competitive culture of Imperial Austria and grown to maturity under the influence of Nazi Germany's doctrine of racial superiority, Lorenz seems unable to distinguish between genetic and cultural influences, especially when it comes to competitive aggression.

It is not surprising that relative sameness is one of the hallmarks of competition and conflict, just as co-operation fosters individual uniqueness and peace in all its forms. Competition requires regimentation and an authoritarian insistence on conformity and uniformity. Again we come up against the fundamental differences between militarist and civilian concerns, war and peace, imbalance and balance, madness and sanity, and patterns of behaviour that match and are matched by the geometric model of game and behavioural strategies, tactics and intentions on which this book is based.

Clearly what may be perfectly normal in one society can easily be judged insane in another. It is, therefore, tempting for anthropologists to pretend relative objectivity in the name of science and refuse to make value judgements. 'After all,' some reason, 'each culture has as much right as the next to insist on its own practices and standards, and to decide what is normal for its members and what is not.' However, seen from a perspective of global survival, especially in today's circumstances, valuative generalizations are essential.

It may seem to have made little difference, except to next-door neighbours prior to the age of exploration and discovery by the West, whether an isolated tribe or society was organized along competitive or co-operative lines; whether, for example, it practised cannibalism because of a lack of protein, for ritualistic reasons, or rejected it entirely. (Ruth Benedict, like Jonathan Swift, preserves a sense of humour about this practice.) However, cultural institutions, what they mean, which behaviours they foster, and their claimed reasons for existence, make a big difference in individual and group behaviours, as Captain Cook discovered long before anthropology became an academic discipline. Today, in a world in which everyone is everyone else's next-door neighbour, the cultural, economic and military institutions of one affect all others. To some extent that was always true, but it has become a burning issue in this age of nuclear weapons.

For example, it would have been extremely difficult, and perhaps impossible, for Arabs, Europeans and Americans to capitalize on the slave trade to anything like the extent that it was practised, had not many African chieftains and tribes been at perpetual war and in competition with one another. Their prisoners of war became their slaves and any surplus was sold to foreign traders. This in no way excuses the European and American slave trade, but puts it into its historic perspective. It also shows how people throughout the world can affect each other. Elsewhere, Europeans did not even have local tradition on their side when they hunted down the natives of Tasmania and killed all of them because they refused to be dispossessed.

Co-operative attitudes among different cultures can therefore be seen to come in many shadings – some that are self-destructive or stultifying and others that are superior. Value judgements can be made about all of them, provided we use a yardstick like the game metaphor that is adequately calibrated and can be fine-tuned. Balance is the operative term throughout – the golden mean – that guarantees that the wrong kind of competition as much as the wrong forms of co-operation do not predominate. History is littered with ill-willed competitors and their willing victims, a disastrous form of co-operation except for the winners, and even they only benefit in the shortest run. This explains the decay of civilizations and empires built on conquest.

The massive kill ratio provided by European firearms defeated or blackmailed even the most warlike American, Oriental, Pacific and African tribes, forced them into submission or wiped them off the face of the earth. During these conquests the more competitive native tribes seemed temporarily to be more successful in withstanding invasion than the more peaceful and co-operative ones. But that was not always true. From time to time relatively few essentially peaceful and co-operative defenders, armed with inferior weapons, who subscribed to guerrilla principles of warfare, managed to defeat much better armed and more numerous aggressors (see Chapter 12).

This truism has been demonstrated again and again by the Ashanti wars during the last century or in Vietnam and Afghanistan in this present one. The guerrilla tactics of a relatively few, dedicated, if often inadequately armed natives who knew the lie of the land and were able to live off it and survive under primitive conditions, roundly defeated substantial and well-armed expeditionary forces again and again. The Ashanti were eventually overwhelmed because no other country came to their aid to provide them with up-to-date weapons. Also, as often as not, defenders can be betrayed by traitors who are suborned and corrupted by the invaders. They tend to be dissidents in their own societies who sometimes seek to revenge themselves for real or imagined injustices visited on them by their own people. That is the chink in the armour of any competitive, conformist culture. No closed society is ever tolerant of non-conformists who deviate from the norm, whatever it might be, and that is often the cause of its undoing.

Ruth Benedict recounts the consequences of non-conformity in the Dobu's, zero-sum, competitive culture:

The most spectacular illustration of the extent to which normality may be culturally defined are those cultures where an abnormality of our culture is the cornerstone of their social structure . . . A recent study of an island of northwest Melanesia by Fortune describes a society built upon traits which we regard beyond the border of paranoia . . . Now in this society where no one may work with another and no one may share with another, Fortune describes the individual who was regarded by all his fellows as crazy . . . one man of sunny, kindly disposition who liked work and liked to be helpful . . . Men and women never spoke of him without laughing; he was silly and simple and definitely crazy.

. . . The concept of the normal is properly a variant of the concept of the good . . . The Dobuan who is not easily susceptible to fear of treachery, who enjoys work and likes to be helpful, is their neurotic and regarded as silly. On the Northwest Coast [among certain Indian tribes] the person who finds it difficult to read life in terms of an insult contest will be the person upon whom fall all the difficulties of the culturally unprovided for. The person who does not find it easy to humiliate a neighbour, nor to see humiliation in his own experience, who is congenial and loving . . . he is abnormal.[18]

Ruth Benedict compares the psychotic Dobuan norm to that of the eighteenth century New England Puritan Divines who burned as a witch anyone who differed from their definition of sanity. The Spanish Inquisition, and the McCarthy hearings in the early 1950s in America, are other examples of highly competitive value systems that branded perfectly normal people as dissidents, heretics and madmen in order to destroy them. Who is deemed sane or insane in any culture seems to depend less on any objective standard and more on whichever values predominate at the moment.

Clearly, a co-operative individual's behaviour in the wholly competitive Dobu culture would be seen by his fellow tribal members as eccentric and mildly amusing at best, and dangerously heretical or insane at worst. If psychiatrists existed in such a society he would probably be required to consult one for analysis and adjustment to the norm. Failing that, he might be killed, sent into exile or committed to an institution for the criminal or the insane. It happens in Western cultures as often as in Russia, although we condemn there what takes place here because we are unable to view with sufficient detachment our own prejudices of what is 'normal'. It is the old story of the kettle and the pot.

Despite the relativistic aspects of behaviour in every society, it is possible to make absolute value judgements as to what is sane and what is not. The fact that sane behaviour is conditional merely means that what may be sane under one set of conditions could be quite inappropriate and insane in another. Absolute sanity in all circumstances would seem to depend on appropriateness. That is a value judgement each of us must make for him- or herself, relative to the world in which we live, modified by our vision of a future that enables all to survive without or with minimal internal or external conflict. It is also one definition of the draw in the context of culture seen as a co-operative game played for the survival of all that is best in our various societies, rather than as a game played competitively that is won by the few and lost by the many.

As this all too brief overview of the 'soft' social sciences demonstrates, most practitioners tend to shy away from making value judgements or, when they do so, they often make the wrong ones. This is even more true in the so-called 'hard' physical sciences where physics and biology are firmly believed to be value free and without meaning – even after the Oak Ridge nuclear physicists and Einstein learned, far too late, that this is a hollow and dangerous pretence. For they only awakened to the meaning of the genie in the bottle at a point when it was half-way out – too late to force it back and keep it where it should have remained all along had these scientists been subjectively aware from the start. That was a mistake from which many have not yet learnt. But – and this is freely admitted among good physicists and most biologists – until 'behaviour' is fully understood, there can be no 'Unified Field Theorem' – a unifying principle of science avidly sought by Einstein and many other physicists. Behaviours are governed by the twin principles of competition and co-operation, chance and certainty, as redefined in the following chapters, providing bridges between human behaviour, physics and biology.

6 The Random Universe

Everything existing in the Universe is the fruit of
chance and of necessity.

Democritus

The meaning of chance, relative to conditions in the universe and
in our lives, is very much a matter of value judgements. An element
of chance seems to exist in all the things we do as well as in the
larger universe that is not affected by human behaviour. But just
what chance is or how it operates are questions about which there
is considerable difference of opinion. Chance is an operational
method of which we seem to know only the consequences and not
the causes.

Every human activity, from safely crossing a busy street to the
effectiveness of birth control methods, seems tinged with the workings of chance. The same appears to be true of inorganic events like
the movements of electrons or radiation from outer space that may
cause mutations, to mention but two of countless examples. Chance
also seems to play a significant role in what we call 'coincidences'
and 'accidents'; so-called chance meetings, convergences of events
or collisions, and even evasions for which there seems to be no
rational explanation.

Chaucer likened chance to a 'wheel of fortune', and other poets
and philosophers compared it to an inexplicable, random force of
nature, an act of God or the working of predestination. It is a
central feature of so-called games of chance. Randomness, chance
and coincidence have been defined in a great many ways. Pliny
described how people viewed chance in Roman times:

Throughout our world at every place and hour, by every voice, Fortune
alone is invoked and her name spoken; she is the one defendant, the one

culprit, the one thought in men's minds, the one object of praise, the one cause . . . We are so much at the mercy of chance that Chance is our God.[1]

Our modern understanding of chance seems similar to that of the Romans; so much so that Lewis Mumford, disparaging the modern belief that creativity is essentially a random process, wrote: 'Chance became God: anything might happen.' [2] Gregory Bateson voiced doubts about the probabilistic methods used today to limit the effects of chance:

In both the theory of evolution and the theory of learning, however, the word 'random' is conspicuously undefined and the word is not an easy one to define. In both fields, it is assumed that while change may be dependent upon probabilistic phenomena, the probability of a given change is determined by something different from probability.[3]

Fritz Mauthner, a turn-of-the-century German encyclopaedist of philosophy, was equally puzzled by this phenomenon:

And when we do not recognize the chain of cause and operations then we speak of coincidence and anthropomorphize it when we call it blind chance . . . What we, as human beings, call order in this world, is certainly no chance event or coincidence [in the probabilistic sense], but a mystery and it will remain a mystery for mankind, because it is equally impossible for our world to be the product of a higher intelligence as of chance.[4]

Mauthner quotes Quetelet, who perhaps came closest to the truth: 'The word "chance" serves to veil our ignorance.' Spinoza said much the same thing. Hippocrates believed that there is no such thing as chance; and that chance events exist only in the minds of men.

Physics is founded on principles like quantum theory of which chance, randomness and uncertainty are innate properties. Classical science has moved from sharing a common deterministic ground with religion to the modern view (and also an ancient one, as shown by the quote from Democritus that heads this chapter) that nature obeys the laws of chance. This is, therefore, one of the characteristics that most aspects of life and science seem to share with certain games.

It is impossible to define chance in terms of the random movements of atoms, electrons, neutrons or quarks, first because there are too many and second because, in order to define anything in a totally objective manner, we must step outside whichever universe of discourse is being considered. That is difficult to do at the best of times. But the universe of games – simple ones especially – does offer such opportunities, as mathematicians of the sixteenth and seventeenth centuries realized.

E. T. Bell in his biography of mathematicians[5] outlined the origins of modern conceptions concerning chance in all branches of science:

The true founders of the mathematical theory of probability were Pascal and Fermat, who developed the fundamental principles of the subject in an intensely interesting correspondence during the year 1654 . . . The theory which originated in a gambler's dispute is now at the base of many enterprises which we consider more important than gambling, including all kinds of insurance, mathematical statistics and their application to biology and educational measurements, and much of modern theoretical physics . . . [such a method] may cause us to revise our whole conception of the physical universe or, as has happened with the application of statistical methods to intelligence tests and the investigation of heredity, may induce us to modify our traditional beliefs regarding the 'greatness and misery of man'.

Bell also quotes Laplace:

. . . It is remarkable that [this] science, which originated in the consideration of games of chance, should have become the most important object of human knowledge.

Chance and randomness are the opposites of predictability, certainty and determinism, and yet prediction is one of the main concerns of science. In science, for example, one of the still unsolved problems is the so-called 'many-body problem' – forecasting the relative position of particles in relation to another or others over a period of time. These are far from trivial matters and, as Bell suggested, they affect 'our whole conception of life and the physical universe', to say nothing of more mundane yet vital concerns like the safety of nuclear energy generation.

Nuclear and other physicists are prepared to make relatively objective (but seldom subjective) assumptions about such problems because they insist that their profession, like all others in science, is value-free. But that is what is so bothersome. The meanings of life and behaviour are not value free, for were this the case ours would be a meaningless, totally materialistic existence.

For example, if physicists wish to put their own lives and those of their wives and children at risk (by making value-free, 'relatively objective' judgements – see Appendix C) that is their business, but they should not be permitted to make judgements that can affect or terminate our lives without our informed consent. For to have such decisions made for us without that and to be faced with the consequences is one consequence too many of a value-free, relatively objective (winning and losing oriented) science. Any 'accidents' such as occurred at Three-Mile Island, Chernobyl and elsewhere that have been kept more or less secret from the public, are the responsibility of those who made the wrong decisions and their scientific advisors, and not matters of chance, bad luck or acts of God.

There is, therefore, a profound connection between human organic behaviour and the inorganic behaviour of atomic and sub-atomic particles, relative to chance. If the inorganic building blocks of our universe move about at random and their affiliations and convergences are matters of chance, as they appear to be, then it is important to be clear about the meanings of the words 'chance' and 'randomness' in that or any other context. Such definitions should be matters of demonstrable fact and games are probably the best way of testing their meanings, as Pascal and Fermat attempted to do.

An ordinary pack of fifty-two playing-cards offers perhaps one of the most definitive ways of analysing the twin concepts of randomness and chance involving both human (conscious) and inorganic (i.e. non-sentient or mindless) behaviour. This was recognized by the physicist Arthur Eddington. The pack of cards analogy was among his favourites:

If you take a pack of cards as it comes from the maker and shuffle it for a few minutes, all trace of the original order disappears. *The order will never come back however long you shuffle*. Something has been done which cannot be undone, namely the introduction of a random element in place of arrangement ... It was scarcely true to say that the shuffling cannot be undone. You can sort out the cards into their original order if you like. But in considering the shuffling which occurs in the physical world we are not troubled by a *Deus ex machina* like you ... So I exclude you – at least I exclude that activity of your mind which you employ in sorting the cards. I allow you to shuffle them because you can do that absent-mindedly.

Secondly, it is not quite true that the original order never comes back. There is a ghost of a chance that someday a thoroughly shuffled pack will be found to have come back to the original order. That is because of the comparatively small number of cards in the pack. In our applications the units are so numerous that this kind of contingency can be disregarded.

We shall put forward the contention that –
Whenever anything happens which cannot be undone, it is always reducible to the introduction of a random element analogous to that introduced by shuffling.[6]

Lest it be thought that the definitions of randomness and chance have changed in the nearly sixty years since Eddington wrote these words, the following was written by A. J. Leggett, another physicist, in 1977:

Let us return for the moment to the occurrence of 'irreversible' processes, that is, those whose time inverse does not occur spontaneously, and which could therefore apparently be used to define a unique 'direction' of time. Such processes are, of course, part of the subject matter of thermodynamics and statistical mechanics, and the conventional explanation of the apparent asymmetry despite the time-symmetry of the underlying microscopic laws goes, very crudely, as follows: if a system is left to itself, its degree of disorder (technically, its entropy) tends to increase as a function of time. To use an often-quoted analogy, if we shuffle a pack of cards we will almost always make it more disordered; if we start with the cards arranged in 'perfect order' (ace, king, queen of spades on the top, etc.) we will almost always inevitably end up, after shuffling, at a less orderly distribution, but it is extremely unlikely that starting from a 'random' pack we would end up, by the ordinary process of shuffling, at a perfectly ordered distribution, and indeed any player who achieved such a result would almost automatically be suspected of cheating. Such an increase in disorder (entropy) seems at first sight to be naturally asymmetric in time and hence to define a unique 'direction'.[7]

But if these game-derived definitions of the meanings of randomness, chance and what occurs when a pack of cards is shuffled are wrong, then conclusions based on this analogy are equally wrong, calling for a revision of some of our perceptions of fundamental processes within the universe as defined in modern physics. Let us therefore examine what actually occurs when a pack of playing-cards is shuffled.

A pack of playing-cards as it comes from a shop consists of four suits, each arranged sequentially from two to the ace. This order exists because of long-standing conventions in the manufacture of playing-cards. However, for the purpose of this demonstration it makes no difference how the cards are arranged as they come from their maker, as long as it is a known and agreed-to order.

There are two ways of shuffling a pack of cards. One is conventional, designed to ensure maximum disordering of the original arrangement, a pre-condition to playing card games. The reason for such mindless shuffling is to prevent any prediction of who gets which cards as they are dealt to or drawn by players in turn. The object of shuffling is to maximize chaos by mindlessly randomizing a previously existing order. It is presumed that, according to the second law of thermodynamics, there will then be a perpetual increase in disorder (i.e. entropy), unless some outside agency intervenes – God, for example, a cardsharp or other kind of cheat. Since science does not admit the possibility of an intervening God, it assumes that order can only be restored dishonestly.

However there is another, mathematical and systematic way of shuffling the pack which makes every future arrangement of the cards predictable, in theory at least. It is not a method I would recommend to card players, but it does provide deep insight into what actually happens when a pack of cards is shuffled, even when this is done mindlessly. It is a method that establishes the sum of all combinatorial possibilities for fifty-two facts – be they playing-cards, atoms, neutrons, electrons or anything else – considered as a finite universe of discourse. It does not matter in the least what the arrangement of the cards may be at the moment when shuffling begins. In other words, fifty-two numbers, each representing one actual playing-card, are rearranged individually, systematically and in every possible combination until all combinatorial possibilities are exhausted.

When we consider the sum of all possibilities, this is usually understood to mean all *permutations*. However, that is an inadequate reckoning. In a pack of cards, for example, any one card, pair or larger combination will recur as many times as there are *combinatorial possibilities* in the remainder of the pack. This means that, if you were to draw two aces in any one hand, one of hearts and another of spades, it is quite possible that you may draw the same pair for the next hand in exactly the same order as before, even though the deck has been thoroughly shuffled and is in a different order than before. The occurrences and recurrences that come about as a result of such recombinations constitute the sum of all combinatorial possibilities for cards or for anything else in any finite universe of discourse.

It is now of some consequence to define what is meant by 'finite' and 'infinite' in this or in any other context. Our universe seems to be finite, but it is infinitely recursive and expanding, although whether or not this is so is unimportant for the purposes of this demonstration.

What does matter is that anything within our universe can be considered as a finite system nested within a continuum of other finite systems that have all the appearance of being infinite in number – something like the painted nesting dolls given to Russian children. Obviously there is a limit somewhere, although we do not yet know what that limit is. Our interpretation of finiteness and infinity may be due to a lack of knowledge and understanding, but the definition given here appears to be a useful way to look at the meaning of infinity when this term is applied to any subject other than the cosmos as a whole (for we have no way of knowing whether one or more parallel universes exist side by side with our own, although that seems highly likely).

A pack of playing-cards is a useful working model by which to demonstrate the mechanisms of chance relative to a finite system. It is made up of fifty-two cards because that is the number that is generally accepted for playing standard card games. Obviously their rules are entirely arbitrary although they may be established by custom and sanctified by Hoyle or by agreement among the players. But none of this concerns us here. What matters is that the arrangement possibilities of such a pack of cards is finite in itself, yet can be expanded to infinity by the addition of jokers, multiple decks shuffled together (as is done in casino blackjack since the advent of the 'counter' – see Chapter 7), or by adding cards imprinted with other than the conventional symbols. Strictly speaking, a deck of cards is a finite portion of an infinite continuum, and the same is true of any other system with which we are familiar.

Any finite system consists of a sum of possibilities that can only repeat itself once all possibilities have been exhausted. Therefore what Eddington and Leggett considered a remote possibility or a cheat is a certainty for any finite system and for every finite portion of any infinite system. The exhaustion of any particular sequence and its recurrence is simply a matter of time.

Therefore and as I showed earlier – and this is crucial – when a pack of cards is shuffled systematically or at random, *every sequence, including the original order, whatever that might have been, will repeat a calculable number of times within the finite combinatorial sum of all possibilities*. In other words every card, and two- or three- or more-card combination in relation to the rest of the deck, up to and including the full permutational sum of all cards in the deck, will occur and recur a calculable number of times in the course of all possibilities being exhausted. Every recurrence within this finite series will be individually unique in one or more respects, despite its identical composition and sequence. Each recurrence will none the less be permutationally redundant (i.e. it will consist of an identical sequence), despite its uniqueness as far as the options it provides are concerned. What this means in terms of a shuffled pack of cards is explained later in this chapter and in Appendices A and B.

A mathematically exhaustively shuffled standard pack of playing-cards generates a finite sum of all combinatorial possibilities that:

$$= 52 \times 2^{1326}$$

Within this huge sum all possible combinations (including the original arrangement of the deck) will be repeated about

$$52 \times [2^{1326} / (52! \times {>}2{<}3)]$$

This mathematical calculation[8] means 52 times 2 to the power of 1326 divided by the permutational sum of 52 times a number larger than 2 and smaller than 3. This number, although still not recognized for what it actually means, has taken on a new significance in recent years as a result of a burning interest shown by physicists and computer scientists in 'fractals' (see Appendix A).

The number of repetitions of every possible sequence within such a systematically shuffled pack of cards is therefore very high indeed and far from impossible or rare, as any player of the card game solitaire (patience) can establish for himself without recourse to mathematics. Shorter sequences recur more frequently than any involving the whole deck of cards and this has profound meanings that are discussed in Appendices A and B. How such vast sums are generated even for very simple games is demonstrated there also.

The number of times that the whole pack of cards enjoys a restitution of its original order, stretched over time as a result of mindless shuffling, mediated by attention and some re-ordering according to the rules, may cause a patience player to lose more often than he wins. But that is due to rules of play and deliberately skewed odds and values assigned to winning combinations. None the less, and even without attentive assistance from the player, the restitution of the whole deck in any given order and that of any of its parts occurs and recurs quite often or often enough to upset the statistical probabilities calculated on the basis of permutations only.

Any intervention that causes deliberate ordering as a result of attentive human behaviour only accelerates the process of restitution to the original order after mindless randomization. But that is all it can do. In time and even without that, every order will repeat a given number of times until the whole series has exhausted itself and then it will begin anew. In other words, even with perpetual randomization and without human ordering of any kind, the original order and all of its permutations in whole and in part will return – not just once, but many times. This is demonstrated by the disproof that order or disorder can be predicted by telepathy.

The attempt to prove the existence of extra-sensory perception is one example of how misleading statistical calculations based on short-run permutational series can be. In the 1940s and 1950s Dr J. B. Rhine and his associates at Duke University in the US tested the telepathic powers of hundreds of subjects by means of shuffled packs of cards, dice and other randomized objects that they were asked to identify or predict without having seen them.[9] For example, subjects were asked to identify individual and series of cards or their order, without being able to see in what order they had been placed or occurred as a result of random shuffling. It was up to the subject to use 'telepathy' to choose or predict. The results exceeded statistical expectations time after time, leading Dr Rhine to claim that telepathy was finally 'proven'.

Dr Rhine used a variety of methods to test his theories, one of which consisted of a pack of 25 cards, made up of five identical sets of five cards, each imprinted with one of the five symbols. He used complex statistical analyses to determine whether the subjects' choices or predictions equalled or bettered what might have been expected by chance. But his calculations were based on permutational rather than combinatorial sums. The following shows how great the differences are between such calculations.

I have confined the calculation to a five-card pack (rather than using one consisting of five identical suits of five cards) for simplicity's sake. The chances of making a correct 'guess' about a particular sequence occurring at any one time in a shuffled pack of five cards are 1 in 120 (or .8333 out of a hundred tries) when the statistics are based on the permutational sum of possibilities. This was one of the statistical 'norms' against which Dr Rhine measured his supposed successes. But the results turned out to be far more favourable than what could have been expected statistically, causing Dr Rhine to delude himself and believers in ESP that he had made a major discovery.

Once we consider the combinatorial sum of all arrangement possibilities for a five-card pack, then the chances of 'guessing' any one sequence equal 41 out of 1,024 (or 4.004 out of a hundred tries) even when the cards are shuffled at random (and in the absence of any ESP). The probabilities of guessing correctly are nearly five times greater when the calculations are based on combinatorial, rather than on permutational sums. Dr Rhine's results came closer to the combinatorial sum expectations than to the permutational ones and were the product of pure guesswork, demonstrating that no ESP was involved. Rhine was never made aware of his calculation error.

But let us return to the mindlessly shuffled whole pack of playing cards and compare it with the systematically shuffled one. We will find that both remain finite systems, no matter how we shuffle them. The mindlessly shuffled pack will generate exactly the same sum of all combinatorial possibilities as the systematically shuffled one in the long run. But the mindlessly shuffled pack will take longer to reach the point at which all individually unique permutational redundancies have occurred and recurred as often as and possibly more frequently than predicted by the systematic method. This will be so because additional, identical but non-redundant sequences that belong to future finite series will have crept into the present one in an unpredictable manner. That, and the disorder in which the finite combinatorial sum of all possibilities will occur are the only differences between mindless and systematic shuffling over long periods of time.

In other words, in the long run there will still be the same finite sum of permutational redundancies in the random series as in the mathematically shuffled pack, plus additional exact copies that rightfully belong to successive finite series. The process of random shuffling creates such disorder that it is impossible to predict which permutations will occur when, and which belong to the original or to any future series. In the mathematically shuffled series all is predictable.

The main differences, therefore, between the mindlessly and the systematically shuffled packs of cards are those of *time* and *order* in which sequences of events occur and recur. In the systematically shuffled pack occurrences and recurrences can be foreseen precisely. In the mindlessly shuffled pack the disordered occurrence of the sequence of events and the time factor combine to make it impossible to predict when individual occurrences and recurrences will take place, but the same ones will predictably occur and recur here as in the systematically shuffled pack.

In the game of patience where mindless disorder predominates and systematic arrangement is relatively incidental, the recurrence of the original order, besides being inevitable, is merely speeded up by the player's attention to detail. It is not caused by it, no matter what the player's intentions may be. That is the best human behaviour can do when a system is randomized mindlessly. Intentionally systematic organic behaviour – mathematically precise, systematic shuffling – eliminates chance entirely.

To reiterate – and I realize that these may seem to be confusing ideas at a single reading – the realization of any finite sum of possibilities is achieved in a minimum of time when the shuffling is systematic, but takes longer with randomization. The mathematically shuffled sequence is totally predictable in the short, intermediate and long run. In the short run anything can take place with randomization, but in the longest run there will hardly be any difference between the two results in the number and kind of occurrences and recurrences, except duplications.

The chief differences between 'short-run' and 'long-run' results relative to time and systemic size require further discussion. A short-run series can either be an exhaustion of a permutational sum (n!) or, if n is a number larger than 2, of a part of such a sum. A long-run series consists of all combinatorial possibilities for any value of n and possible repetitions of that sum. When n = 4, the short-run permutation series = 24 (when it should actually be greater than 2 times and less than 3 times that number – see Appendix A), but the full combinatorial sum of all possibilities = 256; a considerable difference. For a pack of cards the full short-run permutational series (and even that is erroneously computed today, as I show in Appendix A) consists (approximately) of 8 followed by 67 zeros, and the single, non-repeated long-run sum of all combinatorial possibilities was given earlier and is astronomical. We are therefore talking about inconceivably large numbers and spans of time that have meaning only in terms of the evolution of our universe and its likely future, of our species, or the number of option patterns generated by our central nervous system.

The larger the system, the smaller the percentage of difference will be in the long run between the systematically and the mindlessly shuffled pack. But there will always be a difference, no matter how minute. This difference defines the second law of thermodynamics which will be discussed a little further on. One reason for the persistence of this difference is that we are not certain about just how many fundamental particles make up our universe, whether their number remains constant, increases or decreases (the current estimate is 10^{40} quarks). We therefore cannot know exactly how long the longest run may turn out to be or how long it might take for the systematically arranged or random sum of all combinatorial possibilities to reach its end, if there is one.

All of this would seem to suggest that the inorganic or pre-organic building blocks of nature are not ordered systematically by a being outside the cosmos. Nor does there appear to be any evidence that a supernatural being is busy shuffling them perpetually. The Book of Genesis states that God created order out of a pre-existing chaos. Conversely, modern science would seem to insist that some force within our universe perpetually increases chaos, starting from a pre-existing order so that no event ever recurs, except by design.

Neither position seems justified by an objective consideration of the available facts. Fundamental particles appear to move about and affiliate with, ignore, collide with or repulse one another in a disordered, random and seemingly unpredictable manner in the short term, presumably from the beginning, whenever that was, and until today. They seem likely to continue to do so for any foreseeable future. However, as the scientist Ilya Prirogine, and some physicists have recently suggested on the basis of research in fractals, a discernible and fundamental long-term order appears to exist even given an apparent shorter-term disorder. Such an absolute order seems to underlie all seemingly random processes, as demonstrated here by a shuffled pack of playing-cards.

Events (i.e. systemic behaviours) from outside any given universe of discourse can affect or limit the occurrences, recurrences and movement of particles in space in a rather more profound manner than human intervention and attentive arrangement of the cards in a randomized game. In physics the rules and values (i.e. the meanings) that obtain are derived from natural law (i.e. cause and effect and the operations that bring them about, viewed totally objectively). But in card games randomness and chance are limited by arbitrarily assigned or deliberately biased rules, values and recognition of likely winning combinations and their arrangement in hand or on the table (i.e. as in solitaire, bridge or poker).

We cannot predict the sequence of cards in a randomly shuffled pack in the short run any more than the short-run occurrences and recurrences of events in any other random universe. Yet the mechanism that is operative for a randomly shuffled pack of cards is equally applicable in any larger or smaller universe. Hence we know that seemingly random events will occur and recur predictably and repeatedly as a finite series in any universe, within mathematically defined bounds over unpredictable periods of time, modified only by the random or sentient behaviours of systems.

Given this easily verifiable definition of the principles of randomness and chance, and if they are found to hold true generally, then we live in a very different kind of universe than that imagined in conventional physics. It means that nature does repeat itself again and again, each repetition being individually unique in one or more respects, and some may even be precise copies of previous ones. The implications of this last possibility we can only surmise. Just think of what this means as far as quarks, electrons, protons, neutrons, you, me, and the whole universe is concerned. It could turn our conception of the meaning of existence on its head. It also means that as far as the inorganic portions of our universe are concerned, time's arrow points in only one direction.

To reiterate: randomness in so-called games of chance is the product of deliberately mindless behaviour and a resulting ignorance and unpredictability (e.g. of the order of the cards in the whole pack, in portions that have not yet been dealt, and those in fellow players' hands), limited by the number of factors that are involved (e.g. the number of cards in the deck or in hand), the assignment of arbitrary or prejudiced rules and values (e.g. which are the winning and losing combinations), how they are rated (what is won or lost), minor re-arrangements of recognized patterns according to the rules (arrangement of cards in hand or on the table), and time.

Games of pure strategy and those of chance are far less complex structures than fundamental particle affiliations. But with every increase in the number of participating components – in games as in everything else – there is a greater than exponential increase in complexity and a corresponding increase in full and partial permutational redundancies and repetitions as a result of the 'combinatorial explosion of possibilities', demonstrated in Appendices A and B.

Rather than a precise match between games of chance and processes in nature, we have a correspondence and equivalence in games, demonstrated by mathematically definable similarities discussed in the following chapter. While certain aspects of nature share characteristics with games of chance, they have many more in common with games of pure strategy in equally unsuspected and surprising ways as we shall see in Chapters 8 and 9. In any event, nature can be analysed and discussed in terms of games of strategy and chance in order to discover its operational principles.

Randomness in card games of chance can only be ameliorated or defeated by waiting until a perfect hand presents itself or by manipulations of one sort or another (e.g. bluffing, betting, inside information, a knowledge of probabilities, psychological warfare or outright cheating). A perfect hand, although it happens, does not occur often enough to do a player much good as far as winning steadily is concerned, given the usual assigned odds, pay-offs and 'skimming' by the 'house'.

Manipulating the cards, odds and other players is therefore the only 'winning' strategy. One of the means of manipulation (the others are discussed elsewhere) consists of a knowledge of probabilities based on statistical analyses of past outcomes. Regrettably for card players and gamblers, a knowledge of statistics does not help them win. Those who rely on this technique can only keep their losses at a minimum, making their capital last longer than it would otherwise, but they will eventually lose, unless they combine statistical knowledge with other methods.

The method of manipulation used in combinatorial mathematics (see Appendices B and C) to analyse what happens when a pack of playing-cards is shuffled is linear, systematic and holistic. It includes all possible rules, conditions and outcomes, irrespective of the number of players, for all games that can be played with a pack of fifty-two playing-cards whether or not they have as yet been invented, within whatever time it may take to play or analyse them. It includes all possible errors and violations of the rules, cheating, bluffing and the intentions and feelings of the players, whether they play systematically or at random. Any statistical analysis of such a sum of all combinatorial possibilities within this finite universe of discourse is bound to provide perfect fore- and hindsight, as it did in disproving Dr Rhine's telepathy claims.

The results are correct to the last digit, not counting rounding errors, and provide perfect fore- and hindsight in mathematical terms. It is clearly impossible, due to a lack of time, to consider the meaning of every game, move and condition, their permutations, individually unique redundancies and the options they offer. Nevertheless, although these analyses are likely to upset some cherished ideas, they may demonstrate principles that could be useful in establishing new truths and confirming some very ancient ones.

Statistical analysis derived from less than the sum-of-all-possibilities is the common method for manipulating random facts in science. As we saw earlier and will see again later, such statistics work but they can be extremely misleading. They can provide a fairly accurate picture (as in image restoration by computer) of strata that lie between a sufficient number of closely spaced marks. Even then this statistically enhanced image is an approximation that is only momentarily reliable. Statistics may summarize what occurred in the past, but they can never be predictive. They can lead to wrong conclusions, as has certainly been the case in

Eddington's definition of chance and randomness and Dr Rhine's ESP experiments.

Conventional statistics are based on an average count of a limited sum of past occurrences and recurrences. 'Weighting' as in Bayesian mathematics can help make them more representative than they would be without it. Weighting means that the samples from which averages are constructed are hoped to be representative of the population at large, as it was in the past. In social surveys, for example, the size of each population sample is broken down according to education, income, home and car ownership among other criteria, and manipulated to correspond more or less to percentages of these groups within the population as a whole. This works well enough for some purposes, like insurance company actuarial (longevity) tables, but only because these companies allow themselves a wide margin of error. This is a form of manipulation (of the odds) that works in their favour so that, like gambling casinos, they cannot lose. But statistics are useless for predicting the actual future or winning.

We will return to conventional uses of statistics in discussing games of strategy (see Chapter 9). This will show just how misleading they are in forecasting any future unless it is an exact repetition of the past. Statistics are bound to be wrong unless they are based on calculations derived from a sum of all possibilities, and even then they can lead to wrong conclusions because they do not take human behaviour – especially learning potential – into account.

My redefinitions of chance and randomness also appear to affect our perceptions in an aspect of physics mentioned earlier – the meaning of the three laws of thermodynamics (there is a fourth, but it is of no apparent significance in this present context). While the laws of games are arbitrary, those of nature are immutable. Simply stated, these laws define energy/matter exchanges in the universe. They help explain the births and deaths of galaxies as well as why an electric motor that generates heat keeps your refrigerator cold.

The first law states that energy is conserved and that all matter and energy in a closed universe are interchangeable. If the first law of thermodynamics were the only one we had, then perpetual motion machines would be possible. The second law states that when 'work is done', loss of energy and disorder increase perpetually throughout the universe and cause all systems to run down at an accelerating pace. This is the law that describes how most current systems operate and was the one believed to apply to randomness and chance. If this law were rescinded, all of us would live forever and nothing would ever wear out or die. The third law states that at absolute zero degree temperature all systems once again reach equilibrium – except, of course, that life under those conditions is impossible.

In modern physics the first and third laws of thermodynamics are usually ignored or believed to be idealized versions of what really takes place. Most attention is paid to the second law. However, my redefinition of chance seems to indicate that we may have our priorities reversed as far as the three laws of thermodynamics are concerned.

According to these findings, the dynamic equilibrium states defined by the first law are far more significant and prevalent throughout the universe than the perpetual rush towards increased entropy and extinction predicted by the second, or a motionless and timeless equilibrium suggested by the third. The first law is defined by the draw in a behavioural context, the second by winning and losing, and the third can be viewed as a non-game. These findings limit the second law of thermodynamics severely – far more than was ever thought possible. I shall return to this theme when discussing games of strategy. The classical definitions of the three laws of thermodynamics are elaborated in Appendix C.

An awareness of the preponderance of dynamic equilibria and balance (i.e. the co-operative draw state) in the universe, where chance and uncertainty were believed to have prevailed in the past, has been growing in a number of fields. As a result, some people have come to the same or similar conclusions as my own, starting from different points of departure but ending up in more or less the same place. For example, in his preface to a series of 1974 lectures on quantum mechanics, H. Haken writes:

In [various] disciplines, such as physics, chemistry, biology and sociology, we observe the phenomenon that out of chaotic, disordered or structureless states there arise completely new states which have well defined spatial structures or which behave in a well regulated manner . . . a new rapidly developing field has come into existence, namely that of studying and comparing co-operative effects in different disciplines . . . The analogies found in these systems go far beyond those which are now well known in phase transition theory of systems in thermal equilibrium.[10]

Twelve different examples of systemic ordering and co-operation in physics are cited in these lectures, including fields like ferromagnetism, superconductivity, the laser and fluid technologies, astrophysics and engineering. According to Haken a new/old ordering principle and paradigm appear to be emerging where chaos was believed to have reigned.

The question of time's arrow may also need reconsideration in the light of my suggested redefinition of the laws of chance and randomness. Einstein appeared to demonstrate that time was dilatable (in effect, reversible like an hourglass) under certain conditions.[11] Obviously every system in the universe is time-bound in one way or another (except those that are subject to the third law of thermodynamics). And while experiments in recent years seem to confirm Einstein's conception of time dilation (e.g. if you were to travel through the universe from earth at or near the speed of light you would return younger than your great-great-grand-child), this is an impossibility for organic systems.

The seeming reversibility of time that some people have claimed to be a consequence of Einstein's theories is a relatively objective, short-term phenomenon that depends on the observer's position within the universe, relative to whatever he observes. But when time is considered in totally objective terms and within a framework of the sum of all combinatorial possibilities (by figuratively standing outside the universe, yet considering yourself to be within and a part of it – a difficult, but not impossible, theoretical vantage point), time's reversibility turns out to be a mirage.

The final belief that may be upset by these findings concerns 'decidability'. It is a problem ostensibly solved by Kurt Gödel, a German mathematician of this century who believed that he had defined the limits of human understanding in mathematical terms. This theory is a perennial matter of debate among computer scientists who claim that artificial or machine intelligence – computers that infer and think in a human way – is just around the corner. The mathematician Sir James Lighthill in his report to the British Government in 1973[12] insisted that artificial intelligence was impossible because of the combinatorial explosion of numbers. He was correct as is confirmed by the findings described in this book.

Gödel's theorem was summarized in non-mathematical terms by M. M. Lehman, a professor of computing science at London's Imperial College, in the two-volume *Encyclopaedia of Ignorance*:

... the latter [Gödel] states that one cannot prove the consistency and completeness of an axiomatic system using only the axioms and the rules of inference of that system. Informally one can state that an assertion about a system (and a model of a system represents an assertion about the system) cannot be shown to be absolutely true from within the system by using only known facts about the system.

Suppose now that we assume that there exists an absolute theory for some artificial system. The latter could be represented by an axiomatic model in which each part and activity of the system reflects either an axiom or a theorem. From Gödel's theorem it follows that the correctness of the model cannot be predicted from within the system. That is, the behaviour of the system cannot be predicted absolutely from within the system . . . By its very nature such activity is a part of the behaviour of the system as represented in the model. Hence there does not in this respect exist an 'outside' to the system. Thus one cannot obtain an absolute theory, a demonstrably correct model . . .

. . . One cannot even determine the state of the total system with any certainty by applying probabilistic judgements as in Game Theory. After all each situation, each sequence of events, will occur only once . . . Total knowledge, the final state, can never be reached.[13]

As illustrated by the vast but finite sums of combinatorial relationships generated by relatively simple systems like a pack of playing-cards, it is perfectly obvious that detailed knowledge of all the facts is impossible even at trivial levels of complexity. But mathematically it is possible to define not only the sum of all combinatorial possibilities for systems as a whole, but also to classify them into their constituent components. This can be done down to the level of the individual uniqueness of every state for systems involving n (i.e. any number of) factors, from $n = 2$ to theoretical infinity, subject only to the limitations imposed by computer processing speeds, time and paper. Further, there is no need ever to consider all possibilities because, as we saw earlier, each sequence and every portion of each sequence of events recurs many times within every finite system.

It is therefore unnecessary to examine every individual card game or player's turn for all the games there are. All that is needed is that representative ones are chosen from the sum of all possibilities and analysed in detail (as I do in Appendix A for the game of noughts and crosses). Better still, generalizations can be made with great precision by analysing the number of individual and groupings of states classified according to criteria that define what occurs and recurs over periods of time. It is therefore possible to understand what goes on within systems, provided we know the principles involved and have sufficient information. It is never necessary to know everything. As the mathematical demonstrations make plain, any attempt at encyclopaedic knowledge or omniscience, were the latter possible, is self-defeating. The level of understanding seems to decrease in direct proportion to the amount of excess knowledge that is accumulated. This is one of the key problems of specialization and a limitation of subject-specific specialist expertise.

The combinatorial sums and their classification show that practical and realistic limitations set on knowledge and information are essential if we are to arrive at whatever truths we seek. For the cluttering of the mind with needless detail tends to obscure rather than illuminate the essential facts. One of humanity's main claims to intelligence, therefore, seems to depend on our ability to jump to correct conclusions without considering everything; to act on principle and to let the details take care of themselves, rather than waiting until we have all the evidence. In the latter case we would have to wait for ever. To jump to a conclusion – right or wrong – is what is meant by intuition.

Even jumping to a wrong conclusion need not be a disaster (except in irreversible situations), for we can always learn from our mistakes. That ability distinguishes us from inorganic nature and especially from computers. The game analogy shows why computers cannot think, reason, learn and make value judgements autonomously. They cannot make value judgements about the relative merits of winning, losing, achieving a draw or a stalemate. They cannot distinguish between perfection and error, unless what constitutes either is pre-programmed into them. Computers are excellent syntactic (permutational) shuffling machines, but they cannot be or become semantic (combinatorial) decoders for all the reasons given here and in Chapter 3.

The revisions made in game theory open doors to a new understanding of how any system works and can be predicted. The behavioural aspects of the game analogy are the missing links that have so far stood in the way of the discovery of a unifying principle in science.

Rather than a universe predominantly governed by chance, as the mainstream of modern science insists, or one that is predetermined by an all-knowing God as religious fundamentalists declare, it turns out to be a *conditionally deterministic* one, as demonstrated by my redefinition of the meanings of randomness and chance. As we have seen, this has many implications in different applications.

The meaning of *conditional determinism*, depends on whether we are talking about ordered or random, organic or inorganic systems, and whether random ones are considered in both artificially ordered and in their naturally random states. Short-term consequences in any random universe in which the odds are not manipulated artificially will remain unpredictable, as at present. However short- and intermediate-term forecasts for any systematically ordered system and long-term forecasts for them and even for random ones will become far more precise than in the past as a result of this redefinition of chance.

Conditions and consequences will become highly predictable wherever a three-dimensional data pattern can be shown to represent reality and analysed *systematically*, limited by the available knowledge (as in today's weather prediction). The intermediate- and long-term future will become far more predictable than it was up to now, because of increased knowledge about the characteristics of events in artificially ordered systems (like the exhaustion of the sum of all possibilities for a pack of fifty-two playing-cards) and their meanings as far as naturally occurring random systems are concerned.

In any other than random systems, short-term forecasts should be more precise than long-term ones because less data needs to be considered. The cone of expectations widens as it reaches into the future and options multiply rapidly. As even the game of noughts and crosses illustrates, the knowledge of facts will always remain incomplete because there are simply too many. Therefore it is the principles that count and not the details when it comes to forecasting any but the simplest events.

A clear distinction must, of course, be made between inorganic and organic portions of the universe. The former are governed by a conditionally deterministic nature that excludes sentient behaviour.

Most of the remainder of this book deals with events affected or brought about by organic behaviour. In human, behavioural terms *conditional determinism* means that we will continue to get what we want and deserve, depending on the conditions we understand and impose. That is especially true for our understanding of the need to impose the correct conditions and the consequences of our failure to do so. If we impose the wrong ones we get nothing but trouble. We are only in the hands of chance if we impose no conditions at all, or if we shuffle the facts deliberately or without thought. In that case we will get whatever is determined by randomly occurring facts and conditions that we ourselves have shuffled, or allowed others to shuffle mindlessly.

Even then success will come to us every once in a while, but only in a random and totally unpredictable manner. It is therefore far better and more efficient to arrange the facts systematically and in a craftsmanlike fashion. That way we get whatever we want in due course. But for as long as we live in a world in which most people and institutions treat one another as if they were engaged in a gigantic game of chance from which only 'the house' (i.e. those who make the laws, manipulate the odds, and systematically skim off the net gains) can profit in the intermediate term, or one of strategy that is won by the few at the expense of the many, our future will remain problematic and uncertain. In the longest run all outcomes tend towards a draw, balance and agreement, the first law of thermodynamics viewed in terms of a never-ending game.

7   Games of So-Called Chance

Never give a sucker an even break.

W. C. Fields

Only the most experienced professional gamblers seem to be aware of some of the true meanings of chance, but they usually lack the frames of reference required to appreciate them in any context away from gaming tables or betting shops. Great differences exist between what actually occurs and what is popularly and scientifically 'believed' to be true about systematically ordered and mindlessly disordered systems. As discussed in the previous chapter, a fundamental order underlies total disorder and randomization. The most chaotic conditions generate series of possibilities in the longest run that are actually or nearly identical to systematic arrangement in the short run. As in a systematically shuffled pack of playing-cards:

- Once the sum of all possibilities is exhausted, no matter how it is calculated, the whole series repeats in the same sequence. All repeated *permutational* and *combinatorial* possibilities are exact duplicates of those in the previous finite series.
- A calculably high number of *permutational redundancies* recurs within every finite *combinatorial* series and its repetitions. Each of these redundancies is identical in content and sequence to every other (i.e. syntax), but differs in at least one or more respects from its duplicates. The most significant of these differences are the options (the possible directions or choices open to the data-flow – i.e. conditional branching – selected as indicated by the arrows on the diagrams in Appendices A and B) offered by each permutationally redundant duplicate (i.e. meanings).

In a randomly shuffled pack:

- The sequence in which events occur is totally disordered.
- It takes longer to generate the sum of all combinatorial possibilities in a disordered manner than in a systematically arranged one.
- The reason for this is that in a randomly shuffled system precise copies that belong to the next series, or even to other, successive ones, creep into any previous series in a disordered manner.
- This means that a random series may contain a far greater number of permutational duplicates and redundancies than one that is arranged systematically within the time needed to generate the sum of all combinatorial possibilities.

Other differences between random and systematic arrangement are:

- Prediction as to sequence (i.e. order in which events take place) is only possible with systematic arrangement and when the object is the achievement of a result that is equivalent to a draw (i.e. a balanced outcome).
- Systematic arrangement and prediction can only be achieved when the arranger or analyst enjoys acute pattern recognition abilities, familiarity with the subject and/or intuitive awareness.
- When a result is brought about by chance and without advance pattern recognition or intuition, it will usually be ignored or misinterpreted. Exceptions exist, but even then understanding comes only after the event that is therefore unpredictable and a matter of chance.

It should be clear that identical results can be achieved by chance as much as by design and systematic arrangement. The differences are those of randomization, time, frequency of repetition and pattern recognition. For example, success in anything, including games of chance, is reached soonest by foresighted visualization or auralization (i.e. imagination), systematic effort and the will to achieve a draw (and not the will to win as is popularly believed), and may then recur with certain but unpredictable regularity. However, randomization means that the results could either take for ever to achieve, or occur sooner or later than anticipated, or, most likely, occur and recur so infrequently or in randomly bunched sequences that they cannot be predicted or deliberately repeated, and may not even be recognized for what they are and mean.

With systematic effort whatever is wanted will occur depending on the options we choose, for we literally create our own future out of the sum of all possibilities. The qualitatively most desirable and worthwhile results require greatest foresight and effort, but are achieved because they can be made to happen far more often than the worst or the wrong ones (except by chance) when the facts are randomized and disordered. And yet we seem to choose the wrong options more often than not despite their relative scarcity, because, due to wrong conditioning or intentions, we employ strategies that turn every endeavour into a game of chance. When this occurs it is due to our subscribing to and following wrong principles (e.g. winning and losing in preference to a draw), and an evident unwillingness or inability to foresee consequences because we place our trust in chance rather than in systematic craft.

The conditions that govern playing to win, and leaving things to chance, or playing for a draw, have profound meanings as far as prediction and forecasting in any field are concerned. Randomness may prevail in the short run in inorganic portions of the universe, or it can be caused by mindlessness, ignorance, stupidity or cupidity wherever human behaviour is involved. When life is lived in a predominantly random and disordered manner (i.e. it is played to be won either as a game of strategy or as a gambling game), history is likely to repeat itself in two ways: precisely (as a result of a duplication of a part of following series), or as permutational redundancies that are sequentially more or less identical, yet individually unique in so far as the options are concerned.

However in that case the periodicity of the occurrences – when they will occur and recur – cannot be forecast. One example was the revelation in 1987 that in the US the FBI had once again 'investigated' and tapped the phones of dissenters from US foreign policy in Central America – disconcerting behaviours designed to tarnish them with the brush of 'subversion', 'communism' and 'anti-Americanism' to blackmail and frighten them into silence (i.e. enabling the Reagan Administration to win by making those who disagree with it lose). This was an exact re-run of the same sequence of events that happened during the Nixon Administration, a bare fifteen years before. Then all sorts of legislation was passed 'because this must never be allowed to happen again in a democratic and free society'.

But this kind of corruption happens again and again in Britain, the US and elsewhere because the reflex reaction of would-be winners in games of chance and strategy is to use every possible dirty trick to try to provoke errors in the opposition that can be taken advantage of. These are the only ways they know how to play and they can imagine no others. That is why history keeps repeating itself at unpredictable times. But, as I have said, there is another way to play, although politicians, like most economists, physicists, biologists and many gamblers do not know about it or, if they do, insist that it does not count. That is why so many seem as if they came out of the same biscuit mould and lack individuality and creativity. It is also the reason why much of modern life is dull, boring and regimented.

When life is lived as if it were a purely strategic game played to a draw, the consequences are highly predictable (although there are innumerable ways to reach this outcome). With sufficient attention the same kind of creativity can produce an endless number of different but benign and imaginative results. It can and should lead to a perpetually invigorated renaissance if playing to win competitively is effectively discouraged or at least not rewarded. There are bound to be exceptions. They are likely to include events that have never occurred or been recorded before or, if they have occurred, for which the periodicity of recurrence is unknown as yet (like earthquakes and volcanic eruptions). They happen, seemingly by chance, but not very often. It is only our ignorance that makes them appear to occur by chance. Once these potentially damaging natural phenomena are understood they can be avoided. The same is true of war (see Chapter 12).

Other events may remain unpredictable because they lie as yet beyond the horizon of the cone of expectancy (see Appendix B). The sequence of events in inorganic, random systems is only revealed over very long periods of time or by systematic analyses. Such models of the past and the future exist, but they are abstract combinatorial matrices for which the details need filling in. They differ in detail from one subject to the next and can apply to games as to anything else, but even here there are limits. They can only include the number of factors that can be taken into consideration, relative to time, space, the present state of knowledge and a past and future horizon that cannot be penetrated except in time and then only with increased knowledge that provides further options.

Our willingness to learn determines how fast and how far that horizon of options can be pushed into the future and our choices enlarged. What was unpredictable yesterday can become predictable today or tomorrow. The principles that govern these natural laws of cause and effect, past, present and future are given in Appendix B.

These statements can be tested in games played by the standard rules (see Appendix A). For example, the rules of different card games limit the sum of all combinatorial possibilities for the past, present and future. The same is true for noughts and crosses, chess or any other game of chance or strategy. They dictate which kind of behaviour is most appropriate for attempted winning, losing, draws or stalemates, what conditions bring them about and when. In some card games, like rummy or canasta, it is a question of waiting until you draw cards that enable you to play various combinations off or out. Other than waiting, drawing cards, discarding, and making minor judgements relative to the cards in hand, those that are discarded, in the other players' hands or that remain in the undealt stack, there is nothing a player can do to reduce chance and randomness (other than cheating).

Getting a winning hand or achieving a draw in those games is mostly a question of paying attention and biding your time. In effect you are continuously shuffling the pack, even while you play a hand, hoping against hope for whatever outcome you want, relative to the stated conditions that a player can affect only minimally. Decision-making plays a minor role in these games. There is very little difference between this kind of game, solitaire or bingo. Given these conditions it is certain that you will win or lose in the short run, and can only expect a draw in the longest run.

Once card games implicitly or explicitly permit bluffing, as in bridge or poker, the psychological manipulations become increasingly important and prediction is hazardous unless a player can read the minds of his game partners. Bluffing and 'mind reading' (i.e. discovering the intentions of other players), far more than the cards in hand, determine winning and losing. In bridge (as in

Monopoly, as we shall see later) things can get to be very unpleasant between partners, either as an effective ploy to disconcert the other side and take advantage of whatever mistakes they make, or because the game strikes at the very roots of an insecure personal relationship. But it is only when such behaviours are subconscious, totally conditioned and reflexive as a result of a subscription to the wrong principles, that history tends to repeat itself in a highly predictable manner like the FBI ploys discussed earlier, except in so far as periodicity is concerned.

On a larger scale, world history in its traditionally chaotic state is unlikely to repeat itself precisely because the number of possibilities are enormously greater than those for any mere game of strategy or chance. Drawn on a larger canvas, history confirms that permutationally similar events recur, each unique in one or more respects, differing from the others by the options they provide (e.g. the First and Second World Wars; Watergate and Irangate; the US-Vietnam war and the Russo-Afghan war; the stock-market crashes of 1929, 1987 and those that are still to come).

It is obvious that the object of intelligent behaviour is to create and maintain a more or less systematic and orderly existence, except when it comes to humour and games of chance. However, orderliness should not be confused with regimentation, for the first is an autonomous, organic act symbolized by the draw, and the second an authoritarian, mechanistic one that applies only to games that are played to be won.

Chance is caused by conscious and intentional or unconscious and random behaviour, and is therefore essentially a matter of awareness (i.e. pattern recognition) and time. Chance can be eliminated entirely in simple games of strategy (like prisoner's dilemma and noughts and crosses), but only limited in more complex ones (like chess) and those involving randomized components (like cards or roulette), except in the longest run. Chance tends to creep into pure games of strategy with any increase in the number of components, their mobility and different characteristics (as in chess); and as a result of a player's wish to win and make his opponent lose. In the last instance chance is a function of human ignorance, inattention, competitiveness, ill-will and conditioning, and not a law of nature.

To repeat, chance is limited by the perpetual recurrence of

permutational redundancies – exact replication of permutations that belong to following series – and by whether sequences of events are random or systematically arranged. Certainty and repetition are therefore matters of time rather than of chance even in a random, inorganic universe, and of evolution, pattern recognition and appropriate behaviour in an organic one. These conditions turn the most random set of events into conditionally deterministic ones. There is also a profound difference between randomness in nature unaffected by organic behaviour and what happens when organic behaviour intervenes.

Mindless randomization rules from the start in so-called games of chance and in mixed games of chance and strategy. Such games depend on uncertainty (i.e. a deliberate, but chaotic creation of chance from the outset), hidden factors, secrecy and unpredictability.

There is, therefore, a conditional structural difference between game categories; one that was not perceived by von Neumann and Morgenstern.[1] They insisted that decision-making determines whether a game is one of strategy or of chance. That is true in determining which kind of game is to be played. But beyond this it cannot be true because then every game would be a game of strategy, no matter how much it depended on randomization, secrecy or chance. If true, then plans on where, when and how to place a bet, or how much to risk would turn the wildest gamble into a tactical decision-making game. Even a guess whether a coin will come up heads or tails could then be considered a strategic decision. A guess is an estimate of a probability. A decision is a declaration of certainty – right or wrong.

If, instead of trying to win a player opts for a draw, then all gambles are taken out of games of pure strategy and chance. Or, if you prefer, the player then gambles only on his own ability to avoid mistakes, to find and point out those made by a game partner, and on that player's willingness to correct them. There is, however, one condition under which the outcome of a gambling game can depend on limited decision-making, although chance is still operative: when artificially skewed odds and values are introduced.

Skewed odds are introduced when, in pitching pennies for example, it is agreed that coming up with heads scores two or more points and tails only one (or the other way round). A mathematically knowledgeable player can then calculate the odds and keep his losses down, while waiting for a short run in his favour.

In other words, in both games of chance and pure strategy, winning is achieved by default, inducing and taking advantage of another player's errors, or by ignorance or lack of co-ordination (i.e. dumb luck). When both players are equally skilled, knowledgeable, fair and honest in games of strategy, equality (a draw) is established as a matter of course and relatively soon. In games of chance draws depend mostly on time and it can take for ever for actual or near-parity to be re-established.

At the best of times one can limit a gamble by understanding the various processes that are involved. Limiting chance in randomized situations does not guarantee winning, but can keep losses down to a minimum, enabling the player to take advantage of whatever manipulations are possible, of luck (i.e. the other player's mistakes) that may come his way in the future, or waiting for perfection to come about by chance. Limiting chance can mean bluffing in games like poker; a good memory in vingt-et-un; or a knowledge of the 'natural' and 'house' odds in craps. 'House' or skewed odds (i.e. other than 'natural' mathematical ones) are imposed in gambling casinos in order to give the house an absolute winning edge.

In pitching pennies one kind of draw can occur when, after an infinite period of time and an infinite number of tosses, heads and tails begin to approach parity – in other words both will come close to having occurred and recurred an identical number of times, provided the odds are 'natural' (i.e. 'tails' has the same value as 'heads'). No one is likely to live long enough to take advantage of this fact (although, of course, it can occur by chance in the short-run). It can occur during the course of any gambling session that ends with each player's recovery of the precise amount of money with which he started, or an equal score for both. Players can agree to play until such a point is reached. But as far as most gamblers are concerned, all this is a waste of time. They find it exhilarating to win and make their fellow players lose and some seem to be excited by losing.

There are only two ways to win with certainty as far as pitching pennies is concerned. One is to use a coin inscribed identically on both sides (i.e. cheating). The other, and far better way, is to learn how to manipulate an ordinary coin so that when you call out your decision and flip it into the air it tumbles over exactly the number of times necessary to give you what you want when it lands. Such exquisite craftsmanship on the part of one player (and not the other) is known as cheating because superb craftsmanship is usually considered just that by those who cannot match it. In order for this to work in gambling games it is important to allow the 'sucker' to win now and then, thus allaying his suspicions so as to clean him out gradually. That is, more or less, how professional cardsharps, gambling casinos and today's stock-markets operate (see Chapter 11).

As mentioned, achieving a draw in pitching pennies can take an infinite amount of time at worst, and a long time at best when this game is played in the conventional manner. But there is a way to achieve a perpetual draw immediately: when both players are exquisite craftsmen and toss the coin with precision at their respective turns. Each then gets exactly what he wants from the start. But then you might as well not play except to demonstrate superior craftsmanship and principles of equality and co-operation.

To return to von Neumann and Morgenstern's errors. They treated every game, including those that are randomized from the start, as games of strategy in which, according to them, the best, most intelligent, and rational strategist wins. Yet von Neumann and Morgenstern, like many Darwinists, ethologists and sociobiologists, failed to define what 'best' means in this context. Their viewpoint implies that the end (winning) justifies the means (dirty tricks and randomization). In playing to win by default the means and ends are always unsavoury, particularly when it comes to games that involve high skill and craftsmanship on the part of both players or teams. When such a value system becomes the common standard then 'intelligence' and 'superiority' denote what is in fact cheating, untrustworthiness and chicanery in play with equals as much as with those who have yet to learn. How true this is even in competitive sports is shown in Chapter 10.

What von Neumann could not grasp is that a player can only win if he plays with another who is not his equal or, when playing with an equal, he creates tactical or psychological chaos, thus turning both games of strategy *and* of chance into games of chance. This can be done in a number of ways. Tactically, and in all games of strategy and chance, the object is to create as much confusion as possible on the game board or playing field by setting tactical traps and diversions in the hope that the opponent will become entangled in them, make mistakes and provide the winner with opportunities to give him the *coup de grâce*.

A would-be winner can also distract his game partner with disconcerting behaviours – pure psychological warfare – to achieve the same ends. Shuffling facts and expectations psychologically (e.g. bluffing), creating chaos and breaking the other player's concentration (or legs) outside the rules are simply alternative forms of randomization. They are the most effective ways of counteracting structural disorder, like the shuffling of the deck, created in games of chance from the start. They are the tactics used in 'dirty' street fighting, political elections and psychological warfare, and were applied consciously or unconsciously by Bobby Fischer, John McEnroe, and former President Nixon. On the other hand the creation of systematic and trustworthy order inevitably leads to a draw in all games of pure strategy and chance. The only differences between the consequences generated by either category of games are those of time and sequence. All wars must come to an end and agreement – and not perpetual conflict – ultimately rules human affairs, despite what is erroneously believed to be human nature. A draw, early or late, defines peace, elections conducted on the basis of the real issues (rather than fought on the basis of mud-slinging, popularity contests or appeals to prejudice), statesmanship and fair trade.

It is the object of every would-be winner to de-systematize the game and seize every opportunity created by his fellow player's inattention or his own duplicity (i.e. the creation of randomness and chance) to take advantage of his opponent's errors. For winners can only win by chance and never by design. Most winners know this in their innermost selves but are reluctant to admit it. Most losers would prefer to think that it is true, but have not got the nerve to say so. Would-be winners tend to set the standards in these matters and have ruled that any loser who protests is a 'bad sport' – the ultimate in hypocrisy.

The following is a simple, real-life example that demonstrates that all games turn into games of chance and that no foresighted decision-making is involved when we play to win, even in games of so-called strategy. All you can do is hope and pray and create or take advantage of maximum confusion. In other words, while it is possible to plan the strategies required for winning, there is no certainty that they will work and success can never be predicted. That is true of noughts and crosses, chess and go, poker or war. It is equally true in pitching pennies, roulette, the stock- and commodities-markets, political elections and in any real-life situation in which the object is to frustrate or defeat an opponent.

Suppose that you are walking down a busy street with your mortal enemy whom you wish to injure. You pretend friendliness to put him off his guard. Ahead of you there is an open manhole on the pavement. You plan to steer your enemy towards it while you distract him in conversation and point out the sights in the hope that he will not notice the danger, will fall in and break a leg. If that happens you will have won and he will have lost.

But there is no way for you to be sure that your ploy will work. Your enemy may refuse to be distracted or he may wake up at the last minute and walk round the manhole. Your planning will have done you no good. On the contrary, your enemy is now on his guard and may well plan a similar trap for you when you least expect it. His decision-making will be as 'chancy' as was your own. Neither you nor he can be certain of 'victory'. But one thing is certain: both of you will have turned a simple strategic exercise (walking down a busy street) into a game of chance. Were it otherwise, there would have existed an implicit agreement between you both to look out for open manholes and to warn each other in time so as to avoid any danger or injury – a draw.

You may think that this is a crude and gratuitously nasty example of game playing, or that I am a cynic. But that is how the Dobu play the game (see Chapter 5) and this is a factually correct analogy of what competitive 'playing to win' really means. Winners in any enterprise are symbolic and sometimes actual leg-breakers. Those who believe otherwise are their potential victims.

Pure games of chance fall into two categories. The first consists of so-called social games like bridge and poker that are actually anti-social, although they are played in company with others. The implicit object is to mislead fellow players, who are pitted against one another far more than against chance. In such games a knowledge of psychology is more important than a knowledge of probabilities. Perpetual psychological warfare is the essential recipe for success and it is this that gets the adrenalin flowing for poker players.

For example, should a poker player get a heart royal flush (the best possible hand that beats every other for which the probability of occurrence is conventionally held to be 1 in 2,598,960), he can still lose if he fails to persuade the other players to bet against him by pretending that he has a very bad hand. Or, even if he holds a hand that is possibly worse than any held by fellow players, he can bluff them out of success if he manages to persuade them that he has a concealed winning combination. The same policies required to win in poker are decisive in warfare, politics, diplomacy and some aspects of business as conducted today.

The second family of games of chance is even more misanthropic than the first. Each participant plays in total isolation except for whatever bets are made with others, as in solitaire, craps and roulette. None of the participants play or compete with one another or even with themselves. Each is only in competition with chance (i.e. time and ignorance of sequences). Psychological manipulations play no part in such games. All that is needed is a good memory (as in vingt-et-un), attention, and a knowledge of the odds. None of these ensure winning, although they help limit losses. They enable a gambler to conserve his cash and stay in the game long enough until dumb luck is on his side. A knowledgeable player understands that he will lose much of the time, hoping for a lucky hit that will enable him to walk away with substantial winnings. But he will only succeed if he has sufficient capital to stay in the game during extended periods of loss.

In this second category of games of chance no friendly or even hostile relationships are established between the players, except for the purpose of betting. Everyone is strictly on his or her own and totally isolated from the other players, the dealer, croupier and the bank. Chance is his only companion. That may be one reason for the seemingly dissociated atmosphere round roulette tables, considered at one time to be representative of an aristocratic manner, which can be an eerie experience for any aware observer. Some people find that being a part of, and yet apart from, this gambling fraternity is more exciting than winning and are quite willing to pay heavy gambling losses for the privilege. That is winning of a different kind, but it is winning just the same. Another attraction of this kind of gambling seems to be a feeling of being locked in combat with nature's laws rather than playing against mere men and women. Dostoevsky understood the isolation and fascination of the chronic gambler and wrote about it brilliantly; an understanding he achieved at great cost because he was a gambling addict.

Gamblers involved in this second family of games of chance are at the mercy of what they do not understand. They are the equivalent of stock-market investors with sufficient capital to ride out minor speculative hiccups and depressions, but who lack inside information, sufficient capital, credit and staying-power for surviving the major ones. They can do very little to affect their fortunes because they have surrendered to what they believe is chance, but what is actually a certainty.

Only the 'house' (e.g. casinos, investment houses, conglomerates, multi-nationals, insurance companies, pension funds and governments) can win because it makes the rules, changes them when convenient, and sets odds and betting limits unless it is backed by more capital than the punters have. Chance is inoperative as far as the house is concerned. It does not need to gamble because it owns the game and rigs the odds in its favour. Eventually it must own most of what the gamblers risk, leaving them enough to try to regain their fortunes by other means, so that they can be cleaned out once more in the future.

In some casino games, like poker, in which house odds do not apply, the house periodically 'skims off' a percentage of the winnings, thus consistently reducing the capital of the players, unless new blood is infused periodically into the game. If such a game were to continue for long enough without re-financing or new capitalization, the house would be the only winner. In a sense, this is what occurs with excess taxation from which most countries suffer today as a result of excessively large and inefficient bureaucracies and self-serving elected politicians. I shall return to this analogy shortly, showing that the gambling metaphor applies in a number of ways to the operations of the modern State and to economics as perceived today.

As shown earlier, limiting risks in business or calculating the probabilities of the random movements of particles in space, for example, are governed by the odds, and have many features in common with games of chance. Methods for calculating the odds in gambles have intrigued mathematicians and astronomers since earliest times; however they excluded human intentions from their calculations or considered them incalculable. Galileo, taking time out from his observations of the heavens, explained to a gambler friend why the combinations of spots on three dice come up as the number 10 more often than number 9. But that knowledge is of little value to a gambler who hopes to win by betting on house odds.

Taking advantage of the odds for any gamble requires comparison between the unfavourable and the favourable ones for 'natural' combinatorial possibilities as well as between these and the house odds. But even that does not enable a gambler to predict winning or losing. Such calculations give him guidelines as to which numbers or combinations are more or less likely to occur or recur in the short run. The closer the odds are to even, the less he is likely to lose – or win. And so all a knowledge of the odds can do is save a gambler money and minimize his losses in the hope that he may get lucky and eventually win more than he lost. That is axiomatic for all gambles, card or other games of chance, stock- or futures market speculations, *and* purely strategic games or real-life situations that are played competitively.

Knowing the probabilities of throwing one number before any other (e.g. a 7 before a second 6 in craps) can help conserve cash for a craps shooter. But if the natural or house odds are greater for some than for other combinations, he had best bet only on those that are closest to natural even ones, as experienced bettors at horse-races know. Occasionally a long-shot comes in ahead of the pack. This means either that the race was fixed, a stable owner entered a 'ringer' (a top-class racer substituted for a loser), or a careless groundsman left a hole in the turf that upset the favourite. It is, of course, always possible that a lame duck suddenly learns to fly. But the chances are remote and not worth betting on.

Most gambling is as primitive and simple as that. Cardano, mentioned in Chapter 2, worked out a great many of the odds for games governed by pure chance. The principles on which he operated were the right ones, although he, like most who followed him, did not always draw the correct conclusions from his experiences at the gaming tables. But he contributed to the discovery of some of the laws of large numbers.

The human inventions we call *the laws of chance and probability* are derived from *the natural laws of large numbers* that define the sum of all combinatorial possibilities (see Appendix B). However, it depends very much on which calculations are used to determine the sum of all possibilities – permutational or combinatorial sums – presumed to be the largest numbers of them all. Permutational sums as shown earlier and in Appendix A, while huge for large systems, are not enough. The brute force sum of all combinatorial possibilities is very much larger, grows at a greater-than-exponential rate with each additional factor and becomes astronomical in size even for relatively small systems. Still larger sums of possibilities may possibly be found, involving a greater number of criteria than those used for the purposes of this book. The present sums must suffice for the moment.

By the time the possibilities for a pack of fifty-two playing-cards are considered on the basis of the given calculations, the gross sums are so large as to be meaningless. However, my classification system (see Appendices A and B) that applies to combinatorial sums of any size now permits rapid 'jumps to conclusion' (i.e. mechanical data reduction), achieved by mathematical isolation of any group or individually unique state within the system as a whole, on the basis of clearly defined criteria. This allows anyone to extract the meanings of any system without having to analyse the whole. It is this method of analysis that has made this book possible.

The law of large numbers could not be understood until such a classification was achieved. As a result it was believed, for example, that all players of pure games of chance have an even chance of winning in the long run. That is absolutely wrong. In the absence of mathematical, manual or psychological manipulations there is an absolute certainty that in the longest run the players of gambling games would eventually break nearly even if they possessed infinite funds and longevity. They will certainly lose in the intermediate term, and may win now and then in the short term. However they must eventually draw. Winning in any situation is therefore only a short-term solution at best. It is often said that in the long run we will all be dead. What is missed is that if we keep playing to win we will be dead that much sooner, given the existence of nuclear bombs.

Wykes, who wrote a book on the history of gambling,[2] tells of a married couple who played the game of bezique for a million points with stakes of one shilling per hundred. It took them three and a half years to reach the million mark, at which point the winner collected a mere four shillings and sixpence – a practical demonstration that in the longest run an actual or near draw predominates, even in games of chance.

The odds of being dealt any one card, two cards or a set of five in poker are exactly equal to receiving any other assortment of one, two or five cards respectively. But the chances of obtaining a particular five-card combination are far more rare than a two-card one. Calculating the chances of drawing one or more needed cards during any future distribution in order to complete a winning combination is a related problem. Calculating whether a hand at any stage of a game is better or worse than the cards the other players hold requires further probabilistic calculations. If anyone refused to bet until he calculated the odds at every turn in order to limit his possible losses, the other players would lose their patience very quickly or each game would last for ever. Good poker players therefore remember as many rule-of-thumb odds as they can to minimize their chances of losing, and then concentrate on the psychological ploys that enable them to enhance their chances of winning.

A common belief is that the law of large numbers ensures that all possible cases happen an equal number of times in the longest run. That can be true only if there are only two choices (e.g. heads and tails, odds and even, red and black). Once any larger sum of options is involved (e.g. $n = 3, 4, 5 \ldots$) and if the combinatorial sum of all possibilities is considered, then it becomes obvious that some events can happen far more often than others within any totally objective, finite universe of discourse – be it that of games or of anything else.

For example, in any game of strategy the number of possible draws is always far greater than the number of possible victories or stalemates. Yet draws are far more difficult to achieve than those victories or stalemates that are the result of an exhaustion of means or a lack of understanding. In a biological and supposedly intelligent environment like the human one, it is theoretically possible to limit the sum of all possibilities to nothing but draws in most purely strategic games, provided we make few mistakes or none. That is the function of intelligent behaviour and it is this that can prevent the worst options from materializing. The fact that this is not true in practice says a great deal about our failure to use what intelligence we have to its best advantage.

The laws of nature define not only the laws of large numbers and the sum of all possibilities, but also *natural odds and values*. There is nothing arbitrary about them, and they are finite within any given environment. Games are governed by a combination of natural and human laws. For example, the sum of all combinatorial possibilities for a pack of playing-cards is finite and absolute. It is the same natural law that governs the combinatorial sum of any finite group of fifty-two facts or factors (n = 52), be they quarks, neutrons, atoms, genes or anything else. The rules that apply to quarks, neutrons and other manifestations of nature are certainly part of natural law. But the rules that apply to a particular card-game – canasta, poker, bezique or any other – are entirely arbitrary and artificial limits imposed by man on the natural law which defines the 'n = 52' combinatorial sum. These limits make game playing possible.

Man-made limits (i.e. rules) impose arbitrary values. They determine, for example, what the winning combinations are. Here again natural law plays a role, for it determines the frequency of occurrence or recurrence of any combination within every sum of possibilities, including those that are arbitrarily chosen. This may sound very complex, but it is quite simple if you apply it to any familiar game without worrying about the numbers. It is a matter of principle, and every principle that applies to games corresponds to one in the real world.

This holds true for games of strategy and those of chance. In games of strategy played to be drawn, as in a pack of cards that is shuffled systematically rather than at random, the possibilities unravel in an orderly manner. In strategic games played to be won and in randomized games of chance the possibilities are totally disordered, and it is this that makes it impossible to predict the short-term future and turns it into a relative gamble. The word 'relative' applies because under some conditions it is possible to counteract chance systematically to a point at which a gambler can win little by little, steadily and with certainty, provided he or she does not get greedy and maintains rigid self-discipline. In addition to the artificial values that apply to any game, the relationship of 'natural' to 'artificial' odds plays an important role in every game of chance. The natural odds are those that are dictated by natural laws. By changing (or 'shaving', as it is called) these natural odds by small amounts, the house (i.e. the gambling casino) maintains its winning edge.

For example, if a pair of dice is thrown mindlessly an infinite number of times over an infinite period of time, the end result will, on average, conform nearly exactly to a repetitive sequence of the thirty-six possible combinations that provide the natural odds established by rotating a pair of dice systematically and in sequence until all possibilities have been exhausted. If you rotate the dice systematically you can get perfect odds from the start and a predictable outcome at every turn of each die. It is the same as playing with an unshuffled pack of cards with the full knowledge of all players. It is not much of a game, but it is significant as far as forecasting, prediction and the establishment of natural odds are concerned.

It is possible to simulate the dice and card shuffling equivalence by drawing the thirty-six spot combinations found on a pair of dice on to each of thirty-six playing-cards. The result is a variation on the game of dominoes. Shuffle the pack and then cut it at random or choose the bottom card in the pack and the effect is exactly the same as tossing a pair of dice in a mindless manner. This shows that each random throw of the dice, like each random shuffling of a pack of cards, is not an isolated, one-time event, but an individually unique, permutationally redundant incident in a continuum of perpetually shuffled events that can however also be regarded as an infinite, if scrambled, continuum of finite series.

The 'natural odds' for rolling a 7 or 11 on the first throw of the dice (a 'win' for a craps player and a loss for the house) are 1 in 6 respectively. That is because there are six ways of obtaining a 7 (or an 11) with two dice. The number of possible combinations of spots for a pair of dice = 36. Therefore the odds of rolling a seven on the first throw are 6 in 36 or 1 in 6. But a gambler is expected to bet the house even money to win on the throw of a 7 or an 11 as a first roll of the dice. That provides the house with a considerable advantage. The punter is only allowed to bet the house that he has an even chance when he enjoys nothing of the kind. That is why the house profits while the punters lose in the longer run, even though they may win once in a while. It gets more complicated than this as the game progresses, but that is immaterial here. The point is that house odds are worse than natural odds and the difference between the two enables the house to cover its expenses and provides its profits.

There is absolutely no contest between the punter and a casino. It may seem to be a gamble from the customer's short-term point of view for as long as he does not compare his winnings to his losses over the longer haul. But it is a 'sure thing' as far as the house is concerned.

The difference between house and natural odds is equivalent to 'skimming' by the house in poker and to paying taxes, as pointed out earlier. In fact the origin of lotteries can be traced to a need for raising funds for public expenditures. The house, like the State, provides opportunities and services that an individual cannot procure for himself. The question always should be, as far as gamblers and taxpayers are concerned: 'Are the services of a kind, quantity and quality that warrant the expense?'

The comparison between the State as it exists today and gambling casinos is legitimate because payments made to both are involuntary – with one difference. You are not required to enter a gambling casino or, if you do not like the service or the decor, you can always play in another or go home. You are trapped, in the case of the State.

Your taxes may be used to pay exorbitant salaries and inflation-proof pensions to rulers, elected officials, bureaucrats and defence contractors who may do their best to thwart the public interest for reasons of political philosophy, self-interest, expediency or catering to vested interests. Or the return in education, health and public services, social security, old-age pensions, public housing, transport and police protection may be inefficient, inadequate and out of scale with tax payments. Or the expenditure on military hardware and personnel may be out of proportion to any possible threat. There is no 'across the street' competitor who might provide a better service. While 'free enterprise' can offer alternatives in some respects to those who can afford them, the poor majority pays the highest proportionate taxes and cannot afford the alternatives where they exist.

A comparison between gambling casinos and the modern State is not as gratuitous as it might seem on several other scores as well.

In certain cases a very few modern entrepreneurs are allowed to win in the short run to encourage losers. In former days, when kings made land-grants to favourites, the winnings were permanent unless an ungrateful recipient offended his master or an improvident and foolish heir gambled them away. But with the advent of elected governments it is the object of politicians to get re-elected. As a result they are perpetually in competition with one another and with large segments of the public, thus turning the electoral process into a gamble. Additionally the various interests that exert pressure on the government – industry, business, unions or the consumer, to name but a few – are all in competition with one another, resulting in a very few people winning and most losing.

Meanwhile, governments 'skim' off their 'take' periodically by taxation (today the average earner on the lower rungs of employment probably pays up to or more than 60 per cent) by direct and hidden means, including VAT on goods and services too numerous to mention. The more you earn, the less you pay (just as in a gambling casino), if only because you can afford an accountant who points out all the available legal loopholes for tax avoidance. The same principle applies, of course, to consumers. The less you earn the more you pay because you can only afford shoddy goods that cost proportionately more and don't last as long as expensive, good quality ones.

As we shall see in Chapter 11, this skimming by government and industry perpetually reduces public funds (exemplified by increasing national and consumer debts) without any opportunity of 'new capital' entering the 'game'. This is, of course, one of the main causes of periodic depressions, claimed to be due to 'economic cycles' which follow natural patterns, but which in fact are entirely man-made and simply represent history repeating itself. All of this can be staved off for a short time, as now, by selling off national assets (euphemistically called 'privatization') in order to delay the inevitable for as long as possible and to stick the next administration (hopefully the 'opposition') with the chaos the exhaustion of funds will bring about. This is similar to a snake eating its tail with the inevitable result that it will devour itself.

Every individual or group enterprise, designed to be competitive, to succeed by winning while making others lose, is a gamble by definition, as I have shown. The government, industry and the general public, like casinos and their customers, are in perpetual competition, with the odds loaded in favour of the government and industry. All should be partners and co-operate in the public interest. But there is a huge gulf between what is and what should be, as everyone knows.

There is simply no way any individual can win or for the government to lose, except for politicians who vie for the reins of government for a while, to become custodians of the house rules and to enjoy the benefits they legislate for themselves and their friends. On those few occasions when a member of the public wins in competition with the government, the rules are usually changed to prevent it from happening again, or the winner is barred from collecting his winnings by feints and evasions. The correspondence between governments as they now exist and gambling casinos is further illustrated by the following.

Blackjack (vingt-et-un) is a card game that depends on a supposed gamble between the house dealer and a punter. As always, the artificial odds ensure that the house wins some of the time in the short run and always in the intermediate term. Conversely, the punter is allowed to win some of the time in the short run but he always loses in the longer term. This makes it a bad risk for the gambler and a certainty for the house. But, as played conventionally, there was a way to reverse the chance/certainty ratio in favour of the gambler, at least for a while.

In this game the dealer deals two cards, or more on request, to the punter and two or more to himself. Whoever goes over twenty-one loses. The punter wins if he reaches exactly 21, or if the value of his cards is higher than the dealer's and less than 21. There are additional rules but they do not concern us here. As played until recently, the dealer placed all discards, face up, on the bottom of the deck after each hand. When the deck was exhausted and the upper-most face-up card came into view, the dealer shuffled and began again. But all of this has changed, thanks to a mathematically aware player who learnt to beat the system – as anyone with sufficient interest, capital and a good memory can.

In the early 1960s Edward Thorp, a mathematician at the Massachusetts Institute of Technology, realized that if a vingt-et-un player could remember the first twenty-six cards dealt to himself and to the dealer, the chances of hitting or keeping below twenty-one with any of the remaining cards in the pack were greatly enhanced. Actually, all you need do is remember all cards valued at and above eight or nine (or those at and below six or seven) by the time half the pack is dealt, in order to make this system work.

That technique gave the punter enough of an edge to reverse the natural/artificial odds ratio that makes winning a certainty for the house in anything but the shortest and longest runs. He could now win more than he lost at the beginning of the game while the second half of the pack was dealt. It took the casinos some time to catch on. Thorp was not gambling. He was playing a surefire system, as the casinos had been until then. From that time, those who were caught using this system were barred from casinos by the 'bush telegraph' by which the world's gambling casinos keep track of cheats, conmen, and those who manage to beat the system honestly. All these are undesirables as far as they are concerned.

Almost anyone can train himself to become a 'counter' as these players are called. Banning those who were caught proved insufficient. The trickle turned into a flood. As late as 1979 *Time* magazine reported that one Kenneth Uston, a vice-president of the Pacific Stock-Exchange, had quit his job and made a fortune playing blackjack using the 'counting' system. He obviously understood enough about his former job to know that, except for investing on the basis of reliable inside information, there is no absolute way to win on the world's stock-markets. But he did have mathematical 'inside information' as far as blackjack was concerned, and that is how he won for a while. Before he was discovered and banned by the casinos, he was winning $700 per hour and had accumulated winnings of $43,000 in sixty hours of play at a single sitting. Winning with certainty on that scale beats gambling any day.

Last week the Resorts International casino in Atlantic City followed the precedent of Las Vegas gambling houses and decided to deal Uston, and at least ten other known counters, out of the game. The casino had cause for alarm.[3]

Eventually the world's casinos changed the rules of play for vingt-et-un without notice to the customers. Some ordered their blackjack dealers to reshuffle once half the pack was exhausted. Others shuffled two or three packs together, defying counters to remember a considerably increased number of cards.

But even that was not the end of the matter. In reply, counters began carrying specially designed mini-computers in their coat pockets which enabled them to keep track of the cards by touch. The numeric value of the cards could be entered by tapping a button and the answer felt by a pulse code response. Others hid tiny telegraph keys and receivers on their persons with which they signalled confederates who operated computers in cars parked outside the casinos. The confederates radioed back instructions at appropriate times based on this information that reached the punter inside the casino by mild morse code electric shocks via the receiver in his pocket. It made no difference to these computer-guided players how many or few packs were shuffled together. The memory of their own or their confederates' computers could defeat the casinos' altered rules of play without difficulty.

The casino owners eventually discovered these tricks as well and prosecuted anyone caught playing them, although it had been perfectly legal for them to change the rules in order to eliminate risks to themselves. The government and the law were still on their side when punters tried to adapt themselves to the new situation created by the casinos. The electronic wizards, who had merely played by the same rules by which the casinos operate, were arrested, tried and gaoled.

Casino owners, faced with these technological attempts to beat them at their own game, learned eventually to stay ahead even when it came to electronics. Many installed security systems that effectively jammed computers and radio transmissions on the premises, other than their own. In this regard it is interesting that a large US computer manufacturer produces a computer-operated roulette table that provides 'perfect' randomization, even when it comes to odd and even and red and black. Before the advent of the computerized roulette table the short-term, random fall of these binary options provided one of the few means for beating that system.

What occurred after the Watergate scandal is comparable to the way casinos punish those who try to recoup their losses. President Nixon, among his other crimes, had been caught authorizing the illegal tapping of the phones of his journalist and other 'enemies' in the hope of winning the publicity game and of blackmailing public critics into silence. Many were severely damaged professionally and economically.

After the scandal broke, the American Congress passed a law which stated that everyone whose home phone was illegally bugged was to be compensated to the amount of $100 per day for themselves and for each member of their families who lived with them. However, the new law stipulated that these individuals were required to sue the government through the courts – a very expensive and chancy proposition. Meanwhile, the FBI destroyed most of the evidence that would have been available to the prosecution under the Freedom of Information Act. The judges further frustrated efforts to collect by those who had been spied on illegally by means of technicalities and chicanery. No one ever collected a penny because the house rules kept being changed.

Nixon, accused and found guilty of all sorts of crimes including tax fraud, was allowed to keep most of his winnings (like some of the people convicted of insider trading in recent US court cases). It was claimed that he had 'suffered enough'. I know of no case where a hungry man, convicted of stealing food, was ever excused on such a basis. Those who exposed Nixon lost (including the janitor who discovered and reported the Watergate burglary to the police. He has never worked again and has suffered acutely ever since). The establishment nearly always protects its own and punishes outsiders who discover its crimes, seek redress or try to re-establish a fair balance. Few outsiders ever stand a chance, except by chance. The cases of Peter Wright's *Spycatcher* and John Stalker in Britain provide similar examples. The British Government's insistence that its former employees must keep quiet about its internal corruption because they have signed the Official Secrets Act is contrary to established international law, especially the laws under which the Nazi leadership was tried and convicted at Nuremberg.

There are a number of well-known systems that supposedly enable roulette players to beat the bank. They include the 'Biarritz' system and 'cross-out', among others. All but one, described below, do not work or, when they do, work only by chance because they are not based on sound mathematical principles. Those who use the system that does work are instantly barred from all casinos when they are discovered, like counters who play vingt-et-un.

The successful roulette ploy is a variation of the Martingale system, but involves two players, each betting on red or odd, black or even respectively. Each partner begins with equal – and substantial – capital and an agreed-to maximum bet that he halves whenever he loses until he has arrived at an indivisible number, and then starts again at whatever maximum is agreed upon beforehand. The winner allows his winnings to accumulate for an agreed-to number of turns, at which point he withdraws part of the winnings and continues as before. At each turn one partner must lose and the other win. To come out ahead requires conditions that may not occur for some time and will do so only periodically, due to the irregularity of winning and losing cycles. They consist of maximized winnings and minimized losses occurring simultaneously over short runs.

It is possible to lose a considerable amount of money over the short haul with this system, and one needs sufficient capital to stay in the game long enough so that it works. You are out of luck if the roulette table is computer operated. Barring this last contingency, each partner must not acknowledge the existence of the other and plays as if he were on his own. In the long run – and it may take days and weeks of uninterrupted gambling – they will come out ahead by an appreciable, but not predictable amount. This system, and there may be others, demands absolute self-discipline, an unvarying routine, total concentration and trust on the part of both partners. It is hard work and no fun, and most partnerships cannot sustain this routine for long enough to come out ahead.

Playing this way is of little interest to most gamblers but has significant meanings in terms of human behaviour. It demonstrates that, given reasonable odds, any gamble can be won for a while by dedicated individuals. They are most likely to lose eventually if the rules are unfair or are changed without notice, or the partners themselves are unreliable. Every gamble must end in a loss to someone in the short and intermediate term and an actual or near-draw in the longest run if you play for long enough and if the house is satisfied with 'reasonable odds' (i.e. enough to pay for overheads, salaries for the croupiers and the management, plus sufficient profit for security, maintainance and improvement of the premises). That is, of course, how an efficient government should be run so that everyone profits. Best of course is to play without randomization or secrecy from the start. That way, what is inevitable in the longest run can be achieved from the very beginning, no matter which games you play. But that takes the gamble out of everything (except what goes on in gambling casinos and what we do not know as yet).

As we have seen, both games of strategy and chance are subject to the law of large numbers (see Appendix B). War is a game of chance because it is a contest that is played to be won. The law of large numbers defeats all military and other aggressors in the long run. It allows them to win battles, but makes them lose wars. Some call this a 'higher law' or 'natural justice'. Alexander the Great, Genghis Khan, Napoleon and Hitler fell foul of it and that is why, despite early victories, their armies lost in the end. It is irrelevant that some of these warriors died before the wars they had begun ended badly for their side. The point is that while peace, agreements and creative achievement can last indefinitely, no one can win and make others lose forever. Conventional victories are risky short-term solutions.

Wykes, the author mentioned earlier, is a firm believer in the laws of chance and ridicules Napoleon who was alleged to have said that security consists of 'the mathematical elimination of chance'. Applying Napoleon's principle to games of strategy played to a draw, this is indeed the best method of operation. If, instead of shuffling a pack of cards, you keep arranging it in its original order before each new hand, the results become predictable with continuous recalculation.

With systematic arrangement and if everyone lays his cards down, face up on the table (i.e. doing away with all secrecy), you don't even need to calculate, but you will not be able to play games of chance. You are in a different reality because all chance has been eliminated and absolute certainty reigns. There is no contest and you are at peace. These differences between chance and certainty, war and peace, competition and co-operation are seldom understood (or deliberately ignored) by, for example, military establishments, politicians, peace study groups, historians, or most game players and gamblers. The claim that war is inevitable in an imperfect world is simply untrue.

If Napoleon meant that with an elimination of chance and secrecy you are at peace, then he was correct. But he was totally wrong if he believed that wars can be won with a systematic arrangement of soldiers, artillery and logistics, and when fought with set-piece tactics. That is traditional military thinking and it ends by the next war being fought with the tactics that applied to the last, which can be foreseen by any shrewd enemy. Former battles are the basis of many of the scenarios used today by the Pentagon's and all other nations' war-game players. This and dogmatic, prejudicial thinking is how wars are lost.

What Napoleon did not understand was that war is never a game of strategy played to be drawn, or a card-game in which all the cards are in order or face up on the table because these conditions describe a reliable peace. War is simply a continuous round of escalating randomization (deliberately created, mindless chaos and dirty tricks), secrecy (playing your cards close to your chest), chance (ignorance and time) and, as in all games played to be won, the biggest randomizer (the biggest bastard) wins, but only for a while.

Napoleon was a brash, greedy egomaniac who became lucky for a while. His luck, as with everyone who plays to win, was derived from the unpreparedness, inattention and indecision of his adversaries and depended on his disconcerting ploys, broken agreements and deceptions. It did not depend on anything 'intelligent' on Napoleon's part. He was a very poor general who treated his own troops badly (they were willing victims who allowed themselves to be butchered for his greater glory), and their wives and children (who never received their promised pensions and were dispersed by his army when they rebelled), and subconsciously used the flaws of his allies and adversaries to his advantage.

Napoleon bluffed, cheated, lied and was thoroughly treacherous and unreliable to friend and foe alike. However, the military advantages he gained by these means were dissipated as soon as he came up against a Russian winter that he had been too stupid to foresee, and once his adversaries stood up to him and used even more treacherous tactical and psychological ploys than those he had employed. That is how wars and games of every kind are won, and chance reduced to the relative certainty of a temporary peace, wrung from a defeated aggressor in the end.

A war is always a gamble; whether it is a little war played on a game board, playing field, arcade machine or computer – or the real thing. The gamble is minimized if you do not strike the first blow; if you defend yourself against an unprovoked attack by evasion or by following your attacker's lead; if you look after and do not take needless risks with your troops, services and supplies; if you have trustworthy allies who can trust you; if you keep well informed about conditions, including the weather, your adversary's intentions and the dirty tricks needed to frustrate them; and if you know the methods needed for ending the conflict and restoring a durable peace in the shortest possible time with minimal loss of life and property on both sides. Or, if you are stupid, you battle on to do maximum damage and achieve the highest body count, until both sides are so exhausted that a stalemate is forced on aggressor and defender alike, or until one or the other side wins by default. That is how the peace is lost before it is ever declared.

The laws of averages and of large numbers are persistently abused in games of chance, and in real-world situations that are believed to operate on the principles of chance. The law of averages, like statistics of which it is a part, predicts nothing unless you live solely in the past, or in a closed environment in which nothing can change, or one in which you can consider the sum of all possibilities – the last two conditions amounting to the same thing. Those who live in such an environment are dogmatists who are impervious to learning. But those who consider all possibilities in a finite, yet infinitely expandable universe can learn perpetually.

This is the real world in which change is the rule. This is true even for the simplest games like noughts and crosses, for which all strategic possibilities are calculable and known, but from which the correct conclusions can always be transferred to the next and all larger environments by learning. Statistics can therefore only be precise and predictive if they are based on the combinatorial sum of all possibilities. Even then they can be upset by 'intelligent' or 'stupid' human behaviour. The law of averages may be a natural law. But in everything, except global applications or predictions made close to an event, the results are nearly always guesswork – although even the wildest guesses can turn out to be correct now and then by chance.

People – and statisticians especially – have all sorts of superstitious opinions about the law of averages. For example, some people believe that after two air crashes a third is bound to happen because 'all things come in threes'. After a third accident has occurred they consider it safe to fly. They believe that the law of averages establishes a quota of victims, after which they are immune.

Another superstition about the law of averages is that some people think that lightning never strikes twice in the same place. That can be a very dangerous delusion because lightning tends to strike only where and when the conditions are right (e.g. tall trees in open country). If those conditions remain the same, the chances are excellent that lightning will strike again and again in exactly the same place.

Andrew Britton, Director of Britain's Institute for Economic and Social Research and a representative of the majority view among statisticians, was reported to assert in *The Times*: 'We try to make forecasting a statistical science, as opposed to people who look at tea leaves.'[4] Yet statistics based on anything less than global information are no better, and are often worse than tea-leaf reading, as we will see in the case of the statistical assessments of personality and achievement by Sutton-Smith, based on game-playing performances (see Chapter 9). The British Meteorological Office abandoned weather forecasts based on statistics many years ago and now uses a multi-dimensional combinatorial matrix similar to that employed here to analyse games of strategy and chance[5] (see also Appendices A, B and C). Yet the use of statistics to make predictions or diagnose systems involving human behaviour is still favoured in the literature on artificial intelligence and so-called expert systems, in economics, sociology, psychology, medicine and many other fields.

One of the most frequently given examples of supposed foresight achieved by statistical means are computer chess programs that are said to 'look ahead' and to be able to foresee the best tactical choices leading to victory for the computer and defeat for its human opponent. Considering that chess, like all other games, is only won by default and by chance, that is one of the most absurd predictive claims of all. Even more ridiculous are claims made for human and computer prediction when it comes to playing poker,[6] horse-races, the stock-market, games of strategy and skill or gambles played to be won. The short-term outcomes of any game involving randomness, secrecy, and disconcerting tactical and behavioural ploys can never be predicted, except that most will be won and lost and others will end as draws or stalemates over longer or shorter periods of time. That is like predicting that it will rain, shine or snow tomorrow, unless it is overcast or foggy – which is what all statistically-based forecasts usually consist of.

The law of averages, despite its shortcomings, does apply to nuclear war. If there should ever be one, virtually all of us would instantly become statistics. That is one of the few instances in which we can trust statistics because in that event they would be based on an elimination of a major portion of the sum of all possibilities on a global scale.

Self-delusion operates across the whole game spectrum, not only when it comes to the meanings of competition, co-operation, winning and losing, chance, randomness and statistics, but also when it extends to the artefacts used to play certain games. It can take different forms. US aircraft carriers are sacred cows in the war-games played by the Pentagon's computers. They can never be sunk by the opposition on orders from the top brass.

One of these days the US government and those who elect it are going to be in for another rude awakening if strategies based on these policies are applied to any future conflict. One example of this kind was what happened at Pearl Harbor in 1941. A more recent example took place on Sunday, 17 May 1987 in the Persian Gulf when the guided missile frigate USS *Stark* was hit and damaged severely (38 men killed and 21 wounded) by an Iraqi-launched Exocet missile, without any effort on the part of the ship's captain or crew to evade or destroy it, even though that would have been possible. The US Navy was totally unprepared because it could not believe that such an attack might take place, despite the military's claims that 'preparedness' is the name of the game they play. That is one of the ways in which history can repeat itself.

The reason for Pearl Harbor was that the US Secretary of the Navy at that time felt that it was ungentlemanly to read the secret messages of other countries when conflict threatens (those sent by Japan to its Washington embassy virtually announced the attack on Pearl Harbor days before the actual attack). This illusion was dispelled once that war-game began in earnest. Even then it took a long time to learn how to decipher secret messages fairly efficiently, not only in the US but also in Britain. The famed 'Enigma' codes, used by the Germans would have been easy to decipher if the British military had not turned down the encrypting machine without understanding it when it was offered to them for purchase in the years before the war. They too went to war without preparation or understanding of how the war-game is won or lost.

A far less lethal example of self-delusion about games of chance prevails in the fundamentalist American South where Baptist ministers inveigh against cards as 'instruments of the devil'. That is hard to understand because the winning and losing principle is deeply embedded in Christianity. It must surely seem to anyone, including true believers, that God would have to be a behaviourist psychologist if only because He expresses His will by means of the carrot (Heaven) and the stick (Hell); that He rewards winners (saints and angels) and punishes losers (the devil and his assistants).

For these, or possibly for other reasons, American Southern Baptists enjoy gambling games including those played with cards. To prevent their sinning, Parker Brothers, a leading US game manufacturer, began marketing a game called Rook in the last century containing fifty-two playing-cards, each imprinted with a picture of the bird and the numbers from one to thirteen. It is still popular and produced by the same company. The cards are divided into four suits, enabling the faithful to play a thinly disguised form of bridge with the approval of their spiritual leaders.

What applies to pure games of chance is true for mixed games of strategy and chance like backgammon and Monopoly. The only way to achieve a draw in either is to play an even number of successive games over an unpredictable period of time. In Monopoly success depends in part on decisions as to when to buy or trade property or keep cash in reserve. In backgammon it involves decisions about which counter to move or play off, depending on the random throw of the dice and the other player's position. These are strategic decisions that help reduce but cannot eliminate chance and uncertainty.

In backgammon, when the dice run against you, you can only improve your chances of winning by distracting your game partner in the hope that you can take advantage of whatever mistakes he or she makes as a result. In games that involve more than two players, like Monopoly, the most promising way of limiting chance consists of waging perpetual psychological warfare against one another, including those with whom you may have made temporary alliances. In real life this is known as treachery. That is the only form of co-operation to which conventional game theorists and mathematicians admit – short-term alliances and co-operation that last only until it is more advantageous to compete against former partners.

The strategy that enables players to limit chance, reduce losses and help them win when playing Monopoly consists of persistent unreliability – as in poker. However, in Monopoly bluffing does you no good. Instead you make temporary alliances (i.e. marriages of convenience) with whoever offers you the most favourable terms. These are dissolved as soon as convenient either because there is an opportunity to sink your partner and gain from his or her loss or because better terms are offered elsewhere. It may not always work, but it works often enough so that those who play in this manner win more often than they lose. That is the very best you can ever hope for in strategic games that involve elements of chance.

In Monopoly chance determines on which spaces you land, allowing you to buy property and to charge rent to those unfortunate enough to be your temporary tenants. Two packs of randomly shuffled cards periodically provide further good or bad luck. By developing your property and building houses and hotels, you increase rents exorbitantly. The object is to bankrupt everyone else, and this game is a spoof of the utter greed of our time and only a slight exaggeration of the competitive Dobuan world around us. I have seen couples literally come to blows over this game because they took it seriously and saw their own competitive, untrustworthy relationship mirrored by it.

None of the foregoing makes much difference as far as gamblers are concerned, except that it introduces some realism into the superstitions, prejudices and myths that surround most games of chance. It does, however, affect our understanding of the correspondence of games to real life, art, and science in which it should be the function of intelligent behaviour to eliminate chance or to limit it so severely that it no longer affects us for all practical purposes in situations that matter.

Having examined how chance functions in particle physics, and behaviour relative to games of chance, I next extend this discussion to biology and to human and animal behaviour in the world at large.

8   Nature Red in Tooth and Claw

> . . . cattle are enemies of grass in that it is still true
> that an individual grass plant would be better off
> not being eaten by a cow . . .
>
> Richard Dawkins[1]

Physics and biology are complementary and overlapping sciences:
the first concerns itself with the inorganic microcosm and macro-
cosm up to the rather blurred line at which organic evolution
begins; the second with the branching of the evolutionary tree from
that point onwards.

Chance plays a significant role in evolutionary biology. We speak
of 'chance mutations' that precede natural selection. The very
beginnings of organic life in the transformation of crystalline
substances or in the 'primeval soup' are still thought of as chance
events and fortuitous coincidences. Mutations can be benign or
malign, caused by 'background radiation' or by man-made events,
ranging from industrial pollution to x-rays, nuclear emissions and
fall-out. In the latter cases chance mutations are usually malign.
However, in natural selection and in adaptive behaviours, strategic
processes are involved that affect the survival of any one species.
These processes have much in common with games of strategy and
are governed by processes explained here and in the next chapter.

The game metaphor is thus applicable to biology in several ways.
Chance mutation in the long term is equivalent to a systematically
ordered process, even when it seems random and chaotic in the
short term. Exactly the same principles of chance, explained in the
two previous chapters, apply in genetics as in particle physics and
the random shuffling of a pack of playing-cards. There is therefore
no need to repeat the re-definition of the term 'chance'. However,

an equally great misunderstanding exists in biology regarding the operation of chance as it does in other fields of specialist expertise. For that reason I first show what Jacques Monod, one of the most prominent biologists of our time, believed chance and coincidence to be; definitions that are still prevalent and widely subscribed to in this branch of the sciences:

... We say that these events [mutations] are accidental, due to chance. And since they constitute the *only* possible source of modifications in the genetic text, itself the *sole* repository of the organism's hereditary structures, it necessarily follows that *chance* alone is at the source of every innovation, of all creation in the biosphere. Pure chance, absolutely free but blind, at the very root of the stupendous edifice of evolution ... It is today the *sole* conceivable hypothesis ...

... Indeed natural selection operates *upon* the products of chance and knows no other nourishment.

... A mutation is in itself a microscopic event, a quantum event, to which the principle of uncertainty consequently applies. An event which is hence and by its very nature *essentially* unpredictable.

... But in other situations the idea of chance takes on an essential and no longer merely operational meaning. This is the case, for instance, in what may be called 'absolute coincidences', those which result from the intersection of two totally independent chains of events. Suppose that Dr Brown sets out on an emergency call to a new patient. In the meantime Jones the carpenter has started work on repairs to the roof of a nearby building. As Dr Brown walks past the building, Jones inadvertently drops his hammer, whose (deterministic) trajectory happens to intercept that of the physician who dies of a fractured skull. We say he was a victim of chance ... Chance is obviously the essential factor here, inherent in the complete independence of two causal chains of events whose convergence produces the accident.

... it must be stressed that, even were the principle of uncertainty some day abandoned, it would remain true that between the determination, however complete, of a mutation in DNA and the determination of its functional effects on the plane of the protein interaction, one could still see nothing but an 'absolute coincidence' like that defined above by the parable of the workman and the physician.[2]

Monod changed his mind about the mechanism of chance and the nature of coincidence shortly before his death,[3] but did not publish his revised views. In the case of his Dr Brown allegory, no chance element could have been involved. The 'coinciding' of the criminally careless and irresponsible dropping of the hammer, with Dr Brown's being in exactly the 'right' place at the precise time when the hammer reached his head, together with his lack of awareness, created an absolute certainty. For had he been aware and looked up he might well have slowed down or hurried along, thus avoiding or perhaps merely postponing the inevitable. Several causal trains of events coincide that make the outcome a certainty. No fate, luck, chance or predestination is involved, given the circumstances. In other words, what may seem to be a chance event as far as the victim is concerned, is actually a certainty when it is viewed totally objectively from outside the system in which such events occur.

The only chance event that could have occurred under these circumstances would have been an evasion of disaster, despite the conjunction of the behaviours of a careless perpetrator and his unaware victim. The same is true of all so-called accidents caused by and involving human beings. Coincidence is a different matter when it involves an inorganic process like a rockfall, and a human victim. In that case the victim's inattention (or, in other circumstances, his inability to escape in time) is at fault. But a still different valuation obtains when a coincidence involves two or more inorganic processes, none of which can act autonomously. We are then dealing with a situation equivalent to a randomly shuffled pack of cards. Monod failed to make any of these distinctions that define randomness and coincidence as conditionally deterministic processes.

It should be obvious that 'mutation in DNA' has far more in common with the shuffling of a pack of cards than the behaviours of Dr Brown and the carpenter, for neither the causes of mutations (except those caused by human stupidity, like exposure to x-radiation of the foetus) nor the DNA are sentient processes.

In previous chapters we found that the difference between random and systematic arrangement in 'shuffled' situations like a pack of playing-cards is simply a matter of time and sequence rather than of substance. This can also be said to be true for mutations. In biology as in physics, the number of factors is, of course, enormously greater than the number of cards in a pack. None the less the longer-term recurrences in a random universe can be more frequent than in a systematically arranged one because two kinds of recurrences – identical ones from the next series and permutationally redundant ones from the present *and* the next series – can and are likely to cluster in the short run.

With mutation it can therefore take rather a longer or a shorter period of time for individually unique, yet permutationally redundant, possibilities to occur and recur than it would in a systematically arranged universe. However, the high rate of permutational redundancy in systems that cause mutations to occur, whether or not they are arranged systematically or at random, ensures that every combination occurs and recurs quite often, especially viewed in the long-term perspective of evolution.

Here it is of special significance to remember that combinations smaller than the full permutational sequence occur and recur with the highest frequency within the combinatorial sum of all possibilities (see Appendix B). These abbreviated sequences – mutational jumps to conclusion – can lead to the same conclusions as the full ones and can affect an organism beneficially or detrimentally and with the same or a similar effect as a complete series.

This redefinition, or more precise definition, of the processes of randomness, chance and coincidence in genetics suggests that the likelihood of life on planets elsewhere in the universe is considerably greater than what is generally believed, except by the astronomer Fred Hoyle and his associates. The permutational, highly redundant recurrence of events, even within a randomized universe, makes it a virtual certainty that the 'coincidences' that lead to the evolution of life are fairly widely distributed throughout the cosmos. Given a relatively high frequency of mutational 'jumps to the same conclusion' as a less frequent, but also permutationally redundant, full series of such events, life on earth or anywhere else may not depend on a single fortuitous accident of nature, as is often believed. No matter how random some of the processes of nature may be, permutational redundancy within combinatorial sums ensures that the same or similar events will occur and recur sufficiently often for the emergence of life wherever the conditions are right – another example of conditional determinism.

Natural selection and adaptation are rather different matters. Triggered by mutation, they are the products of a succession of minute changes that prove fortuitous or disastrous to the survival of a species in a particular environment. They can also lead to speciation (the formation of different species, none of which are able to mate with any other species) in widely differing or separated environments. The objective of every species is to survive, and this has given rise to speculation about whether natural selection and the survival of the fittest are due to inter- and intra-species competition, and whether success accrues to the strongest and swiftest members of each species – in other words to the winners in a purely strategic game of existence.

Strategic and so-called competitive games, as we have seen, are lost as a result of a loser's spontaneous errors, or by randomness and chance created wilfully and maliciously by a would-be winner to distract an inattentive loser. A defeat occurs when one player falls into the traps set deliberately or mindlessly by the other – a coincidence of deviousness and lack of attention. Strategic game and real-life losses are certainties unless they are avoided with sufficient awareness and when both partners play for a draw (balance, error-free play and perfection).

Before going into this subject in greater detail, it is necessary to digress. The implicit question in natural selection is which kind of selection nature favours – that of the individual or of the species? It should be obvious that the survival of the species comes ahead of that of any one individual, yet some authors, like Richard Dawkins, are convinced that individual self-interest takes precedence over group responsibility. That is the result of wrongly interpreting individualism – namely that the winner in any enterprise is a 'superior' individual. I have dealt with this misconception, but it is important to keep it in mind in the context of this chapter.

Two kinds of postulated competition are involved in natural selection: within (intra-) and between (inter-) species. Let us consider the processes that determine survival not only within and between species, but even within an individual of any species. Surely, internal co-operation between the various organs, muscles, the central nervous system and an organism's environment is the first rule of biology that favours the survival of individuals and species. Internal neural, organic or muscular conflicts of any sort manifest themselves in ill health, handicaps or degeneration as a result of mutation, genetic defect, maladaptation, environmental injury, disease or old age.

Co-operation must therefore predominate within the organism itself, and between it and the larger environment. Conflicts occur, but then the organism is always the loser (e.g. cancer or AIDS). The only way for the organism to 'win' is to establish and maintain or re-establish a co-operative relationship and balance within itself and between itself and its environment. That is how an organism maintains life and its individual identity. You might say then that traditional game theory, being based on competitive principles, has nothing to teach us as far as this aspect of biology is concerned. But that would be wrong.

The concept of inter- and intra-species competition has been the subject of intensive controversy from the time of Darwin until today. Niko Tinbergen, the Nobel laureate biologist and ethologist, is among the few who define survival and adaptation as an essentially co-operative enterprise:

The study of social behaviour [in animal species] is the study of co-operation between individuals. There may be two individuals involved, or more ... The care of the eggs might be called social behaviour, for from the time of being laid the eggs are individuals ... As soon as the eggs hatch, however, the relationship between parents and offsprings is truly mutual ... Many animals aggregate in groups larger than families. Such groups may be composed of several families, such as a flock of geese or swans, or they consist of individuals which are no longer united by family ties.
... The relationship between an animal, for example a bird, and its young begins in essentially the same way as that between an individual and one of its organs.
... When studying the way in which a community [of animals] is organized, one is often struck by the many parallels that can be drawn between it and an individual. Both are composed of constituent parts; the individual is composed of organs, the community of individuals. In both, there is a division of labour between the component parts. In both, the parts co-operate for the benefit of the whole, and through it for their own benefit. The constituent parts give and receive ...
... we have seen that co-operation between individuals is ... by no means confined to relationships between animals of the same species; we know numerous cases of inter-specific co-operation ...
... co-operation is ensured by a system of innate activities in the actor, and of (usually innate) responsiveness to the actor's behaviour in the reactor. The satisfactory functioning of these behaviour elements is as a rule ensured by 'preparedness-in-advance'.[1]

The innate potential for co-operation and competition of every kind exists within each individual in any species, but needs to be

triggered by what the psychologist Renée Spitz has called genetically inherited Innate Release Mechanisms (IRMs), modified by
learning. IRMs may generate an appropriate response on the part
of a fledgling, for example to spots of colour, silhouettes, sounds,
postures and gestures of other individuals of the same or other
species. The resulting behaviours are elaborated and perfected by
trial and error. The combination of innate (reflexive or instinctive)
endowment and the learning of more elaborate, error-free moves
and responses is achieved by the transmission of key behavioural
triggers genetically from one generation to the next, activated by
environmental stimuli and then refined and elaborated by nurture
and experience. Tinbergen and Lorenz have demonstrated the
existence of these IRM-triggered behaviours in several bird species.
They are equally observable in many others, including our own
(e.g. the sucking instinct of infants that is eventually elaborated into
speech).

These species specific behaviours enable healthy individuals and
groups to reach implicit agreements (concerning essentials like
staking out and marking or defence of territory, mating rituals,
submission, establishment of rank in the hierarchy, and flight or
fight responses). In effect they are the tactics of players in a game
in which the instinctive intention of both partners or teams is to
achieve a draw rather than a victory; an agreement-to-agree rather
than perpetual conflict; an error-free result rather than success by
default; balance rather than imbalance. Yet there are other behaviours, also partially triggered by instinct and partially learnt, that
are often misinterpreted as being competitive and equivalent to
'winning and losing'. They concern the relationship between predator and prey, or as Richard Dawkins would have it (see the quote
that heads this chapter), between eater and what is eaten, even
when the latter is vegetation. On the other hand Tinbergen writes:

When an animal is cornered by a predator, it will often fight. This type of
fighting, the defence against a predator . . . usually does not involve animals
of the same species. Nor is it as common as the fighting of animals which is
directed at individuals of their own species . . .[5]

Most intra-species fighting is ritualistic or a challenge rather than
a fight to the finish. It can be territorial and designed to space out

individuals, pairs and groups, help establish and maintain temporary or permanent territory sufficient for successful reproduction and the rearing of the young, subsistence and a pecking order. It consists mostly of threatening behaviour rather than actual attacks. Physical damage or death are exceptions rather than the rule. Further, and as discussed in Chapter 3, 'territory' can mean something quite different in the human than in any other species.

Neither co-operative nor aggressive behaviours in any species are entirely spontaneous and innate or entirely learnt. The potential for both must exist in the very genes of all. But fully fledged behaviours of either kind can only be learned after being triggered by IRMs, including inhibiting and displacement behaviours in response to certain signs. The overall object of processes in nature appears to be balance – a draw in game terms – for the sake of long-term qualitative benefit to all species. Nature appears to favour diversity and conditional equality rather than short-term quantitative gain for one individual species – or individual member of any one species – at the expense of all the rest. Yet this last proposition is the favourite theme of conscious and unconscious social Darwinists.

The same principle applies to predators and their prey as to other forms of competition. Both are usually more or less equally matched. The predator's size, speed, teeth and claws can be neutralized by the prey's matching swiftness of foot, camouflage or defensive equipment, or an ability to bolt into small holes in trees or the ground where the hunter cannot follow. Only the prey's error or weakness perhaps due to age, ill-health, defect or inexperience for example, gives the predator an advantage – just as it does in the strategies that lead to victory in games. But, strange as it may seem, even here predator and prey are engaged in a tacit agreement to agree – a draw situation seen in a larger genetic and ecological context.

The prey species benefits through the weeding out of its surplus population and especially those members that are accident-prone and, for that reason, are not desirable breeding stock. The predator species needs this surplus in order to survive. Both predator and prey species co-operate in the broadest sense of the term, although this does not mean that any individual welcomes death or being eaten for the benefit of its own and the predator species. It is unlikely that any animal species or individual is ever altruistic. We tend to attribute this purely human characteristic to animals because we seem not to understand what co-operation really means.

The rabbit and dingo population explosions in Australia and the choking of the upper Nile by water lilies are typical examples of what can happen in the absence of inter-species co-operation in population control. In both instances no conditions existed to limit the proliferation of species that were artificially introduced into an environment in which they multiplied and prospered without hindrance because they had no natural 'enemies'.

Because no 'natural predators' (other than ourselves) exist to limit human populations, we must be careful to avoid jumping to wrong conclusions in these matters. Euthanasia is suggested from time to time as a possible solution to the threat of over-population. But the dangers of this approach are so great, as demonstrated by Nazi Germany, that they do not recommend themselves. Euthanasia is a zero-sum (winning and losing) form of population control except when it is done by agreement. But that poses obvious problems in our society. Matters were much more simple for certain Eskimo tribes among whom it was the custom for those who were too old to travel or be autonomous to allow themselves to be sealed inside igloos and abandoned, so that they froze to death. They really had no other choices. But we do have choice. Self-disciplined and voluntary birth-control (abstinence, 'natural', artificial, or surgical) are our current options for a self-regulating form of population control by agreement (equivalent to the non-zero-sum draw), at least among reasonable people in our day and environment, given the current population explosion – choices that are unique to our species.

Other than disease, self-control and agreement, we have no built-in or natural limiting factors to the proliferation of our species, except lack of space and the global food supply. Our populations are not kept in balance by any predator species that ranks higher than we do on the evolutionary ladder. Even the world's food supply could support a far greater population than space on earth permits. The belief that war acts as a check on human population is discredited by two world wars that helped to increase rather than decrease our numbers in the long run, despite great short-term losses. Nuclear war would have a similar effect, if only because it would force a small number of possible survivors into vastly reduced areas that might still support life, causing excessive crowding due to a lack of habitable and farming space.

On the other hand we must be careful not to anthropomorphize. Every species differs from every other in the techniques it employs to achieve a balance between population density and the ecology in which it exists. Some have certain characteristics in common with others and with man. It would be foolish to generalize from the exceptional behaviour of the female black widow spider who kills and eats her mate immediately after copulation. Yet that is exactly what social Darwinists are fond of doing. Anthropomorphism means an attribution of human characteristics to animals. Children's books often feature animals that speak and reason as we do. In the literature on evolution it means attributing the wrong game-derived conclusions to animal behaviour. While all animals play, none 'hunt for sport' *in their natural environment* (not even cats).

An amusing, if superficial, comparison could be made between the behaviour of the black widow spider and that of the competitive, human female which leads to huge alimony payments and a symbolic 'killing off' of the male in American divorce proceedings. 'Bleeding the male' is a product of greed, vindictiveness and 'winning' in the classical, competitive sense. (This is not an 'anti-feminist' statement.) But female black widow spider behaviour is consistent with a purely instinctive and involuntary maintainance of a balance in nature in the interest of keeping its population in check. In that sense such behaviour leads to a draw between the spider and the larger environment in which it exists.

The origins of the misconception that ruthless competition, winning and losing lie at the root of natural selection make a fascinating story, part of which is worth recapitulating for it relates directly to the game mythology of the superiority of the winner that may be as causal in this instance as it is in any other context.

Darwin himself held confused and self-contradictory views on the subject. According to his contemporary and fellow biologist Alfred Russell Wallace:

In my last conversation with Darwin he expressed himself in very despondent terms about the future of mankind, basing this on the observation that in our modern civilization no natural selection is taking place and that the fittest do not survive. The successful ones in the struggle for wealth are by no means the best or the most intelligent specimens, and, as you know, in each generation our population is renewed to a greater extent from the lower than from the middle and upper classes . . .[6]

There is an innate contradiction here, because if Darwin believed in 'the survival of the fittest', and if this is interpreted to mean those 'best equipped to survive' in whichever society or environment they exist, then those who own most assets are certainly the most likely survivors. If survival means achieving the best educational credentials or getting the highest marks in examinations, then we are talking about yet another kind of survival. Equally, in an army, an authoritarian state or in many schools, survival could depend on following orders and doing exactly as you are told, even when it may be wrong; or again, survival could depend on skills that are required for existence in an urban, political, social or other jungle.

In this sense it is difficult to determine exactly what Wallace intended by this report on his conversation with Darwin. However the facts are, as Darwin may have surmised, that success, wealth, social class or even superior strength do not necessarily determine intelligence or fitness to survive. Instead, the yardstick of intelligence must be appropriate, craftsmanlike behaviour in all circumstances, relative to environment, frame of reference (i.e. experience), adaptation and learning. In other words, an exquisite craftsman in anything – baking bread, childrearing, science or technology – is superior to the unskilled, whether or not he or she has a formal education.

In our society those without art or craft in the sense defined here become politicians, bureaucrats, administrators and managers, or join those trades and professions in which being a third-rater, sheer opportunist, catering to vested interests, not thinking for yourself and not acting responsibly are among the prerequisites. All of these 'professionals' tend to insist that they belong on top of the hierarchical tree by right and have more and greater 'rights' than anyone else (e.g. tenure, inflation-proof pension schemes, stock options and tax advantages).

Of course, politicians, bureaucrats, administrators and managers can indeed be craftsmen. Regrettably only very few qualify and they do not last very long. They are quickly driven out by the schemers and cowboys (i.e. the classical winners). While originally legitimate, labour unions, once they became powerful enough, began to lay claim to greater rights for their members than for anyone else in some modern societies, whether or not their members were superior craftsmen. This then brings us to the crux of the matter: who is superior and who is not, who deserves to survive and prosper and who does not, in every species, including our own?

The question of superior ability and use of intelligence in animal species is easily resolved. Poor 'craftsmen' usually end up as someone's dinner. We have a similar paradigm when it comes to a choice between a craftsman and a cowboy, except that in our perverse cultures the cowboys often thrive and the craftsmen go under. That is the latter's fault to a large extent, for they usually do not learn how to survive in those societies that discriminate against them. In our cultures the problem is complicated by the need for task specialization. Who is to say whether a shop-foreman or a shop-floor worker, a surgeon or a plumber is more intelligent or skilled? Which of these is superior or more intelligent is easily established on the basis of performance (and not, as is popularly thought, on the basis of credentials).

However – and this is where permutational (syntactic – i.e. sequence) and combinatorial (semantic – i.e. meaning) subtleties come into any hierarchical paradigm – I know of some surgeons who would make better plumbers and vice versa, and some surgeons even manage to be both. But I doubt if I would trust my insides to either without some evidence of his skill and experience. Very few would qualify if we applied a similar test of craftsmanship to today's economists, military leaders, bureaucrats, politicians or game theorists. Exactly the same standards that apply in the animal world should also apply in our own. You do not deserve to prosper (physically among animals; economically among ourselves) unless you are as skilled a member of your species as possible.

If you happen to be a cheetah, superiority means running speed, success in keeping others of your kind out of your territory except for a mate, hunting skills sufficient for feeding (but not so efficient as to 'win' every time and endanger future food supplies), and avoiding human predators. The lack of absolute hunting success is important for animals so that they do not strip their territories bare of the stock required for regeneration of their means of subsistence, as we do.

Examples of this kind of human stupidity are legion: the mindless

stripping of the world's irreplaceable hard-wood and other forests –
which are one of the chief suppliers of the world's oxygen – for
short-term profit by paper and lumber conglomerates and multi-
national corporations; overgrazing by greedy cattle barons and
primitive herdsmen that turns grazing lands into deserts within a
few years; the destruction of the world's ozone layer by the over-use
of petro-chemicals; or the undisciplined consumerism of most of the
world's populations, among other malpractices too numerous to
mention. All stem from the predominance of 'winning against nature
and one another' and other indefensible academic, political, social
and commercially competitive attitudes.

For an elephant, a herring or an ant successful survival depends
on skills and abilities rather different to those that enable cheetahs
to prosper. But no species other than man tries to win by making
nature (and itself) lose by destroying its own territory, habitat and
future food supply. There are plenty of different examples that show
how all species other than man survive in the best sense of the word
by co-operating with nature, with members of their own species and
those of others – in effect, playing for a draw rather than to win by
making others lose. Animals are ethical by definition, but not by
choice. They cannot choose to be anything else, as we can. Being
ethical by choice seems to be an option that many human beings
deliberately ignore, making those of us who fail to live up to this
obligation inferior to animals.

Rabbits are not known for brawn but manage to survive rather
well as a species by hiding in small holes and making up in what
they lack in combat readiness by breeding faster than they can be
eaten. Practically, and taking a long view of predator survival, prey
species and the ecology as a whole, the eaters and those they eat are
each other's 'best friends' and not one another's enemies as Richard
Dawkins supposes. They could not get along without one another,
as the Australian rabbit and dingo experiences have demonstrated.

An essentially symbiotic and task-specialized relationship seems
to exist between animal predator and prey species, one that aids the
process of natural selection by co-operation, rather than by competition and conflict. For if war to the death were the first rule of
survival, we would live in a world of starving predators stalking one
another after they had finished off all other species. Only 'civilized'
human beings seem to lack such self-restraint, for shortly we may

be the only species on earth and we are endangered by ourselves. Even locusts swarm and ravage the land only once in ten years, giving the foliage time to regenerate. We are the only competitors who want to win it all, all the time, and that is how we may lose. The game paradigm should be our warning and caution.

But happily not all human beings are 'unnatural' or inferior to other animal species. A co-operative relationship exists between some primitive human hunters and their prey. Many beg their victims' pardon before the hunt begins, thus hoping ritualistically to assure themselves of success in killing their prey by eliciting its co-operation. Among American Indian tribes a close symbiotic and totemic relationship existed between the human and animal world in which hunter and hunted were interdependent, as is or should be the case in any balanced ecology.

Darwin was not the first to regard nature as a perpetual battle-ground. Linnaeus, to whom we owe the original classification of plant species, had this to say 100 years before publication of the *Origin of Species*.

... I am inclined to think that war occurs where there is the greatest superfluity of people. At least it would seem that, where the population increases too much, concord and the necessities of life decrease, and envy and malignancy towards neighbours abound. Thus it is a war of all against all.[7]

Although the war of all-against-all theme recurs in Darwin's writing, other and contradictory strands can be found. According to the editor of and commentator on Darwin's unpublished notebooks: 'Charles Darwin characterized living beings as struggling to survive, not to defeat each other.'[8]

Darwin was a pacifist who had signed an anti-war declaration at the onset of the Crimean War. He insisted that all races of man had an equal potential for intelligence, in contrast to his cousin, Francis Galton, who used a *Dictionary of Men of the Time* to rate the intelligence of judges, high-ranking military officers, government leaders and men of science and art 'according to their reputation' and family connections. Galton 'proved' statistically that a strong correlation exists between family status, wealth, political power and intelligence. This was a rather convenient prejudice for Victorians in support of a twisted interpretation of the meaning of the survival of the fittest – and in the interest of maintaining the status quo.

Galton, although an African explorer, carried his prejudices so far that he credited African tribal chiefs with intelligence superior to their subjects (on the basis of their genetic inheritance and reputations), but insisted that tribal chiefs ranked only on a par with European (white) factory foremen in these respects.[9] All of this may seem ridiculous today, but Cyril Burt (now discredited, yet one of the most influential psychologists of our age who faked his statistics[10]) was Galton's devoted disciple. We can therefore see where some of our modern ideas about intelligence, superiority and competition originated, and why they have survived, contrary to all logic, reason and factual evidence.

Darwin was pushed very hard by a belligerent anti-evolutionary opposition to his ideas and it is perhaps understandable, if not praiseworthy, that to appease some of his critics the fifth and sixth editions of the *Origin of Species* had undergone a considerable metamorphosis since the first in favour of depicting nature as a competitive enterprise.[11] Darwin was undoubtedly influenced by Malthus whom he had read in 1838, and even more so by his friendship with Herbert Spencer who was the first to use the phrase 'survival of the fittest'.

Spencer wrote volumes on just about any subject you might care to name, each considered from every conceivable point of view, so that you can find justification for anything depending on which page you happen to read and whichever prejudices you care to justify. None the less a persistently authoritarian, and what would today be considered right-wing extremist ideology, interspersed with pseudo-humanistic (and one suspects hypocritical) social concerns, run through much of his work, including his ten-volume series entitled *A System of Synthetic Philosophy* which includes *The Principles of Ethics*. In the latter he writes:

Doubtless, as I have elsewhere admitted [in a section on altruism], it seems, from one point of view, unjust that the inferior should be left to suffer the evils of their [innate] inferiority, for which they are not responsible. Nature, which everywhere carries on the struggle for life with unqualified severity, so as even to prompt the generalization – 'the law of murder is the law of growth', cares not for the claims of the weaker, even to the extent of securing them fair-play ... For with the admission that the ferocious discipline of brute-justice which issues in survival of the fittest, has, in societies of men, to be much qualified . . .[12]

Similar veins run through much of the evolutionist literature, including the works of more recent authors on the subject, among whom are Konrad Lorenz, I. Eibl-Eibesfeld, Anthony Storr, Desmond Morris, Robert Ardrey, Edward O. Wilson and Richard Dawkins. Each of these, with the exception of Ardrey, are scientists of repute who have fallen victim to their game-derived prejudices. Ardrey might be excused from submitting to the demands of scientific logic and consistency, but journalists also have responsibilities in not yielding to prejudice and myth.

The following are examples of how Desmond Morris views the game of survival and his version of how the pacific and vegetarian hairy ape turned into a merciless, flesh-eating, naked killer. The conclusion can only be that our whole species is torn between its acquired taste for altruism, co-operation among fellow combatants, and competitive murder of everyone else. The game of existence and survival as played by mankind and all other species, if we are to believe Morris, would thus lead inevitably to a Dobuan culture consisting of a war of 'us against everyone else' without respite. It may seem sometimes that Morris might be correct but, as we shall see later, this is so only because the exception has turned into a rule as a result of long-standing operant conditioning.

Aiding and abetting this mayhem is our specially evolved co-operativeness. When we improved this important trait in connection with hunting prey, it served us well, but it has now recoiled upon us . . . Loyalty on the hunt has become loyalty in fighting, and war is born. Ironically, it is the evolution of a deep-seated urge to help our fellows that has been the main cause of all the major horrors of war . . . because of the vicious combination of attack remoteness and group co-operativeness, the original goal has become blurred for the individuals involved in the fighting. They attack now more to support their comrades than to dominate their enemies, and their inherent susceptibility to direct appeasement is given little or no chance to express itself.[13]

Morris then proceeds to suggest four methods for ending war that are not worth quoting. Robert Ardrey in *African Genesis* carries the 'us against them' theme even further.

Human behaviour in its broad patterns cannot with any assurance be attributed to causes lying within human experience.

. . . It is a law of nature that territorial animals – whether individual or social – live in eternal hostility with their territorial neighbours . . . It seems probable that the demands of civilization, not the yearnings of an inherently genial nature, account for any temporary lapses in human belligerence.

. . . the drive to acquire private property; social groupings based on the defence of a territory held in common; the commandment to gain and hold individual dominance within such a society; the contest between males for superior territory or superior status; sexual choice exercised by the female in terms of the male's acquisition of property or status; the hostility of territorial neighbours whether individual or group; and the dual code of behaviour, prevailing in the members of a group, demanding amity for the social partner and enmity for individuals outside the territorial bond. All these are human instincts derived from ancient animal patterns. But to them must now be added those particular attributes of the hominid line: the way of the predator, and the dependence upon weapons.

. . . We are Cain's children . . . Man is a predator whose natural instinct is to kill with a weapon. [See Geoffrey Gorer's 'Ardrey on Human Nature'[14] for an entertaining demolition of the 'Cain' mythology.]

Our history reveals the development and contest of superior weapons as Homo sapiens' single, universal cultural preoccupation.[15]

Ardrey, in the inconsistent manner typical of the literature on evolution since the time of Darwin, then turns around and pleads for co-operation and attributes the spirit of competitive winning and conflict to our 'animal nature'. But if we adhered more closely to our animal nature we would be far more pacific than we are:

The territorial instinct, so ancient in its origin that we cannot mark its beginnings, demands of all social animals, with equal force, the capacities for co-operation as well as competition . . . Strip man of his social instincts and we will be left with Huxley's jungle law, with no higher authority than dog eat dog, and no way of existence beyond screams in the night . . . The dual nature of man is the supreme product of the social territory.

. . . No man can regard the way of war as good. It has simply been our way. No man can evaluate the eternal contest of weapons as anything but the sheerest waste and the sheerest folly. It has been simply our only means of final arbitration.[16]

But on page 372, Ardrey returns to his main theme once again. The killer/competitor, the football hooligan, the criminal, the delinquent and the compulsive winner are sane, and everyone else is neurotic and mad:

And we find the delinquent, by and large, superior to the non-delinquent in energy and physique . . . among five hundred boys who had rolled up in every individual history a fair record of repeated burglary, larceny, assault and public disturbance – among the ranks of this inglorious five hundred we find far fewer neurotics than in the ranks of the non-delinquents [who conform].

. . . Man is a wild species, and every baby born is a wild young thing. Advancing age, weakening vitality, and a long accumulation of fears and experiences may at last work a general inhibition on certain animal sources of human behaviour . . . [But] every accouchement delivers to society a creature who somehow must be tamed. Every accouchement – today, tomorrow and until the end of our species' time – presents civilization with an aspiring candidate for the hangman's noose. Yet truly to domesticate him means probably to destroy him.[17]

The myth of the vicious nature of animals in the wild was also adopted by Karl Marx who, like most evolutionists, blamed them for a predominantly human flaw: '. . . nothing discredits modern bourgeois development so much as the fact that it has not yet succeeded in getting beyond the economic forms of the animal world.'[18]

The curious belief that nature is a fiercely competitive enterprise in which the spoils go to the winners in evolutionary and genetic terms is still shared by scientists and non-scientists alike who have convinced themselves and one another that all of nature, and particularly human nature, is ruled by what is erroneously called 'the law of the jungle'. Compared to human civilization, the real jungle is actually a benign place where peaceful coexistence is the rule and violence the exception for its inhabitants.

Almost as disturbing as the prevailing view among ethologists like Morris, psychologists like Storr and journalists like Ardrey, are the views of critics like Ashley Montagu who, while he is correct in stating that human behaviour is mostly learned, discounts instinctive, innate, genetic inheritance and insists that no comparison can be made between animal and human behaviour, and that all analogizing is wrong.[19]

The development of bird song in some species illustrates the manner in which innate, genetically determined, instinctive behaviour is elaborated by learning. The real question must be what is innate and what is learnt? What is due to nature and what to nurture? Voice prints made of fledgling chirping clearly reveal visible innate patterns that form the basis for mature bird song, required for the establishment of territory and mating rituals. The fundamental sound patterns are present at birth in an abbreviated, yet clearly recognizable form. They mature to a full song repertoire as a result of contact with parents and practice until they become acceptably adult. But orphaned fledglings reared in isolation chirp permanently in an infantile manner, are not recognized by their own species at maturity, and cannot establish territory or find mates.

Given that human beings require a longer learning period and childhood than any other species, it is safe to say that the ratio of acquired to innate characteristics is far greater for us. Therefore our innate, reflexive and instinctive behaviours lend themselves to far greater modification and variation than those of any other species. In other words we have choices that are not available to them. That is a benefit of being human; but it can also be a curse. As I said earlier, all animal species are ethical by definition because they cannot choose to be otherwise. Only we can tell the difference between good and evil, although few of us seem to exercise that potential. Most people today think that ethics are matters of opinion rather than of fact.

The genetic programme provides what Jean Piaget, the Swiss psychologist, has called 'schemata' in human infants and what other psychologists and ethologists call IRMs. They form the basis for elaboration through learning and experience. Konrad Lorenz borrowed Piaget's vocabulary but his meanings are very different.

Unfortunately Lorenz, like Spencer and many others who have written on this subject, tends to want to be all things to all people. In his best known book *On Aggression*, he equates aggression with violence and insists that it is innate and not learnt, requiring periodic release by means of 'harmless' sports like football. Despite Lorenz's credentials as an ornithologist, his skill as a writer and raconteur and periodic expressions of humanistic concerns, he is as authoritarian and wrong today about the causes of competition and aggression, superiority and inferiority as he was even before and during the Second World War. When it comes to these matters he, like so many of his countrymen and women, seems to have only learned a new vocabulary. The old convictions, intentions and meanings remain unchanged in all he says, except when he writes about the things he knows. The problem with him, as with John McEnroe and possibly many other would-be winners, is that he is unaware of the true meaning of what he says and condemns himself with his own words. He is convinced that winning is all and writes in *On Aggression*:

I believe – and human psychologists, particularly psychoanalysts, should test this – that present-day civilized man suffers from insufficient discharge of his aggressive drive . . . There cannot be any doubt, in the opinion of any biologically-minded scientist, that intraspecific aggression is, in man, just as much of a spontaneous instinctive drive as in most other higher vertebrates . . .[20]

These views are reiterated and elaborated by Eibl-Eibesfeld [21] who has taken over Lorenz's position at the Max Planck Institut, which he uses as his platform to spread a similar gospel and in the same, probably sub-conscious way (see Chapter 12). The casual reader can be taken in and confused by the writings of such men unless their works are read with great care.

Richard Dawkins, the Oxford biologist mentioned earlier, has amplified the myth that competitiveness, selfishness and the instinctive need to win are embedded in our very genes to the exclusion of all other options. Altruism as the sole mediating factor can only be acquired by learning, according to him. Worse is that he also sincerely believes (see below) that altruism, like everything else, can only be taught by means of the carrot and the stick. In his book *The Selfish Gene* he writes:

Like successful Chicago gangsters, our genes have survived, in some cases for millions of years, in a highly competitive world . . . I shall argue that a predominant quality to be expected in a successful gene is ruthless selfishness . . . However, as we shall see, there are special circumstances in which a gene can achieve its own selfish goals best by fostering a limited form of altruism at the level of individual animals . . . Be warned that if you wish, as I do, to build a society in which individuals co-operate generously and unselfishly towards a common good, you can expect little help from biological nature. Let us try to teach generosity and altruism, because we are born selfish . . .[22]

Dawkins's beliefs include that computers can learn how to win at chess and that: 'The programmer's actual role is rather more like that of a father teaching his son to play chess.'[23] As a result,

Dawkins believes, along with behaviourists, that operant conditioning with reinforcement (i.e. carrot and stick training) is the only
form of learning potential built into our genes. But, contrary to
what he believes, it is not the only one. Many forms of conditioning
and learning exist.

In these respects Dawkins has much in common with Alan
Turing (the mathematician who provided the basis for electronic
computing and helped break the German 'Enigma' encoding system
during the Second World War) who persuaded himself and a great
many other people that 'artificial intelligence' was a possibility,
stemming from his belief that computers might eventually learn and
think. The reason for this common error is that people like Turing
and Dawkins do not understand what is involved in human
intelligence or learning.

Turing, Dawkins and many others perceive conditioning to be of
the operant type only and, since computer programming is equivalent to operant conditioning, they conclude that computers could
learn to be intelligent, if not exactly like us, then certainly in an
equivalent manner. But whoever is programmed or conditioned by
these means can only do as it, he or she is told and that is the
human tragedy. Operant conditioning is the main reason for human
stupidity.

Dawkins is so convinced of the rightness of his beliefs that he has
extended the principles of operant conditioning even to genes:

One way for genes to solve the problem of making predictions in rather
unpredictable environments is to build in a capacity for learning. Here the
program may take the form of the following instructions to the survival
machine: 'Here is a list of things defined as rewarding: sweet taste in the
mouth, orgasm, mild temperature, smiling child. And here is a list of nasty
things: various sorts of pain, nausea, empty stomach, screaming child.[24]

Desmond Morris, the ethologist quoted earlier, has written an as
yet unpublished book, in collaboration with Peter Marsh, that was
serialized in *The Times*.[25] The authors seem to have carried Morris's
favourite theme – the competitive nature of nature and of human
nature especially – to new heights. Whereas Dawkins blames genes
for our supposed innate need to win by making others lose, Morris
and Marsh believe that the female of our species is responsible to a
considerable extent:

Love and war are basic to human culture . . . The former is, in fact, linked to the latter. The human female is partly to blame . . . her constant [sexual] availability has the effect of increasing competition among the men on a sustained basis.

These authors also attempt to explain football hooliganism and other 'tribal' violence in a similar vein.

These are tragic mistakes made credible because they are backed by specialist expertise and a great deal of publicity that affect students and public attitudes. Like all unsubstantiated beliefs, they are caused and perpetuated by means of operant conditioning, becoming increasingly entrenched and more difficult to dislodge the longer they prevail. Our understanding or misunderstanding of games of chance (e.g. what occurs when a pack of cards is shuffled and why) and of strategy (why we win, lose or draw) is shown to affect our thought and behavioural processes in complex and profound ways. As I have indicated, wrong game-derived ideas have become deeply embedded in the physical as much as in the behavioural sciences. An understanding of these matters could mean the difference between peace and war, survival and extinction.

9 Games of Pure Strategy

> As is reasonably well known, noughts and crosses
> is a game in which, providing certain rules are
> followed, the player who has the first move can
> always ensure a draw.
>
> Igor Aleksander and Piers Burnett[1]

As we have seen, the games we play can be divided into three categories – those of pure chance, those of pure strategy, and those that consist of a mixture of both. All forms of behaviour can equally be divided into these three categories. We examined the meanings of games of chance in the contexts of physics and biology in earlier chapters. We have also seen that in behavioural terms we create chance, accidents and coincidences for ourselves or for one another. It remains to examine the meanings of pure games of strategy in a general behavioural context.

Prisoner's dilemma, noughts and crosses (tic-tac-toe), nine-men's-morris, draughts (checkers), chess and go are pure strategic games. They are played on a diagram, board or terrain, and involve a fixed number of players and counters that are placed or moved according to given rules. Strategic games are finite in as much as they end when no further moves are possible or because the rules prohibit repetition of the same move more than a given number of times on successive turns.

'Theoretically' and 'conventionally' everything, other than the intentions of the players, is in full view and no secrets or randomizing factors are involved 'in advance' of tactical moves. I emphasize 'theoretically' because in practice it is impossible to foresee all possibilities, especially for complex games like chess and go, or even draughts. There are simply too many – far more than is generally supposed. 'Conventionally' is stressed because, as a new modelling technique shows, it is now possible to gain deep insights into the players' intentions (see Appendix A). Randomization 'in advance' is a requirement only for games of chance.

As discussed earlier, if a player's intention is to win a strategic game more complex than prisoner's dilemma, then he must use randomizing tactics *after play has begun* in order to mislead or entrap an opponent on the board or playing field. Disconcerting ploys of a purely psychological nature may not be explicitly allowed, but they are not expressly forbidden by the rules. They can make the difference between winning and losing, and their use is epitomized by some chess (Bobby Fischer) and other champions (John McEnroe) who, being thoroughly conditioned 'winners', may use such tactics subconsciously. They are a form of psychological randomization. Tactical and psychological 'warfare' and 'randomization' are essential when the sole object is to win purely tactical games, especially when the players or teams are equally skilled. Systematic (i.e. non-random), fault-free and non-deceptive strategies can only lead to a draw between equally matched players. However, a stalemate can come about when a draw is played out to the bitter end, when players do not understand that this can be a draw played to the last turn, as a result of an exhaustion of means on both sides, or when the draw principle cannot be extended to any larger universe of discourse. None the less stalemates, like draws, 'do not count' as far as would-be winners and losers are concerned.

Games of pure strategy can be classified into five families: territorial games of occupation (e.g. noughts and crosses and go); killing games involving tactical disposition and movement of opposing forces (e.g. draughts or chess); quisling games of perpetually shifting allegiances (reversi or Othello); those that combine some of these characteristics (e.g. nine-men's-morris) and games of physical feats of strength and co-ordination (sports and athletics – see Chapter 10). Race games, except in sports, (e.g. snakes and ladders and the royal game of goose) depend primarily on dice or spinners and are therefore games of pure chance. These classifications run parallel to strategic and tactical human behaviours in all walks of life.

The intentions and psychological orientation of the players (i.e. to play for a draw, to win, or to play at random – the last two objectives amounting to the same thing) count for a great deal. Many people feel, but seldom express, resistance to playing solely to win or they cover up their discomfort by platitudes like: 'It's not winning, but how you play the game that counts.' That sort of advice leaves one entirely at sea as to 'how to play'. The object is still to achieve something, but what that is – presumably a draw – is never spelled out.

Playing for a draw in pure strategic games precludes the use of deceptive strategies. The precise dividing line between causal preconditions for war and peace, competition and co-operation, conflict and agreement, is thus clearly drawn, defined by the players' intentions to play for a win (to compete, maximize confusion and uncertainty in order to induce and take advantage of errors), to play for a draw (co-operate in achieving an error-free result and an agreement-to-agree) or a stalemate (an agreement-to-disagree after all other possibilities have been exhausted). There are significant differences between these various outcomes that do not seem to be generally appreciated.

It is, of course, easy to achieve a draw in noughts and crosses. But once the game diagram is enlarged to an 11×11 or 19×19 board with a 'winning' requirement of 'five-in-a-row' (as it is in the game of go-moku or the Japanese game of renju), it requires progressively greater concentration and considerable pattern recognition ability to ensure the earliest draw ending (see Appendix A). All that is needed in order to win, on the other hand, is to wait until the other side makes a mistake (or to induce it) and then to pounce.

A victory is always more easily achieved than a draw. But when both are considered in terms of the combinatorial sum of all possibilities, there is in fact a far greater number of possible draws than victories to be obtained in any game I could name. One can therefore legitimately conclude that rarity is not necessarily a criterion of value. That, of course, is our salvation because people like Ghengis Khan, Napoleon and Hitler are relatively rare historic phenomena – all dedicated would-be winners on a global scale.

The similarity of meanings between the causes, consequences and operations that bring about various conditions and outcomes in games and in the real world are not generally known or admitted. For example, we may ask ourselves whether 'first-strike capability' offers an advantage in war. Games of strategy provide us with the resounding answer 'NO', unless the other side is totally unprepared or unwilling to defend itself. Is 'more better'? Games of strategy show unequivocally that less suffices for those who understand enough, based on practical demonstrations that can be verified by playing noughts and crosses (see Appendix A).

In the past it was simply assumed that the means employed for winning meant success, superiority, greater achievement and intelligence, and survival of the fittest, but in no branch of science, from mathematics to biology was it ever conclusively demonstrated by application of a replicable scientific method that any of this was true for human or animal behaviour. Just as with the pronouncement that the earth is flat until it was found to be more or less round, no proof was ever sought or required. And now, as then, it is likely that many will go to their deaths, insisting that the original dogma is correct and the 'round earth idea' ridiculous, eccentric or insane. Edward O. Wilson, a Harvard zoologist, who coined the word 'sociobiology' does not juxtapose co-operation and competition. Instead, like Dawkins, he sees only 'altruism' as an alternative to competitive and combatively aggressive behaviour.

If 'aggression' and 'competition' are genetically innate, as they must be to be behavioural possibilities, then so is co-operation. The expression of any form of behaviour, however, depends on the interaction between what is innate and the environment and requires a conscious decision as to how to behave in various circumstances. This does not require an 'aggressive', 'competitive', or 'co-operative' gene, but merely a genetic potential – gene structures and relationships that make 'appropriate' (i.e. intelligent) behaviour possible in response to environmental stimuli.

For to be less than aggressive in either flight or defence in the face of an unprovoked attack means to co-operate with those who seek your destruction. To be anything other than co-operative in the absence of any threat is to be paranoid and a menace. To be altruistic without enlightened self-interest can be suicidal, an attempt to manipulate others and make them dependent rather than autonomous, or a way of surreptitiously making up for having caused deprivation (e.g. the altruism of nineteenth-century robber barons like Andrew Carnegie to whom we owe most of our public library systems).

But such altruistic behaviour is less a product of wishing to do

good by co-operating with others and more of another form of
winning: obtaining recognition, publicity, being deemed superior,
or to gain sainthood and a reserved place in Heaven. But some
people give their time, money and skills to those in need in order
to help them stand on their own two feet. They are not altruists
but co-operators in the best sense of the word. They get something
out of whatever they do for themselves – a sense of a job well done
in collaboration with others, as well as money if they need and
deserve it.

Because games of strategy, played to be won, are usually considered as proof of intelligence, attempts to demonstrate 'artificial
intelligence' (i.e. computers that think for themselves, learn and
make decisions autonomously and become 'expert systems' or
'inference engines') centred until recently on trying to prove that
computers are superior noughts and crosses, draughts and chess
players and winners. Although I have made this point before in
relation to learning, a more detailed explanation is required to see
how computer experts have been misled by their beliefs in the
superiority of the winner.

Computer programs written by investigators in artificial intelligence *have
demonstrated conclusively* that in certain activities (including activities that
most people say require intelligence, *such as playing games*) the computer
could out-perform human beings . . . Programs that play games such as
chess, checkers [draughts] and backgammon are informative examples of
heuristically [i.e. trial and error learning] guided search. Many of the
programs now play at levels of *experts* or master human players . . .[2]

Even as distinguished a man as Charles Babbage, who built the
mechanical prototype of the modern computer in the nineteenth
century, believed that computing engines could 'win' games and
demonstrate something akin to autonomous logic, despite the fact
that his friend and interpreter, Lady Lovelace, discounted any such
possibility.[3]

After much consideration I selected for my test the contrivance of a
machine that should be able to play a game of purely intellectual skill
successfully; such as tic-tac-toe, draughts, chess, etc. . . .[4]

Babbage, a brilliant mathematician and engineer, hoped to finance
the development of his computing engines by building noughts and

crosses and chess playing machines that would invariably win. He abandoned this idea without ever recognizing what was wrong with it.

A noughts and crosses playing machine was built in America in 1878 and its originator seems to have been one of the very few to have understood what this simple game is all about. It is not known whether he grasped the generalizations that can be inferred from this game which apply to all games of pure strategy as well as human behaviour:

At a recent meeting of the Franklin Institute, US, Mr F. T. Freeland presented and described a machine, designed and constructed by himself, for playing the game of tit-tat-to. The machine is so designed that the move made by the person playing against it determines the next made by the machine, the latter being accomplished by the simple movement back and forward of two levers, and the most skilful player is unable to win any one of the vast number of variations of which this simple game is susceptible.[5]

The possibility of a chess-playing automaton was discredited early in the nineteenth century,[6] but revived in 1890 by Torres y Quevedo, then President of the Spanish Academy of Science.[7] This same idea was proposed once again by Alan Turing,[8] the man who made modern digital computing possible. A noughts and crosses machine, built by Turing's erstwhile associate Donald Michie, persuaded the latter that machine intelligence was an inevitable byproduct of computing.

. . . after 150 plays the [noughts and crosses] machine had become capable of coping with anything . . . I would have done better to return to 'best strategy' and put up with an endless series of draws, or retire from the tournament. This I eventually did after sustaining eight defeats in ten successive games. At every stage, I used tactics I judged to be the most hopeful. It is likely, however, that my judgement was sometimes impaired by fatigue.[9]

Some of the fallacies about games, learning and intelligence are reflected in an educational noughts and crosses playing computer program, written for the BBC Acorn micro, used in schools throughout Britain. An accompanying brochure explains that this program purportedly demonstrates how computers can learn to win at best and at worst not lose.[10]

I played 100 games with (or against) this program. I won, and the computer lost 62 games; 38 were drawn; and the computer did not win a single one. What did the computer learn? The Acorn computer can only keep 600 games in its memory store, and had we played all of them, the proportion of draws would have increased somewhat and those I would have won declined, but the computer could not have won even one game unless my attention flagged. At the same time it would have continued to lose a substantial number. If a future computer could store all possible games (9×2^{36} if we consider all combinatorial possibilities, or 'merely' 943,488 if we limit ourselves to the permutations – see Appendix A), it would take 3,527,694 years of uninterrupted play in the first case and only $5\frac{1}{2}$ years in the second (at 3 minutes per game, played 24 hours per day) to discover that all games would be drawn, and the computer would still not have won a single one, nor could it ever do so unless the human player became inattentive due to fatigue – not unlikely after staying awake all that time.

The BBC micro noughts and crosses program additionally offers an option that enables the computer to play against itself. Out of a hundred games the X side won 47; the O side won 41; and 12 were drawn. If the fastest modern mainframe computer were to play out the combinatorial sum of all possibilities (which it could probably do quite rapidly, given today's parallel-linked, mainframe computer data processing speeds), 96.966 per cent of the 9×2^{36} games would be drawn and only 3.034 per cent would be won and lost as a result of errors. The meanings of these sums are interesting, for they illustrate an intriguing new way of representing the three laws of thermodynamics (defined and discussed earlier) relative to intentional and non-intentional behaviour. They show that there are many more ways of achieving a draw (i.e. achieving actual or relative perfection) than a victory (inducing or taking advantage of spontaneous mistakes); that the former are more difficult to achieve than the latter; and that there is always more than a single answer to any problem. All of this runs counter to modern dogma.

In pure strategic games like noughts and crosses the conventional calculation of the sum of possibilities (i.e. a wrong calculation of permutations – see Appendix A) is inadequate, made worse when only the symmetries of the game are considered, and even more so because it fails to take psychological factors into account. Once we include those we can literally read other people's minds and be certain about the past and the future as far as games and many, but by no means all, aspects of human behaviour are concerned. In the presence of intelligent and aware behaviours, the percentage of error should be zero (a definition of the first law of thermodynamics in behavioural terms – see Chapter 6). In the absence of any wilful organic behaviour and intelligence (i.e. when play is mindlessly at random, as it would be when the computer plays against itself), there is a percentage of inevitable error (the second law of thermodynamics) which, while the number of won and lost games may be large, is statistically small yet significant (i.e. 3.034 per cent for noughts and crosses when the combinatorial sum of all possibilities is considered). This margin of error is more or less the same as the 'longest run' percentage for pitching pennies mindlessly, which is only possible to predict approximately because that is an infinite game of chance.

It may be difficult to see that the contentions made here for noughts and crosses apply equally to other games of pure strategy. None the less it is inescapably true that unless one or both players are inexperienced or inattentive, every game of pure strategy must end as a draw. Like all other such games, noughts and crosses can only be won by default, by playing dirty tricks on a fellow player and taking advantage if he falls for them, or if the loser plays without knowing the game, without paying attention or is unable to do so because he is mentally damaged, too young or too old. Games of strategy are never won by any qualitatively 'superior' tactics or 'intelligence' on the part of the winner.

Noughts and crosses, trivial though it is, demonstrates in a simple way that the draw defines error-free perfection between equals. This outcome constitutes the only predictive and predictable state before and at any time during a game. Playing for a draw is the only condition that involves foresight since, as I showed earlier, playing for a victory always involves chance, uncertainty and dirty tricks, the consequences of which can never be predicted.

The game of noughts and crosses shows that it makes no difference who goes first when the intentions of both players are to play perfectly. As demonstrated later, this is even true for games like prisoner's dilemma where the first moving player must always win in any single encounter. His opponent has the same opportunity in any return engagement, thus balancing the score. The quotation that heads this chapter is therefore in error because it is impossible in noughts and crosses or in any other purely strategic situation for the first or second moving player to force a draw on an insistent would-be winner. The latter is unequal from the start and will inevitably defeat himself by trying to win, losing by not paying attention and making mistakes. His fellow player may show him where he is wrong, but unless he is willing to learn he will continue to compete and lose in what should have been a co-operative situation from the start. It is impossible to force anyone to learn or co-operate unless he wants to.

The disadvantage of the first turn for any player hoping to win is easily demonstrated (see Appendix A). The only advantage a first moving player enjoys is that he is able to take advantage of the other player's errors, if any, one turn earlier. If both players are equal in all respects, neither has any advantage, nor would either seek to take advantage of his or her partner. That is what co-operation, friendship and peace are all about. The same principles apply to chess and may end the perennial debate as to white's supposed first turn advantage.

The implications for those who advocate the advantage of first strike capability in war are more important. The game of noughts and crosses shows clearly that whoever strikes the first blow in any contest (i.e. the aggressor) suffers a severe disadvantage in winning terms, unless the second moving player (the defender) is totally unprepared or blunders persistently. All the defender has to do is follow the first moving player's lead and one of three kinds of a stalemate (one of which is a draw played out to the end) is guaranteed, unless the aggressor spontaneously makes – or can be induced to make – enough mistakes so that he will lose if the second moving player takes advantage of them.

Some of the properties common to different games of strategy are generally understood, although the generalizations that can be inferred from noughts and crosses (or any other simple game of strategy) are usually not understood and appreciated. Additionally, conditions and rules that change from one game to the next can be confusing. The varying conditions of 'captures' in games like chess and draughts are representative examples.

The term 'killing' is far more appropriate than the more usual 'capture' because the latter is a euphemism for what actually occurs. Soldiers prefer words like 'frag', 'total' or 'eliminate', to 'killing', while gangsters 'rub out' their rivals, thus reducing the murdered person to a thing rather than a human being. Strategic game players tend to disguise reality in a similar manner. Those who play games of chance seem to lack such inhibitions and speak freely of 'making a killing' in poker or on the stock-market, an accurate, if symbolic description of what winning involves when games are played, but literally true in many other situations.

Important differences exist between mandatory and optional killing. Killing is mandatory in draughts where total war – 'kill or be killed' – is the rule. Unless you kill whenever the opportunity presents itself, the piece that failed to do so is killed, giving the opposing side an advantage. But in chess it is up to each player to decide whether killing is opportune. At times it can be an advantage not to do so. This then defines one form of classical 'chivalry' – another word for 'altruism'.

Killing can determine whether a game can be drawn, won or lost. A draw or a stalemate can only be achieved when no one is killed or when killing on both sides is balanced and equal. If that is not the case the game may, but need not, be lost by the side that suffers the greatest number of casualties. With every 'murder' (and with every 'reincarnation' that can occur in chess and draughts) a game requires total recalculation because each death or resurrection alters the sum of future possibilities.

The underlying complexity of even the simplest games seems to be responsible for much of the confusion and misunderstanding reflected in the following quote from a book by Professor F. George, one of the early proponents of artificial intelligence:

To put the matter [of machines that think] at the simplest level and to give a preview of the mode of thought to be pursued, look at a machine playing a game. If we make it an easy game like noughts and crosses . . . we can see how the machine learns to play it . . . The machine keeps a record of games won, lost and drawn, and gradually 'learns' only to make moves followed by a W [the sign for winning]. This way it eliminates all errors and never loses. If it plays against a player who has also learned to play perfectly, every game is then, at best, drawn, so it will have to *settle* [my emphasis] for a D [the sign for a draw] instead of W. The main thing is to avoid L [losing] . . . This is an example of reinforcement, sometimes called the Law of Effect [it is actually the law of the carrot and the stick, and, where emotions are involved, it has been called the pleasure-pain principle which is the same as operant conditioning with reinforcement or the way performing bears are made to dance]. Where something is done which satisfies, it is repeated, and vice versa. To win therefore *must* [my emphasis] satisfy, either by some emotional state or by building in a rule which is the equivalent.[11]

Here then is absolute proof of how computer experts confuse operant conditioning (programming) of the crudest kind with learning and believe that one is the same as the other. They are not alone. Behaviourist psychologists and some biologists agree with them and seriously conceive of 'rewarding' or 'punishing' a computer in this symbolic manner.

Even Anatol Rapoport failed to appreciate the possibilities of combinatorial analysis when he stated that:

. . . In the case of very simple games like tic-tac-toe [noughts and crosses] a game tree could conceivably be drawn, but a matrix of the strategies remains out of question. The number of strategies of tic-tac-toe is enormous even if the symmetries of the game are taken into account.[12]

The prevailing confusion and contradictions concerning this simple game are typical of the muddled thinking that surrounds the subject of games, competition, co-operation, winning, losing, draws and stalemates. Authors who have written about noughts and crosses range from Igor Aleksander, who heads a computer department at London's Imperial College, to Claudia Zaslavski, an American curriculum specialist, mathematician and author of a children's book on this game in which she wrote that: 'If you go first you probably won't lose. If you go second, you probably won't win . . . A smart computer will never lose a game of tic-tac-toe.'[13]

Ms Zaslavski turns out to be wrong on all scores. Professor Rice, a mathematician at the University of Georgia in America, believed that he could use noughts and crosses to analyse predictive and committee decision-making processes. His whole approach was based on the wrong premises because he was apparently unaware that only drawn game outcomes can be predicted:

. . . Some recent work has been directed toward the problem of modelling human behaviour in an attempt to use game theory as a predictive device . . . In this paper, we consider a formalization of the idea of 'looking k turns ahead' . . . In order to introduce the ideas involved, consider the game of tic-tac-toe . . . As Kalin (1959) emphasizes, a strategy for this game is quite complicated . . .

In view of the fact that there is no strategy which guarantees a win for the first player, it is only necessary to check that the opening move does not present the opponent with the possibility of forcing a win, and that each subsequent move guarantees a win when possible, or a draw when a win is not possible . . .[14]

A 'scientific' study of children and young people playing noughts and crosses, conducted by Brian Sutton-Smith and a team of fellow American psychologists, shows how ingrained game-derived prejudices can be, and how they corrupt thought processes and reasoning powers.[15] Sutton-Smith is a leading expert on the educational and behavioural aspects of play and games. He has written any number of books and articles on the subject, including a 21-volume *Studies in Play and Games*, and is widely quoted in the professional literature. In the cited study he and his associates 'discovered' that 5 per cent of all elementary grades schoolchildren, 20 per cent in secondary grades and 30 per cent of all college students who were tested, succeeded in *winning* when playing noughts and crosses. Naturally an equal percentage lost, leaving a residue of players who deliberately or unwittingly achieved a draw.

These psychologists concluded that an increased ability in *winning* signifies learning, achievement and maturation, when in fact the reverse is true. The 90 per cent of elementary grades children who drew (5 per cent won and 5 per cent lost) came close to the 100 per cent draw result anyone should achieve with sufficient attention, or even the 97 per cent of draws achieved when the sum of all combinatorial possibilities is played out in a purely mechanical (i.e. mathematical) manner. But the percentage of drawn games declined drastically with further education, conditioning and chronological maturation. The ability to achieve a draw declined from 90 per cent in early years to a mere 40 per cent (30 per cent won and 30 per cent lost) at college levels.

The only conclusion that can be drawn from these statistics is that trickery and deviousness had increased substantially among the winners with education, conditioning and maturity, and that losers had grown less attentive in the years between early grades and college ages. Both winners and losers had, in fact, become less intelligent as they grew older.

What is equally interesting is that this research tells us nothing about whether these changes are due to home and environmental influences or to formal education in schools. At the very least the personalities of these young people had taken a turn for the worse through their years of growing up. But that is the exact opposite of the conclusions reached by the researchers, whose premises about this or any other strategic game were wrong from the start.

In the second part of this study the children's development was predicted by correlating noughts and crosses success with personality in typical statistical and psychological assessment fashion. As a result of his researches Sutton-Smith claimed to have established that:

Winning [at noughts and crosses] was correlated for girls with . . . dominance . . . [over] other girls, with instigating both verbal and physical aggression, with a preference for gross motor activity with uncontrolled motoricity . . . hyperactive, impulsive, aggressive and a tomboy . . .

This altogether unattractive and unflattering assessment of the 'winning girl' differs from the personality predicted for the 'winning boy' whose assessment:

. . . suggests that this is the model of his general approach to successes . . . one who gets leadership as a result of his ideas . . . [the profile of the winning boy] correlated with [high] scores on arithmetic, and intelligence tests . . . and intellectual achievement . . . a model of a more general strategic style in boys, though that does not appear to be the case with the winning girls . . .

The prejudicial judgements that favour these stereotyped sex roles become clearer when the psychologists define the characteristics of the 'drawing girl' they extracted from their statistical analyses:

. . . a picture of sex appropriate orientations and actions . . . preferring feminine games . . . neither aggressive nor interested in gross motor (traditionally masculine) activities . . . ladylike behaviour . . . the good girl plays it safe . . .

On the other hand the 'drawing boy' comes off badly as a plodder, a swot and a 'mother's boy'. According to this assessment such males are most likely to:

. . . display high need for achievement . . . have experienced high accelera-
tion pressure from their mothers and that they seek approval from adults
. . . unduly dependent on adults to define success for them . . . plays it safe
when the situation is not clearly structured for him by adults . . .

Altogether an unpleasant personality compared to the male winners
who are clearly favoured by Sutton-Smith and his co-workers. This
study says a great deal about the value of intelligence and psychological testing, statistical analyses and the criteria by which personalities and learning abilities are assessed. It also suggests that
fundamental prejudices are perpetuated by what passes for science
not only in psychology and education and among practitioners in
these fields, but in our society as a whole.

Examples given by Sherry Turkle demonstrate the disorienting
effect on young children of the all-pervasive conditioning for winning at any cost that runs right through our modern, purely
materialistic cultures. Sutton-Smith's research, while worthless in
other respects, dramatizes the consequences of such conditioning of
children, parents, teachers and psychologists. Miss Turkle's studies
reveal part of the cause:

Robert is playing with Merlin, a computer toy that plays tic-tac-toe . . .
Merlin follows an optimal strategy most of the time, and if neither player
makes a bad move every game will end in a draw. But Merlin is
programmed to make a slip every once in a while. Children discover a
strategy that will sometimes allow them to win, but then when they try it a
second time it usually doesn't work . . . Robert [age 7] accuses it of being a
'cheating machine'.

As Laura [age 6] plays she becomes less composed. Merlin's 'tic-tac-toe
mind' turns out to be a formidable opponent. 'How does he win so much?
It tries to make me lose.'

Lyndon is seven years old. He is angry with Merlin, which has been
trouncing him at tic-tac-toe for fifteen minutes straight. 'It's not fair. It's
too tricky. It's cheating, because it wins all the time.' Kelley, six, his
'girlfriend' and sometime tic-tac-toe partner, is equally convinced that
Merlin's steady triumphs are breaking the rules. 'It cheats. It's not nice to
win all the time.' Kelley confides to me that sometimes she 'cheats back' so
that she can beat Merlin. She does this by taking two turns in a row. 'But
when I do it,' she is quick to insist, 'it is not breaking the rules. It's just to
make things even.' At six, righting a moral balance is not cheating.[16]

The same misconceptions about winning and losing in noughts
and crosses and other strategic games affect perceptions in many

different specialist fields. 'Experts' tend to believe one another without asking whether ideas they accept as gospel have ever been tested, before they conduct research based on given or presumed premises. The absurd beliefs surrounding the superiority of the winner (i.e. you win by playing 'better' than your opponent and by making fewer or no mistakes) in noughts and crosses have even invaded research in neurophysiology, as illustrated by the following. If considered superficially it may seem as if this were a small error on the part of the researchers. But the consequences can be serious when conclusions that affect human brain surgery, electro-chemical or even psychiatric intervention in the treatment of supposed diseases of the brain are based on such serious misconceptions:

With a computer that records brain-wave patterns you can know *in advance* how a person is going to react to a question or a problem, and take action. John Hanley of the Brain Research Institute at the University of California, Los Angeles, found that such mind-reading was possible with chimpanzees. A chimp named Jerry was taught to play tic-tac-toe. (The game can usually be mastered by humans only after the age of four or five.) Once Jerry had mastered the game, Hanley's group planted electrodes in his brain. These were to record his brain-wave activity while he decided what move to make next. They restricted their observations to the times when he had a chance to make a winning move . . . To their surprise, and delight, they found that they could tell at least fifteen seconds before he made a move whether it would be correct or incorrect. Their forecasts were right 99 per cent of the time! All aspects of Jerry's brain-wave pattern showed more activity if he was about to make an error . . .[17]

These 'findings' may well be mechanically correct but they are conceptually wrong and prejudiced. Jerry the chimpanzee's increased brain-wave activity certainly reflected anxiety, but it was not caused by any fear of losing the game. As with any 'skill' learnt by means of operant conditioning, Jerry was either afraid of being punished if he failed to do what was expected of him or, if his trainers were made angry by whatever he did next (and he really had no idea what was expected of him, other than that he must make a move that pleases his keepers), they would withhold his reward. These are classical reactions of species (including man) when subjected to sometimes unbearable, externally created psychological pressures and inner conflict brought about by unrealistic expectations coupled with conditioned greed.

To expect a chimpanzee to understand noughts and crosses – a totally artificial, human abstraction, the object of which is to win by disconcerting a fellow player or by trading on his spontaneous mistakes – is sheer anthropomorphism and, in a way, cultural provincialism. These concepts are totally foreign to the ways of chimpanzees and their survival needs. No chimpanzee has ever discovered any such game or the tools, symbols and rules required to play it. Chimps are like the pigeons who were taught how to play ping-pong by B. F. Skinner, simply because he exploited their pecking instinct and rewarded them with grain every time they pecked the ball over the net, even when they were not hungry. Those pigeons had no idea what they were doing. They did not understand ping-pong, but they understood enough to know that they would receive a reward when they did as they were told, like every good consumer.

If their pigeon-brains were wired up to an EEG machine it would show increased brain activity because presumably the pigeons, like Jerry, feared that they might not get their reward, rather than knowing what they were doing, trying to win, or being afraid of losing the game. Jerry was rather like an aspirant for a college degree who studies frantically for his examinations, not because his subject interests him or because he hopes to master it, but because he fears that he will not get a well-paid job without credentials. That is why 'numbskulls' often come out ahead of students who are interested in learning for its own sake. The fools treat education as a game to be won, and they are quite correct in terms of the expectations of their teachers and future employers. They are only studying (but not learning anything) for the sake of the reward. But they do not understand the game they are playing any better than Jerry the chimp and his psychologist trainers, Skinner's pigeons or Skinner himself. People get ulcers or become mentally deranged for these reasons; they fear the stick (getting fired or demoted) or not getting the carrot (a rise or being promoted).

All this would seem to indicate that chimpanzees and pigeons may suffer stress when they become compulsive would-be winners – just like human beings. They can become terrified that their artificially conditioned expectations might not be met. They then become uncertain and the electrical discharge of their brains, caused solely by greed and fear, come to the notice of psychologists who are just as anxious as they are to succeed, publish and get their reward without understanding what they are doing.

However, 'success' can mean many different things. It can mean succeeding in learning something new, or in getting a banana. Rather than calling a spade a spade, psychologists invent 'noble' reasons for their own and their chimpanzees' anxiety (i.e. 'success in problem solving'). Both are playing to win, rather than for a draw. One wants a banana; the other tenure or a Nobel Prize.

The point I wish to make here is that when principles of game playing that may seem trivial in actual play are misunderstood, the resulting errors in applications that matter become magnified to an extent that can do serious harm.

On and off the board, disconcerting ploys within and outside the rules are least likely to succeed in games as simple as noughts and crosses. That is, however, not the case once the game board is enlarged (as in an 11×11 square noughts and crosses game) and when the rules become more complex (as in chess). Then tactical confusion usually reigns in the middle game, supported by psychologically disorienting ploys, although simplicity is restored towards the end if the game lasts that long.

Chess, of course, enjoys its own mythology. It is supposedly 'a game of kings' in which victory comes to those who are 'superior' players, who possess greater intelligence and foresight than losers or those who 'merely' draw. The following are quotes from chess champions, computer scientists and others that show how misleading a belief in the superiority of the winner can be. Additional ones are cited in the References.[18] The most significant of these concerns the fact that the draw and stalemate were considered 'winning' and 'superior' chess outcomes in medieval and Renaissance times in some parts of Europe and in Britain.

Chess is a game that indisputably requires intelligence on the part of the player, but its rules, the world within which the intelligence must be applied, are clear and well-defined; it is a 'game of perfect information' (that is, there is no element of luck or bluff as in poker) ... one of the fundamental skills in chess is the ability to calculate the implications of a particular move for the future ... The actual mechanism employed takes the form of a 'decision tree' ... Naturally, the player who can look furthest ahead along the most branches will have an enormous advantage.[19]

Man can solve problems without knowing how he solves them . . . Chess is an intellectual game *par excellence*. Without a chance device to obscure the contest, it pits two intellects against each other in a situation so complex that neither can hope to understand it completely . . . If one could devise a successful chess machine, one would seem to have penetrated to the core of human intellectual endeavour . . . Humans play chess, and when they do they engage in behaviour that seems extremely complex, intricate, and successful.[20]

. . . is intelligence the ability to play chess well? If so, then AI [artificial intelligence] is well on its way, since chess-playing programs can defeat most good amateurs; and the level of artificial chess will probably continue to improve slowly.[21]

If the number of feasible chess games were not so enormous, a computer would be able to play perfect chess. It could analyse the initial position out to mate or to a mandatory drawn position at the termination of every line of look-ahead analysis. But the number of possible games (more than 10^{120}) far exceeds the number of atoms in the universe and the time taken to calculate just one move in the perfect game would be measured in millions of years.[22]

Human chess skill does not depend on deep analysis (although that is part of it); rather it requires an ability to form plans, generalize from examples, learn from experience, etc., and to recognize important features of a position . . . [23]

Studies by Binet [one of the original authors of the Stanford-Binet intelligence test] and de Groot have revealed that the skills of chess masters lie in their powers of conceptualization, together with a vast accumulation of knowledge of past games and positions. Nor do they look ahead more than ordinary players: according to de Groot, six or seven half-moves tends to be the limit, with a total of perhaps thirty positions considered on the look-ahead tree.[24]

The distinguished applied mathematician I. J. Good, himself an expert chess player, believes that when a chess program has been developed capable of defeating the world champion, we shall be no more than five years away from the appearance of the 'ultra-intelligent' machine, intellectually superior to man in all departments of thought.[25]

It remains to look at recent world chess championships to see that the 'best games played by equals end as draws' principle applies in practice as much as in theory. The facts can be obscured by a clever – but stupid – manipulation of the scoring rules (e.g. the 'best' 6 out of 10 games, when 'best' means winning). But when all games won, lost and drawn in both 1985 contests between Karpov and Kasparov are added together (even with the artificial and prejudiced valuation of 1 point for each 'won' game and only $\frac{1}{2}$ point for each drawn one, according to the championship game rules promulgated by FIDE, the world chess federation), the final, combined scores added up to a draw.

The first of the two sets of title matches was halted by FIDE after 48 games because it looked as if a perpetual draw was in the making. Kasparov, the challenger, protested that FIDE was trying to protect Karpov's crown. But he was wrong. FIDE was protecting its vested interest in a contest that ends in victory for one and defeat for another. Most but not all professional chess players go along with the myth of the superiority of the winner, hoping to become sole and temporary possessors of the crown and the prize money for a while.

The 1987 international chess championship between Karpov and Kasparov was a re-run of the 1985 games. Kasparov remained the sole champion according to FIDE rules, despite the fact that the outcome was a draw after 24 contests. They had played 120 championship games against (or with) one another, of which 87 were drawn and the rest won and lost due to error on one side or the other. But, according to FIDE and other modern valuations, the 'best', actually or relatively error-free games in which both players showed great foresightedness did not really count. The world will have to wait until 1990 when these champions are likely to try once again to psych each other out, each hoping to beat the other by default and by chance.

David Spanier, author of a book on chess, is correct when he writes: 'It's not the moves that matter . . . it's how you make the moves. The object is always to disconcert, intimidate and infuriate the opposition.'[26] Anyone to whom such behaviour becomes habitual is in serious psychological trouble sooner or later, especially when it is applied away from the chess board. Compulsive winners and perpetual competitors in any field – in politics and business, as much as in chess – tend to lose touch with reality and become insecure and psychologically unbalanced for exactly the same reasons that caused Jerry the chimp's increased brain-wave activity and anxiety. This, of course, explains why such a large percentage of past chess masters like Paul Morphy, Howard Staunton and Wilhelm Steinitz suffered serious psychological difficulties later in life, became paranoid and were diagnosed as clinically insane. A few, like Lasker and Grunfeld, who understood the draw principle, remained rational until the day they died.

It is unnecessary to provide more examples, for they would merely show how varied and psychologically hazardous erroneous beliefs can be when they are based on fundamental misconceptions. But far more damaging is that they are said to be indisputable, when all the evidence points in a different direction. The folly of these beliefs is illustrated by a Hindu tale.

It was the custom among Indian maharajas to play a version of chess by having palace courtyards constructed to serve as life-size game boards, using their retainers gowned to represent the playing pieces – white on one side and black on the other. The maharajas made their moves from balconies overlooking the 'board', cooled by punka flappers and attended by wives and admirers. Two such chess players decided to lend the game a little more realism and zest by ordering 'captured counters' to be removed from the board and beheaded on the sidelines. The losing chess-playing maharaja eventually ran out of retainers and the winner found himself without a partner. Undaunted he continued to play chess, albeit by himself, using and beheading his own retainers as demanded by the situation on both sides. This maharaja soon depopulated his palace and eventually his state, leaving him the sole victor and ruler of a country without punka flappers or enough subjects even for a game of chess.

My own less bloody tale explains the principles of chess in a different, although related manner. Suppose that God invited you to play chess with Him (for the purposes of this demonstration let us leave aside questions like whether or not you believe in God, or whether God is male or female). We could equally substitute Douglas Hofstadter's fantasized universally intelligent machine,[27] but the largest, parallel-linked mainframe computer in any foreseeable future would not do. It could only generate the sum of all combinatorial possibilities and is therefore subject to the second law of thermodynamics (see Chapter 6). In other words it has no way of finding, eliminating, correcting or forgiving innate mechanical, mindless or psychological friction or errors, as may God or perhaps even Hofstadter's science fiction master computer. (But you and I can eliminate mindlessness and psychological and tactical friction if we want to.)

God has all the answers as far as chess or anything else is concerned, from first move to last, if for no other reason than that He is the game's inventor: we merely discovered it. He knows all the games that can ever be played – the classified brute force sum of all combinatorial possibilities that includes the best and the worst. He can, of course, achieve any outcome He wants – the ultimate chess master who never makes any mistakes. Such a champion has perfect fore- and hindsight and nothing is unpredictable as far as He is concerned. Compared to Him all human chess champions are mere novices.

Are you going to play 'with' or 'against' Him? You are God's friend or enemy, depending on your choice. In the latter case nothing – neither skill nor luck – could help you, for there is no way in which you could ever defeat God.

The next point to be settled concerns who 'gets white' and enjoys the first turn – a presumed advantage (like first strike capability). Would you suggest that God tosses a coin to see who goes first? He would know in advance what the outcome will be, no matter who tosses the coin. Further, if He tossed it, He could make it come up heads, tails or stand it on edge because He is the perfect craftsman. But that would be cheating and God cannot cheat. He is the fundamental ethic, in addition to His other characteristics.

Further, and especially if white were to enjoy an advantage, God would decline to go first because He would not want to take advantage of you, for that would be a violation of His principles. Would or could you try to take advantage of God? He would probably resolve this dilemma by graciously offering you white and the first move, insisting that you accept. You could hardly refuse. In any event God knows that your belief in the first turn advantage is superstitious and a fantasy. The questions that remain are:

'Who wins this game?' and 'Can the outcome be foreseen?'

We have already established that games are only won and lost by default. God will certainly not make any mistakes, or trick or disconcert you so that you make them, or take advantage of those you make. Any of these acts would be violations of His perfection. He would follow your lead, defend His pieces perfectly and create the conditions for an eventual draw. That would be His advantage as an omniscient player, even if you tried to win. He would point out your errors as they occurred, forgive and show you how to correct them if you were willing to learn. If you are reasonable, trust in God's expertise and play for fun and to learn to become perfect, rather than wanting to win by trying to make Him lose, that game is bound to end as a draw – as God knew it would from the beginning. While you and God may have been unequal at the start of the game you can become His equal at its end, for that is His intention.

There is, however, one way in which the outcome might be uncertain as far as you are concerned, although God (and only He) could predict even that. You could lose or stumble into a stalemate if you dogmatically refused to learn, insisted that your wrong moves were really the correct ones, or if you ignored God's advice. God can predict, but he will not intervene to prevent human intransigence, arrogance and stupidity.

In other words, the outcome is totally predictable if you co-operate, play with and learn from God, nature, or anyone who knows what he is talking about. You are in the hands of chance if you compete, and only God can predict the consequences. Since we live in a conditionally deterministic universe, our actions determine which segment of the future is brought into being. The quality of our future depends on the conditions we ourselves recognize and understand within the limits provided by a bountiful nature, by the rules we invent for whichever games we choose to play, and by how we interpret both natural law and man-made rules.

Whether we win, lose, draw or achieve a stalemate is never a result of the will of God. God and nature only give us all the choices there are. Whichever force or being to which you may ascribe supreme powers has actually loaded the dice by establishing a vast preponderance of the best (co-operative) options in our favour, as against a tiny fraction of the worst ones (winning and losing) which are only to be invoked in relatively rare and extreme circumstances. We choose the right or the wrong options because we are given free will by that same supreme power, as the game of chess demonstrates.

The expression of will is certainly a matter of options and choice. How free or limited human will is or can be therefore depends on the number of options that are available to us or that we perceive. The permutational sum of all possibilities for chess is about 10^{120} and the combinatorial one is very much larger. It is certainly larger than the number of atoms in the universe, which means that there are so many options in this game that we could never exercise them within the time available in the cosmos – past, present and future – even in the rather limited universe of chess. If we consider the game of life in an environment bounded only by our central nervous system and the universe itself, the option sums grow calculably larger.

The human central nervous system consists of about 10^{11} neurons, each containing 100 bits of information that it can exchange with many of the others. If we consider each neuron as a square of a chess board and the bits of information as playing pieces, we are talking about an occupied portion of a chess board that is 316,228 squares wide and long, of which each square contains about 100 playing pieces of varying powers. The universe itself constitutes the as yet unoccupied portions of the board – a universal commons of vast but unknown dimensions. The options offered by such a universe of discourse are so large that we would run out of time if we tried to exercise all of them. We therefore have unlimited free will for all practical purposes, despite the possibility that our universe and our central nervous systems are finite.

Once we consider fundamental questions of life and existence in game terms, the answers become relatively simple to extract, opening up possibilities that can occupy us until the end of time. While discussion, deeper exploration and agreement as to what all of this means can expand human horizons indefinitely, the facts of these matters lie beyond argument, for me at least.

To return to strategic games of movement, the game of draughts is very different from chess. The sum of all permutational possibilities for draughts are 10^{40} options. At a rate of three of these exercised every millimicrosecond, it would require 10^{21} centuries to exhaust all of them.[28] If all combinatorial possibilities were calculated they would run to a much larger sum, and the time it would take to exhaust them would be correspondingly greater – much greater than noughts and crosses and smaller than chess.

Draughts differs from noughts and crosses and chess in as much as a draw cannot be achieved, although a stalemate is possible. The reason for this is the rule that requires mandatory killing. In many respects draughts has a great deal in common with the game of Othello and with the First World War. Players cannot foresee or reach an agreement (i.e. a draw) until the very last moment when the possibilities for winning have been exhausted. That is the point at which no further mistakes can be induced by trickery or made spontaneously, and then taken advantage of. The means of both sides are exhausted at that point or the options have been reduced to a balance of minimal means that cannot be upset at any future turn. When such an outcome occurs the game will have ended as one kind of a stalemate. As in most other game outcomes, how a stalemate is perceived depends on the intentions of the players (see Appendix A) – whether they are played for fun, to win, for a draw, at random, to wear one another out, or to learn.

There is no possibility of agreeing to limited or balanced murder in draughts, just as there is no possibility of limiting treachery and switching sides in Othello by agreement among the players. In draughts, no matter how either player moves or what his intentions might be, a point is reached at which killing cannot be avoided until the game is won, or until both sides have reached absolute parity in impotence in their ability to harm one another. In Othello a stalemate is rare because it can only occur on the last turn if an equal number of turncoat pieces have sided with each player, no others remain to be corrupted, and the whole board is occupied.

A stalemate in draughts can also be likened to nuclear war after all populations have been destroyed. The governing bureaucracies would emerge from their fall-out shelter command posts without the power to do each other further harm except, perhaps, by guerrilla warfare. At some point they would presumably reach an agreement and make peace – but at what cost to themselves and a de-populated, barren and highly irradiated earth?

A stalemate in Othello is equivalent to the morning after an election in which two political parties have bribed voters with promises they know they cannot keep. The polls swing back and forth between the contestants until the very end. On that 'morning after' the opponents discover that they have both managed to corrupt an equal number of the electorate so that the outcome is 'hung'.

In both draughts and Othello, if a player seeks to win he must make a number of timely sacrifices by exposing one or several of his own pieces to force the other side to expose a greater number to imminent death or corruption. Both are therefore games of alternating provocation and sacrifice (i.e. altruism) in order to force an advantage and to lure the other side into unavoidable disaster, just as in today's politics and in war.

One of the objectives in draughts is to reach the other side of the game board as quickly as possible so that an ordinary playing piece can be elevated in rank to become a king. Kingship under such circumstances is a misnomer because only a single king could properly be said to exist on each side. It would be more appropriate to call such pieces bureaucrats (or aristocrats) because they enjoy special privileges without any obligation. Each player aims to prevent the formation of such a privileged class by his opponent at any cost, as political parties do when they have won or lost an election.

Having reached elevation to the bureaucracy (or aristocracy), a piece is given the privilege of running down the other side's plebeian counters, being able to move in all directions, while the latter can try to escape their fate only by moving towards one or the other side of the board. If both players command only high-powered pieces and when there are no commoners to pursue, the game is reduced once more to the same provocative, sacrificial ploys as in the beginning; a falling-out among opposing ruling elites, limited and perpetuated because no low-ranking soldiers are left to be exposed and hunted down. A stalemate can only be reached when the number of commoners or high-ranking pieces on both sides is reduced to a level at which they can no longer damage one another.

Draughts is much simpler and more ruthless than chess, mainly because of the application of mandatory brute force. Its consequences are inescapable for both sides, as determined by the rules. In chess there are possibilities for optional killing or no killing whatsoever, and an early, foreseen draw or a flawless late one when the game is played out to the end by chance, or by design when both sides are equally matched. But chess can be just as hypocritical, chancy and murderous as draughts when it is played to be won.

Nothing, of course, prevents players from changing the rules of these games, but that is not the point. The object here is to show when and whether winning and losing are the only possible outcomes in any strategic game as it is currently played; how, when and why victory and defeat occur; whether, when and how draws and stalemates can be achieved under the existing rules; and what these various outcomes mean when translated into real-life terms.

The necessarily ruthless, simplistic manipulation of forces, and a selection of clear-cut, if less than humane strategies or praiseworthy goals required to play draughts, make this game much easier to program on a computer than chess. There are no alternatives to murderous intent, other than exhaustion.

In chess a certain pretended gentility can be preserved in all but championship games played for prize money; an impossibility in draughts or Othello where a stalemate means that one or the other players was not sufficiently ruthless. Draughts is a game of total external control (as differentiated from self-control and a valuative choice of options). It should therefore not have been surprising that A. L. Samuel, an American computer programmer, created a draughts-playing computer program in 1959 that once (and only once) managed to defeat a US state champion.[29] It was instantly hailed by computer scientists, eager to win support for their ideas and research grants to which they aspire, as an example of artificial intelligence, learning and independent thought on the part of a computer.

... He [Samuel] never enjoyed playing checkers himself, and despaired of learning anything about the game's general principles by reading literature on the subject ... he invited checkers masters to help him work on the program, but always without success ... 'We got simply nowhere,' Samuel reports. The more he attempted to analyse his own thought processes, the more confused he got ... Samuel has long maintained that his ignorance of checkers was helpful in getting the program going ...[30]

Feigenbaum [in his book, *The Fifth Generation*[31]] for example, reports that 'by 1961 [Samuel's program] played championship checkers, and it learned and improved with each game' ... In fact, Samuel said in a recent interview ... the program did once defeat a state champion, but the champion 'turned around and defeated the program in six mail games.' According to Samuel, after thirty-five years of effort, 'the program is quite capable of beating any amateur player and can give better players a good contest ... It is clearly no champion ... The experts do not know enough about the mental processes involved in playing the game.'[32]

The same appears to be true for many other experts on games, in psychology or artificial intelligence.

One last game of pure strategy is worth exploring. It is called prisoner's dilemma and is perhaps the simplest game there is. Its meanings were dramatized in 1978 by a computer program, written by Anatol Rapoport. The 'super-simplex' solution to prisoner's dilemma I provide here is even simpler than Rapoport's 'Tit-for-Tat' program, but before I explain it, it is important to understand this game and its applications.

Melvin Dresher and Merrill Flood invented prisoner's dilemma in 1950, while working for the Rand Corporation – one of the Pentagon's 'think tanks'. Albert W. Tucker, another game theoretician, named and wrote about it. This game has been used as an analogue for the story that gave it its name, for the East/West conflict (under the name of 'chicken'), and as an economic paradigm.[33] It has since been enlarged to a 4×4 game from its 2×2 origins, the subject of two competitions among game theorists (won by Anatol Rapoport on both occasions), and a book written by Robert Axelrod, a psychologist at the University of Michigan, [34] the sponsor of these contests. Axelrod (instead of Rapoport who had, after all, written the winning program) claimed to have discovered the wellsprings of co-operation, but denied emphatically that the draw is the appropriate metaphor.[35]

Prisoner's dilemma has been used to analyse competitive situations ranging from the stock-market to the cold war. The latter was the subject of an article that appeared in *New Scientist* in 1983: 'The arms race: is it just a mistake?'[36]

P. G. Bennett, one of the authors, was a member of the Operational Research Group at the University of Sussex and the other, M. R. Dando, worked in the School of Peace Studies at the University of Bradford. They cite John Maynard Smith who has applied conventional game theory to evolutionary biology and believes, as do so many of his colleagues, that nature favours winners, although he acknowledges that co-operation plays a rôle in evolution.[37] The authors also refer to Steven Brams as one of their authorities, an American game theorist who has made an analysis of the first book of Genesis and concludes that God is a 'would-be winner' and involved in a perpetual game against the creatures of His creation, starting with Adam and Eve.[38] The authors of this *New Scientist* article try to explain the so-called East-West conflict in terms of prisoner's dilemma and come to the conclusion that: 'The moral of this [application of prisoner's dilemma] is that rationality, at least as narrowly defined, does not "add-up".'[39] They were correct as far as they were concerned, given their understanding of this game at that time.

Prisoner's dilemma is noughts and crosses played on a 2×2 field, made more complex than it needs to be by a 'pay-off' matrix that enables a number of different outcomes to be postulated. In other words, entirely artificial odds that obscure the obvious are superimposed on this game. Presented as it was by Dresher, Flood and Tucker, the game seems paradoxical, but not if it is considered realistically and without recourse to artificially imposed values. Basically, the story is this:

Two criminals are arrested by the police who know that they have committed a crime, but there is no evidence on which to convict them. They are separated and placed in individual cells so that they cannot communicate. The police promise immunity (or a shorter sentence if you prefer to change the odds) to whoever talks first, telling each that the other is ready to implicate his partner. Whoever 'grasses' wins and goes free (or stays in jail for a very much shorter time), while the other is prosecuted and jailed for many years on the basis of his partner's evidence.

Neither is jailed if both remain loyal to and co-operate with each other, and refuse to play. But distrust and suspicion are sown by the police who try to persuade each of the two prisoners that 'if you don't talk first, you'll be the loser'. As stated earlier, variations on this theme exist, including one in which whoever grasses gets a lighter sentence than the other. Introducing such complications merely confuses the main issue without altering the principles that are involved (e.g. the prisoner who grasses and gets a lighter sentence had better not go into the jail's exercise yard, where he is likely to be fatally injured by an 'accident' arranged by his former partner or his friends). The 2×2 game paradigm, if played as a simpler version of noughts and crosses, makes it perfectly plain that in this strictly limited environment and because the sum of squares is even, whoever goes first wins every game. But the designers of the game have overlooked a number of significant issues.

Rapoport's program (showing that conditional co-operation works best in economics) indicates, as he has argued for a long time, that there should be honour among thieves; that they should have a conscience or feeling for one another and operate on the basis of trust. His Tit-for-Tat program showed that there is a practical basis for ethics in any quid pro quo relationship. The conclusions drawn by Axelrod were that people should be 'nice', retaliate in a restrained manner when their reasonable expectations are not met, yet be forgiving. Axelrod vigorously denied that this has any connection with playing for a draw in any game.

None the less, Rapoport's solution makes it perfectly obvious that the ethics dictated by natural laws of cause and effect are implicit in all games of strategy and chance and are not limited to prisoner's dilemma. They are defined by the draw or, in instances of unprovoked attack, by withdrawal and a refusal to play, or by a vigorous defence and achievement of a temporary victory for the purpose of restoring a balanced peace. Such a definition of rational behaviour also sets limits (i.e. defines the rules) of ethical behaviour.

Ethics are defined by appropriate (i.e. intelligent) behaviours that are innate, and do not need to be 'taught' or imposed by moralistic platitudes. Unless we are misdirected by culture or by leaders whom we follow blindly, it is best to trust instincts that are finer and better than any religious, philosophical or other dogma. And even when misdirected by Church, State, parents or self-conditioned greed or fear, every individual can learn for him or herself by placing him or herself in the shoes of others and imagining the consequences of whatever behaviour might be questionable. That defines the mechanism of foresight. There is never any need to try everything once because we cannot and need not do so. The number of possibilities is too great. It is enough to act on the right principles for then our instincts will seldom let us down.

But we can only discover the correct principles if we remain open to all possibilities; if we refuse to play to win except temporarily in response to an unprovoked and persistent attack; and if we are willing to accept responsibility for our own mistakes, correct them and make up for whatever damage was done as soon as, and to whatever extent is possible. Then, and only then, can we be forgiven for being immoral or even unethical now and then.

Winning at any cost is unethical in itself. It is caused by self-conditioning or conditioning by others. It results in a poverty of the imagination, a lack of foresight and consequences, and is characterized by a total lack of concern for others. Such behaviours are self-reinforcing for as long as they are tolerated and range from the inconsiderate and the psychotic to the criminal.

Unfortunately, unethical, highly competitive behaviour has become increasingly acceptable and entrenched in most parts of the world as a result of artificially stimulated and often unrealizable expectations of material possessions to which people feel entitled as a matter of course. This results in a stifling of foresight and causes a lack of awareness of consequences, generating internal and external conflicts similar to those experienced by Jerry the chimpanzee who was trained to play noughts and crosses – a game he did not understand – by being bribed with bananas. This example demonstrates a terrifying similarity between some human beings and chimpanzees, for both can be bribed to do things they do not understand. There are, however, three significant differences. Human beings enjoy a much larger sum of options than chimpanzees, can always resist the wrong forms of conditioning, and can learn to understand anything.

The ethical aspects and the options provided by prisoner's dilemma are generally ignored. Nor is this game usually understood. The analogy itself concerns unethical behaviour from the start. The game, as defined by Tucker, does not involve 'legitimate' conduct. It concerns known criminals who, by definition, are competitive with the 'straight' society, and co-operatively devoted to winning by making it lose (like many 'legitimate' business enterprises and politicians today). They have, in effect, declared war on society. If they are co-operative and loyal to one another, both will refuse to play and will win together (i.e. achieve a draw) by defeating the forces of law and order. But if the first moving player is treacherous and disloyal to the other, considers himself engaged in a 2×2 contest and plays 'against' the other when he is caught by the police, he (who now co-operates with the police and is in conflict with his former partner) will certainly win in the short run.

However there is a catch that game theoreticians overlook, tending as they do to remain locked into the limited paradigm they create without looking beyond into the larger 'real-life' environment. Games of this kind do not necessarily end with the first round: that is where the 'super-simplex' solution lies. There is usually (or should be) a repeat game or, as it is known, a 'revanche'. If all games between the criminals were to end as draws, and if those are understood for what they are, they will remain trusted and trusting friends and confederates for life. If not, they will begin to play a winning and losing game with one another and become bitter enemies.

The jailed criminal will continue to play after the first round is lost. Only this time he will have the first turn as a matter of course and win, while his former partner who grassed will necessarily go second and lose. The jailed prisoner can have one of his friends or relatives on the outside take out a contract on his former partner, or wait until he is released and then 'bump him off' (or have him 'taken care of' in the jail's exercise yard), thus winning the second round. Obviously he will also be a loser because he will probably be caught and receive a life sentence for murder. Like all would-be winners, both criminals are losers from the start – as are those who play any game with the object of winning without understanding what is involved. There is, however, one way of avoiding the truth of this interpretation of prisoner's dilemma, and it was brought home to me forcibly in 1980 while I was in Germany.

I was invited to the home of a prominent German game theoretician (a specialist in prisoner's dilemma) in order to explain my new game theory. After I had done so, and after coffee, Strudel and Gemütlichkeit, my host insisted that we play a game of prisoner's dilemma to show me how wrong I was. It was clear that he wanted to win and make me lose. He, of course, insisted on the first turn and triumphantly won. When I requested a return match in order to illustrate my point he refused huffily. One game, he insisted, was enough. When dealing with certain kinds of academics, there is no comeback, return match or any way to even the score. Such 'experts' are at war with you from the start; are always right even when they are wrong; never admit an error or provide any opportunity for discussion. They want to win. Additionally, the concept of a 'draw' is foreign to German ways of thinking because, as we saw earlier, there is no word to express such an idea in that language – a significant cultural signpost.

Rapoport's Tit-for-Tat solution to prisoner's dilemma resembles my own – one of the many ways of achieving a draw. Axelrod cannot accept that both solutions are merely different versions of the conventional draw, common to games of any kind, save those that involve actual or symbolic mandatory killing, perpetual turn-coat treachery, argumentation and randomization. Those are the signs of Cain.

There are, of course, many other purely strategic games like nim, nine-men's-morris and go that illustrate the behavioural meanings and subtleties of winning, losing, achieving a draw or a stalemate. All of these are variations on the same theme, although each may contain illuminating features that are unique. I leave it to others to discover and elaborate them. But what perhaps deserves much more discussion than I have room for is, as I have said, that all strategic games played to be won and lost turn into games of chance by virtue of this intention alone. That subject is worthy of a small book of its own and needs to be understood far better than at present by politicians, economists, many academics and all would-be winners of both sexes in the game of life.

In the following chapter I explore what all of this means when it comes to sports and athletics for which, although the details may differ, the same conclusions hold true as for games of pure strategy. What is perhaps more intriguing is that it is possible to demonstrate clearly how attitudes involved in games and sports affect all aspects of our individual and collective lives and behaviours in the arts, sciences, government, business and in the home.

10 The Sporting Life

We'll take the Tottenham in half a minute
We'll take the Arsenal and all that's in it,
With hatchets and hammers,
Carving knives and spanners,
We'll show those Tottenham bastards how to fight!

British football fan song [1]

Sports are often believed to differ from games of strategy in that they depend more on physical than mental co-ordination, but that is not necessarily the case. To be successful in sports and athletics it is essential to be physically fit, but attitude plays a major role. 'Mind-set' and the psychological aspects of winning and losing or playing for a draw can be as crucial on a football field as over a chess-board. Like all games played to be won, sports and athletics performed solely for the sake of winning turn instantly into games of pure chance. Even golf and tennis have been turned into gambling games, overtly wagered on by participating champions.

Excellence in sports and athletics depends very much on psychological factors that play important roles in how these activities are perceived by players and spectators alike, and in how both groups behave on and off the playing field. The abrasive behaviours of some sports champions have become commonplace, as have drug use and 'accidents' on playing fields, physical damage to players and, of course, football hooliganism.

Today's frequency of these phenomena is not accidental. They are certainties like all coincidences that involve human behaviour. The reasons given by psychologists for these unpleasant behaviours are also predictable. They, together with governments, sports promoters and football hooligans themselves have different, but equally self-serving explanations for the increase in anti-social behaviour in and related to sports and athletics. Essentially all of them protect (perhaps unwittingly) highly competitive attitudes of others that mirror their own (see References, Chapter 10: 13).

For example, psychologists and journalists have made much of John McEnroe's tantrums on the tennis courts. They try to explain them by attributing contradictory motives to him and others like him.

In a recent issue of the *Bulletin of the British Psychological Society*, Steve Murgatroyd . . . suggested that according to 'reversal theory', McEnroe's tantrums are a device to increase his concentration by stoking up his adrenalin flow. 'Careful observation,' writes Murgatroyd, 'suggests that McEnroe's outbursts typically occur when the game is becoming too easy for him.'[2]

Why McEnroe or anyone else should need extra adrenalin when the game becomes too easy, and less rather than more effort is required, is something of a contradiction.

According to the official biography of McEnroe . . . the former champion's outbursts can be explained by . . . 'a rage for perfection'[3] . . . The lay president of the Institute for Psychoanalysis refused to be drawn on the subject, saying rather stiffly, 'You must understand that analysis is a long, subtle and very judgmental process . . .' A Jungian in private practice, while saying she would need details of McEnroe's dreams to know the true archetypal basis of his temper tantrums, explained that in nearly every case, extreme perfectionism masks a deep sense of personal inadequacy . . . A Freudian analyst . . . could see a clear and classic pattern running through the uncourtly behaviour of a raging perfectionist . . . 'and in Freudian theory, the root of this sort of personality pattern is, at the unconscious level, powerful feelings of love and hate – usually towards the mother'.[4]

Presumably McEnroe confused his feelings for umpires, line judges and photographers with those he normally reserves for his mother, if we are to believe this Freudian analyst's interpretation of his motives and behaviour.

In one match in Paris he [McEnroe] swore at the umpire and line judges, telling one official: 'You moron. You haven't got the guts of a French Frog fag.' He also attacked a photographer who was annoying him.[5]

The clues to McEnroe's behaviour, or that of any other ill-tempered game player, and the bizarre explanations offered by psychiatrists, can be found in the nature of ruthless competition itself. Consciously or unconsciously, the tantrums are designed to disconcert and break the concentration of umpires and opposing players so that they make mistakes that the would-be winner can take advantage of. That is how such games are won and lost, especially those played between equally skilled players. A rage for perfection is certainly involved – a rage of perfectly malicious psychological warfare.

Tennis deserves additional comment for it is sometimes claimed that a draw is impossible to achieve in this game: someone must win sooner or later according to the standard rules. But here, as in all games played to be won, two principles apply. The first, as I said earlier, is that all strategic games of skill played to be won by equals are bound to turn into games of chance. Second, the artificial values (i.e. scoring rules) and not the players' superior play guarantee that one side wins and the other loses as far as game, set and match are concerned. For if the score for each game, or the number of games required to be played in a set or match, were even rather than odd, drawn matches between equally skilled champions would be common. The problem – and the solution – are similar to those that hold true for prisoner's dilemma.

A recent development in tennis, known as the 'Stakes Match' (which has also been introduced in golf where it is called the 'Skins Game') is one that is bound to spread; this overtly relates playing to win to gambling, not only on the part of punters but by participating players. In November 1987 Lendl, McEnroe, Cash and Edberg were the first to compete in such a corrupt form of tennis in Florida:

Instead of a series of sets, for example, a Stakes Match encounter will be a single 15-point game. And instead of prize money going to the winner at the end of the three-day tournament, the four players will each be awarded a \$250,000 stake at the beginning of play.

They will play one another on Friday and again on Saturday with the winner of each game receiving \$30,000 from the loser's stake. The two who accumulate the most money in the first two rounds will meet on Sunday for a three-of-five game series of 21-point games, with the value of each game rising in \$30,000 increments from \$30,000 to \$150,000.[6]

Additional winnings consisted of $2,000 per ace (a serve that shuts out the other player) and a penalty of the same amount for a double fault serve that the loser pays to the winner. $200 is won every time the ball crosses the net and twice that amount in the finals. Roulette anyone?

While the sports metaphor has long been an important feature in British education and politics, an awareness of its penetration of American culture has only surfaced in recent years. As two astute sociologists and sports commentators write:

Americans want winners, whether it be in school, or business, or politics, or sports. In sports we *demand* winners. Coaches are fired if they are not successful. Teams are booed if they play for ties . . . Coaches do all they can to socialize their athletes with the value of winning. They reinforce winners with praise, honour, and status . . .

To focus on one institution – sport – is, we believe . . . a technique for understanding the complexities of the larger society . . . The games people play, the degree of competitiveness, the types of rules, the constraints of the participants, which groups benefit and which do not under the existing arrangements, the rate and type of change, and the reward system in sport provide us with a microcosm of the society in which it is embedded.[7]

These statements mirror a minority view. But they also indicate an awareness among a growing number of people that sports today are symbolic of an increasingly competitive attitude throughout the world, not just in America. Nor is this a particularly new phenomenon. Who wins and who loses and how victories are achieved within the sports arena have been symbolic of what occurs outside it for a very long time. These symptoms – and they are symptoms and not causes, which makes matters worse – wax and wane in direct proportion to the lessening or intensification in competitiveness in the larger society. The main difference between the US and the rest of the world seems to be that there the symptoms are more exaggerated and lie closer to the surface than elsewhere, and are therefore more easily identified.

In *The Winning Edge*, the Proceedings of the 1973 First National Sports Psychology Conference, Eugene Gaier of the State University of New York expressed the conventional assessment of the winning syndrome in a paper called 'The Self Concept of the Winner: What if the Dream Comes True?'

The oft-repeated cry, 'It's not the winning, but the taking part, not the conquering, but the playing fair,' is enough to bring tears to the eyes of the most naïve coach. While this may be mouthed for the press and boy-scout pow-wows, athletes are trained to win . . . Romantics may tell us that the ancients were content merely to participate in the game. Not so . . . In sports, success in one area often becomes the stepping stone to success elsewhere (that is, there is a transfer of learning or of success) . . . Winning and/or success can be viewed as a favourable termination of a venture or contest.

But even winning has its toll . . . In his essay, 'Those wrecked by success', Freud observed that . . . it is forces of conscience which forbid the person to gain the long-hoped-for enjoyment from the fortunate change in reality . . .[8]

Freud, like Gaier, never understood what winning and losing imply. According to Korzybski, founder of the School of General Semantics, who did understand, enjoyment of success depends on how it is achieved: 'God may forgive your sins. Your nervous system won't.'[9]

Players, coaches, club owners and politicians are usually less subtle than psychologists – in the US as elsewhere – and often say exactly what they mean without realizing what they are saying about themselves. It is a common failing among real life's would-be winner game players. They are so thoroughly conditioned that they do not stop to think before they speak. Their statements are often sub- or unconscious. The following is a sampling of sports quotes gathered by Don Atyeo and Jonathon Green, two authors who have made penetrating studies of this subject.[10]

No one ever learns anything by losing. (Don Shula, US football coach)

. . . I said, Sonny, how's it feel to see a man lying on the canvas with his eyes rolling in his head, his body twitching and his tongue hanging out. He just looked at me matter-of-factly and said: 'Makes me feel good.' (Sonny Liston, US boxer, interviewed by Pete Hamill, a reporter)

The more brutal it is the better I like it. (Lillian Carter, mother of the former US President and a born-again Christian, speaking of wrestling matches)

It is the work of the Lord. (Vince Foster, British boxer, after winning a fight)

A Christian is always keyed up before a game, because he knows he is playing for his *real* coach. (Paul Newman, US Sports Ambassador)

We Americans are a competitive race. We bet on anything, we love to win. In this next fight, you are entering the greatest sporting competition of all times. (US General George Patton, addressing his troops prior to the invasion of Sicily during the Second World War)

It's a good thing there's a law or else I'd get myself a tank or a howitzer and I'd kill deer by the bus loads. (Herb Miller, deer hunter)

[football is] . . . the law of the jungle. You know it's exactly like nature, the survival of the fittest. (George Atkinson, professional football player)

Other voices are none the less heard even above the din made by competitive winners:

Our mass spectator sports are geared to disguise, while affording expression to, the acting out in elaborate pageantry of the myth of the fittest in the process of surviving. (Eldridge Cleaver, US black activist)

Serious sport has nothing to do with fair play. It is bound up with hatred, jealousy, boastfulness, disregard for all rules and sadistic pleasure in witnessing violence: in other words it is war minus the shooting. (George Orwell, *The Sporting Myth*)

There is big money in sports; relatively modest amounts are paid to the players, no matter how much they earn, compared to the damage many are expected to do to themselves and one another, and what is raked in by promoters, advertisers and TV networks. The amount of money paid by US TV networks for broadcasting rights to collegiate and professional football rose from nearly $14 million in 1963 to more than $201 million by 1975. In 1981 NBC, a major US network, paid $6 million to the National Football League for the privilege of broadcasting a single game during which it cost advertisers $12 million – more than $500,000 per minute – to promote their products on the air. Nearly all US basketball teams earned close to $1 million per year each from national and local TV contracts. ABC, another TV network, paid $225 million for the broadcasting rights to the 1984 Olympics.

305 million spectators were paying customers at various US sports events during 1979. 730,000 paid to attend football games

every Sunday afternoon and another 22 million watched any one of these on TV. Proportionately equally large numbers hold true for sports events in other so-called developed nations of the world and in most Third World countries as well.[11]

Britain has become infected with the same values. By 1988, with the advent of satellite TV, the BBC and commercial networks were competing to obtain exclusive rights to major sports events, thus commercializing them beyond previous levels with foreseeable consequences.

Meanwhile NBC, one of the three major US TV networks, sold $550 million worth of air time to sponsors for 5,000 commercials shown during the broadcasts of the two-week 1988 Olympics held in Seoul. Despite record-breaking performances by drug-stimulated athletes, the network, advertising agencies and their clients were disappointed by the relatively small US audiences viewing these events. US viewers are evidently bored by competitive events that do not draw blood and that are far less dramatic than the mayhem seen regularly on TV.

Competitiveness in American college and professional football, soccer, rugby, hockey on and off the ice, and basketball has become increasingly violent and physical damage in the form of broken limbs, kneecaps, heads, backs, concussions and crippling neural, brain and internal injuries done by players to one another is in direct proportion to the commercialization of these games and the amount of money involved. Injuries have increased year by year according to medical authorities – just like the payments to the players, advertisers and everyone else connected with sports.

Spectators attending games, athletics and racing events or watching them on TV, sponsors and 'successful' (i.e. winning) players, want victory for their side at any cost for commercial and psychological reasons. For example, and according to Eitzen and Sage,[7] Mark Spitz, who claimed amateur status during his Olympic performances, turned pro like many other athletes once he had won some medals, earning $5 million from endorsements and personal appearances in following years.

There is, of course, every reason why a top performer in any field should be handsomely rewarded. But it often seems as if the initial claim to amateur status (from the Latin 'amare' – to love for its own sake) is a pretence maintained only until a player has won enough acclaim or medals to turn professional and cash in on his success. The endorsement of products by athletes, sports figures – or stage, film or TV stars – is usually a farce because they are not competent to evaluate most of them. This is, of course, part of the whole competitive media and advertising hype of capitalist societies.

However, the same situation prevails in communist countries where so-called amateur sports figures and athletes are subsidized by the State once they show any promise, and are exploited for national and international propaganda purposes as soon as they can be put on show. They, like most Western champions are in training to be professionals from the start, and it is back to the tractor factory if they are not made of the stuff that produces winners.

The legitimate aims of sports and play – doing a thing for the sake of the thing itself, for fun and exercise, or to improve one's own performance – are corrupted once the game is played for cash. When winning by default, by disconcerting behaviours, steroid consumption and 'stomping the opposition' are acclaimed and rewarded on a par with superior performance, the whole concept of achievement is debased. The only measure of success then becomes money in the bank.

In line with this is the manner in which today's sports and athletics are conducted, which leads to injury and mayhem on the playing fields – deliberate and inadvertent. But media commentators and the authorities often pretend or honestly believe that sports injuries are 'accidental' and regrettable exceptions. Spectators have come to expect and enjoy them, and players tolerate them as occupational hazards. Thus the whole society becomes increasingly immune to hostility and violence. Both become acceptable attitudes on and off the playing field.

Violence is an essential ingredient of games in which the sole object is to win by competing against others. Amateurs must also win, be willing to be injured and cause injury in order to qualify as pros and make money. That is why fees for professional players are high and why amateurs turn professional at the earliest opportunity. For many it is the only way of securing an income for themselves and their families during what are for other people the most productive years of their careers, because they can be crippled for life after a few seasons of 'play'.

In athletics the effect of perpetually escalating competitiveness has a similar effect. There violence done to others is rare except in events like boxing, but athletes often damage themselves. Drug-taking for muscle building or in order to heighten aggressive performance is common. Drugs are also used by athletes to kill physical pain due to excessive training or to anaesthetize themselves when they try to exceed the limits of endurance. Training is often begun at too young an age and is too intensive, without concern for the long-term effects on the athletes themselves. Everything is carried to extremes and many successful performers suffer burn-out at relatively early ages. One football player did a survey among his teammates in the 1970s and discovered that 48 per cent used amphetamines, a drug accurately known as 'speed'.

These practices are endemic. They can hype up the performance of racehorses as much as of team players, athletes, ballet dancers, stockbrokers, business and government executives, college students and all who try too hard to win. Alcoholism is also a problem connected with the cult of ruthless competition. It dulls the psychological pain suffered by those who try to win by making others lose and who discover that they themselves must become eventual losers. It is known that stress resulting from competition against others for the sake of winning is the main cause of ulcers and heart attacks, as it is of mental disturbance. Contributing factors may exist, but they are relatively minor. What is not admitted, or in many cases not known, is that there is a healthier and more profitable way to compete . . . playing for a draw. It is the cure for many of the social, psychological and physical ills of today's excessively competitive societies.

The Olympics have never lived up to their avowed ideals since those held in pre-Second-World-War Nazi Germany. The original Olympics may have served as a more or less lethal method for selecting an annual king or chieftain, as we saw earlier. In ancient Greece these games were legitimate if the selection was based on qualitatively superior performance. But more recent Olympics have been nationalistic and political propaganda vehicles or commercial ventures. There's not much difference between them. All are competitive in the extreme.

A correctly motivated athlete co-operates with his physical and mental capabilities, his trainer, team, fellow performers and environmental conditions. He (or she) will define his goal and do his very best to reach it, but he must also refuse to allow himself to be pushed beyond reasonable limits. He will reject the idea of winning at any cost. An athlete may wish to test and expand his limits with gradual practice, but must recognize that beyond them lie psychological disorientation, injury and possibly death. Any of these can be caused by the dirty tricks, outright cheating, physical and psychological warfare and drug-taking to which many athletes resort, with the tacit encouragement of their managers, in their drive for success. But success won by these methods is not worth the cost, as many people inside and outside the sports world keep discovering – some too late to do them much good, and others never.

The psychological orientation of a genuinely successful athlete determines whether he or she will excel by approaching natural limits as a result of interest and dedicated exercise for the sake of the thing itself or whether he pushes himself or allows himself to be pushed beyond reasonable limits merely to win medals and glory that can be converted later into cash.

The limits of athletic performance depend to a large extent on health, build and environment. Equally important are concentration, will and dedicated practice. The mile race is one example of where reasonable limits lie. Roger Bannister's four-minute-mile is being bettered micro-second by micro-second each year. Certainly no one will ever run the no-minute mile. The ultimate limit lies somewhere in between, relative to human size, age, conditioning and the conditions of the moment. Anyone sharing the same characteristics and interests who reaches that limit at that same time and place is the equal of everyone else who may be similarly endowed. Here as everywhere else the draw played out to the last turn (would-be winners call this a stalemate) defines the absolute limit shared by equals. That is one definition of a survival oriented, co-operative outcome. No one can do better than that and it is foolish to try.

The Oxford and Cambridge boat race of 1978 was a typical example·of how a team lost by trying too hard to win. The Thames was more choppy than usual on the day of the race and the Cambridge crew, favoured to win, rowed as hard as it could, paying no attention to the condition of the river. They rowed so hard that

choppy water, spilling over the bows, capsized them near the
starting line. They had literally sunk their chances of success by
rowing themselves under water. Oxford won by taking it easy and
staying afloat – an example comparable to the race between the
tortoise and the hare.

Snyder and Spreitzer,[12] citing another author, compare the
American culture of sports to the society as a whole. Again what is
true for the US is true for most other parts of the world:

State activity is increasingly being cloaked in the rhetoric of the sports
world; at times it even appears as if the language of politics is being
completely absorbed by the language of sports. Thus the President becomes
the 'quarterback' who, along with his Cabinet and White House staff
'team', pursues 'game plan' policies designed to reach the 'goal line' and to
'win' the political 'ball game'. This corruption of the discourse of politics
by the discourse of sports alerts us to a possibly profound transformation in
the way in which governmental activity in America is defined and understood: to envelop politics with the symbolism of sports is to translate the
meanings which we attribute to the latter to the former. Thus the political
ascendancy of the sports metaphor may well signal the increasing importance of sports as a legitimating mechanism of the American state . . .

The authors continue: 'The underlying value theme of . . .
[sports] slogans is that certain behaviour patterns must be adopted
in order to excel, succeed, and win . . .' The authors then cite seven
themes that reflect the dominant US value system in which those
values that apply to sports are adopted within the American society
in general. Needless to say '. . . preparation for life in the sense of
facilitating subsequent success [i.e. winning] for the individual . . .',
the relationship of sports to 'traditional American Christianity . . .
patriotism and love of country . . . red-bloodedness' loom large in
this sports-derived and sports-related value system.

Thus we suggest that sport provides a means of expressing some of the
dominant values of society. Indeed, a common justification for sport in
schools is that participation in sport serves to transmit the values of the
larger society. In other words, the youngster is ostensibly learning not only
to play a specific sport but to 'play the game of life'.

This 'game of life' can take many different forms. It does not need
to involve ruthless competition, as demonstrated by how the

Gahuku-Gama play football, described in Chapter 5. This is a co-operative method of play that reflects their value system in other aspects of daily existence. Playing games co-operatively conditions their children to that way of life. We, on the other hand, condition our children to subscribe to competitive and purely materialistic values, which are reinforced by what is praised and rewarded inside and outside the home.[13]

Children at earliest ages often cry when they lose games. They know there is something wrong with the idea of winning and losing. Parents, teachers and older children who are already conditioned by our culture then tell them one of three things:

It doesn't matter. It's only a game.

As a result children may not learn to concentrate, pay attention, or expend effort.

Learn to be a good loser.

Children who heed that advice may become willing victims.

Learn to be a winner.

The children who learn this lesson can turn into devious and unpleasant adolescents and adults.

It never occurs to anyone in our culture to show children how to achieve a draw, even in simple games like noughts and crosses. That is why they cry. They know that winning and losing are unfair. That knowledge is programmed into their very genes. Any young child who is not yet conditioned to believe in our false value system as an article of faith, and to whom you demonstrate the draw principle in simple games, will be your friend for life. He or she will also learn better, faster and more quickly, be more attentive and generally more co-operative, friendly and trustworthy than others who become conditioned to the prevailing standards. Equally he will not be any winner's willing victim, but will defend himself aggressively whenever that is required.

Educational and employment opportunities beyond school years reinforce earlier conditioning. Young people, irrespective of social or economic class, who prepare for the shrinking world of employment in an increasingly automated and roboticized world, turn into winners who are rewarded in the conventional sense. They become academic and commercial Yuppies; in it for short-term profit and early retirement – just like most sports figures and athletes. The values to which they subscribe were formerly found only among the worst kind of bureaucrats and those 'on the make'. But now the whole world has adopted the most unpleasant criteria of success and laid aside satisfying, public-spirited and craftsman-like ones. The 'cowboy' trader ethos is near-universal. Competent craftsmanship and service in trades and professions (including public service) are rarities today.

The whole of society pays a price for this increasing incompetence which goes hand-in-hand with competitiveness. Nothing works as it might and should, if those who do the work assumed responsibility for their performance.

Young people who cannot be absorbed by our society are unemployable or restricted to occupations in which it is cheaper to use menial labour instead of machines. The more energetic ones trade in whatever comes to hand, often joining a growing black economy, or go in for petty crime. The rest become apathetic. The numbers of unemployed, under-employed or anti-socially employed young people keep growing despite the manipulation of statistics by governments that would have us believe otherwise. This population knows that they are life's losers today, tomorrow and for a long time to come. They see no future for themselves or for their children.

They also see football players paid what to them are huge sums to do as much damage as possible to the opposing team. That is what they understand to be the winning strategy in football and everything else. Cheering 'their' team and disparaging the 'others', they feel cheated because they are not in any position to participate in any of the games they see played within and outside the football grounds. Ganging up on others is their only way of feeling at one with 'their' team and to be successful fellow-competitors.

Trained in the winning ethic and knowing no other, they also want to win by making others lose. There is only one significant difference between football hooligans and their peers with a future: the former are not hypocrites. Football hooligans know that winning means total war. Without having read Hobbes's *Leviathan*, they have been conditioned at home, in school and via the media to believe that life is a contest of 'all against all'. Excited by what they anticipate or see on the football field and lacking any opportunity to compete, they try to break heads and legs to defeat 'the other side' in pitched battles on terraces and in the streets. Like McEnroe, they also hope to disconcert the opposition and somehow help their team win in this way. There is really no difference in fundamental motivation between excessively dedicated football 'fans' and right-and left-wing brawlers. They often join forces at these games and it is the 'winning' spirit found among all of them that is the cause of football hooliganism. So much for the 'cathartic effect' of football games favoured by Konrad Lorenz and Anthony Storr, or the 'rage for perfection' postulated by others on behalf of John McEnroe. However, these are not new phenomena:

In 70 A.D. an audience at the Pompeiian Games rioted and hacked to death victims who were being held back for performing on another occasion. Rival chariot team backers caused a near civil war in Constantinople in 532 A.D., killing tens of thousands of bystanders and nearly causing the downfall of the Emperor Justinian. Hence football riots and football hooliganism, whether it occurs in Glasgow, Brussels or Washington, DC, deplorable though they are, are nothing new. Equally old is the refusal on the part of sports promoters, the keepers of the peace, psychologists and governments to face up to the real cause of these often murderous outbreaks of collective violence.[14]

None of this is very different from today:

. . . Each Saturday from August through April, crowds of up to 60,000 assemble to watch each match and over one million watch football [on TV] every weekend. Practically every Saturday throughout the season, the media features another grim episode of what has become a national problem – soccer hooliganism . . . [it] is seen as aggressive and antisocial, perpetrated by adolescents who are not really interested in the game and concentrated in a small core of troublemakers in the crowd – the potentially criminal elements. It is argued [by magistrates, judges, psychologists, politicians, football club owners and the police] that if these renegade individuals could be excluded from the ground and perhaps reformed in some penal way, then the football terraces would be safe for the vast majority of the spectators who come only to watch and enjoy the game. As to the origin of this behaviour, many blame the lack of discipline in the family and in schools, or the permissive society generally . . .

Some sociologists believe that hooliganism is part of the more general delinquent and vandalistic tendencies of youth [reared in a permissive society] and thus no more than a currently fashionable example of the general social malaise. The current concern arises from the belief that sports should be free from such negative aspects. It is for this reason that sports administrators have been reluctant to acknowledge that hooliganism may now be an integral part of the sport, and to sponsor relevant research . . .[15]

In one sense the authors are correct. Hooliganism is an integral part of sport and always has existed in Western cultures, although it waxes and wanes depending on the emphasis on competition in the society at large. It is not necessarily due to any criminal element among the football fans, unless we are prepared to characterize most of our society as criminally inclined. It stems from the existence of a sizeable segment of economic losers in our societies who have been conditioned, like most other people, to consider winning the prize of manhood and success. Football hooligans generally come from poor and often authoritarian homes (contrary to the popular belief that they are products of a 'permissive' upbringing) and have little to look forward to, their frustration heightened by unrealistic expectations raised by TV and the consumer society.

Social scientists, whenever they see any problem, demand government and foundation research grants to enable them to 'study' the problem scientifically. Typical are innumerable studies conducted periodically in Britain and the US, asking whether media violence affects children and young people deleteriously. I investigated many of these studies in great detail some years ago and found that all, except the most penetrating and earliest one – the Payne Fund Studies conducted in the US between 1929 and 1932 – came to the wrong or muddled conclusions. The Payne Fund Studies have been totally ignored ever since and are seldom or never referred to in more recent reports. They were conducted at a time when large segments of the US child population had as yet never seen a film and provided interesting and 'clean' control groups. These, like most of the 'primitive' co-operative cultures studied by the anthropologists discussed in Chapter 5, no longer exist and, as a result, more recent surveys are purely speculative and useless.[16]

Current football hooliganism and media violence studies consist of assembling meaningless statistics through interviews and by means of 'laboratory' research that is far removed from reality. The researchers and their sponsors are themselves infected with the 'winning spirit' and see nothing wrong with it (that was even true to some extent for those involved in the Payne Fund Studies). Testing that hypothesis does not seem to occur to them or, if it does, they are careful to avoid it. Psychologists and politicians debate these problems 'in committee' over and over again without ever coming to grips with them. Politicians get elected by not dealing with sensitive issues. Psychologists make their money by researching without coming to any conclusions. That is also how and why practical solutions to soccer hooliganism and other social ills are evaded.

Governments of the right or left usually recommend the suppression of football hooliganism by increased police presence at games, but also like to sponsor psychological research and social studies. The forces of law and order make a show of having won, some heads are bloodied and a few offenders made examples of and gaoled. Others are studied. The problem is sufficiently contained to escape public notice for a while until a major riot and bloodshed bring it back into the headlines and the cycle is repeated. Both sides enjoy the escalation for it challenges their will to win. The hooligans turn to more vicious and devious forms of antisocial behaviour (e.g. muggings or vandalism away from sports grounds). Competition – and the spurious excitement and pretended individualism it generates – is the object of the exercise. In effect the police, the courts, social scientists and the hooligans unwittingly co-operate. The society as a whole is the loser.

The ways in which politicians campaign to be elected or behave in opposition are other expressions of the same competitive spirit that motivates the players of team sports, athletes and football hooligans. Conditioned for existence in highly competitive societies, they act out variations on the same theme, while blaming each other for not singing a different tune (the SDP/Liberal Alliance feuds in Britain were typical examples). It is axiomatic that only a few can win at the expense of the many. Yet our competitive cultures insist that everyone can be a winner by competing with everyone else. The contradiction in this pretence is only understood by unwilling victims. Both winners and willing victims insist that only winning and losing count. Unfortunately winners, willing victims and many unwilling ones jointly believe as an article of faith that draws do not count. That is why we are engaged in perpetual warfare of one kind or another, even in sports and athletics.

One reason why football hooliganism is less of a problem in the US than in Britain is that the American employed, unemployed and under-employed share the mythology that everyone who is sufficiently competitive can be a winner. In France it was once held that every *poilu* (conscript) had a field marshal's baton in his haversack. In the US it is widely believed that anyone can get to be President – of the US or of General Motors. All except the criminal fraternity – and even some of those – are convinced that the route to success is through individual enterprise and hard work. That should be the winning formula in every case, but it usually is anything but that. Most people never discover this discouraging truth – or only discover it when it is too late to do them much good. They believe that in football, as in everything else, 'winning' in play between equal teams is brought about by strategic superiority rather than through leg-breaking. US sports fans therefore look up to collegiate and professional football players as heroes and superior beings with superior skills.

In Britain, especially since the breaking down of superficial class barriers, the fans know that football players are no different from themselves. The unemployed or under-employed, more than the middle-class, are fully aware of what is involved in 'winning' in the conventional sense, and pattern their own behaviours after that of the players on the field. As these examples illustrate, the different behaviours of people in the same circumstances depend largely on their beliefs.

It is also thought by those who subscribe to the conspiracy theory of history that circuses, sports and athletic events of yesterday and today are deliberate attempts by governments to divert the attention of the populace from the real issues of the day. That may occasionally be true. Most of the time governments encourage quantitative competition in school and in daily life, as well as in violent competitive spectacles to foster the virtues to which they themselves subscribe. They never suspect that this can be suicidal. The hooliganism that followed Roman spectacles sometimes turned into political riots, as we saw. The same could happen again, because related motives are involved.

It does not seem to occur to economists or politicians that, given a sufficiently long time without reinforcement, today's unemployed may someday rebel, once they are roused from their lethargy. Societies, unlike the gambling casinos that they resemble, do not allow the suckers to win once in a while. Hence past revolutions. Every competitive society nurtures the seeds of its own destruction. It is only a matter of time. Rebellions could be averted by an evolutionary change towards re-education for a more fair, just and co-operative society that encourages and rewards qualitative competition and success.

Revolutions do not change things in substance because they are carbon copies of the societies they replace, just as football hooliganism mirrors what takes place on the football field. As in Soviet Russia, one tyranny tends to replace another – Stalin became in effect an arbitrary tsar by another name. Therefore the criteria by which we live will beggar most of us sooner or later unless things change in an evolutionary, rather than in a revolutionary, manner.

There are, of course, many contributing factors in the escalation of paranoia and hostility generated by today's sports and athletic contests. They are only one expression of the 'winning spirit' that has poisoned generations and whole cultures. Typical of this closed feedback loop are the many extraneous practices that have become part of modern sports. They tend to escalate the symptoms and consequences that the organizers, players and spectators themselves first create and then deplore. Players and coaches bait referees. Deliberate fouls and brawls on the field rouse partisan spirits. Spectators demand action and they usually get what they pay for. At football matches it is possible to feel the disappointment when the crowd considers itself let down by a goalkeeper's brilliant defence. The fans do not like that and want a maximum imbalance between opposing teams. A score is better than none and the worst fear – worse than losing – is a draw or a tie which is believed to be worthless (except on football pool coupons).

The massed bands, flag waving, drum majorettes (in the US) wearing the teams' colours, the cheering and jeering are intended to heighten the blood lust of spectators far more than that of the players. These are the rituals of warfare, which at other times and on different occasions arouse patriotism and hatred of the enemy. The difference between genuine warfare and combat in the sports arena is that when attending the latter the spectators can be in on the kill from their 'safe' seats in the stands. That safety is threatened by football hooliganism, and 'respectable' spectators become inordinately outraged by the violence on the terraces which they condone and encourage on the football field itself.

At car rallies, the fans, stimulated by the angry buzzing of hornet-like motors, are openly out for blood. Stirling Moss, the British racing-car champion, knew what he was talking about when he replied, on being asked whether people attend Grand Prix races to see crashes rather than the races: 'I don't think we'll see that question answered definitely until someone works out a way to fit 50,000 lie detectors to 50,000 people watching the Grand Prix race.'[17]

Things are only slightly different at horse and dog races where spectators want their favourites to come in first and any injury means a loss of money. There are probably bettors who feel the same way at car-racing meets. But in any of these sports it is a question of gambling on actual or symbolic death. The imponderables at the racetrack of dogs chasing a mechanical hare that they can never catch – all for money – determine who wins and who loses. The losers in the race, as much as those who lose money, are symbolically 'dead', for the time being at least, just as captured chess pieces are 'dead' for all practical purposes. The same is true of the America's Cup sailing races.

It is often maintained that racing-car contests, sailing competitions and horse-races serve to 'improve the breed'. Occasionally a navigational advance surfaces as a result of disproportionately huge investments, as for example in the design of Australia's America's Cup winning boat keel. But that does not really make much difference as to who wins and who loses. Winning is mostly achieved by adroit manoeuvres at sea to steal the wind and get in the competitor's way so that his boat loses the precious few seconds that make the difference between winning and losing.

In urging industry to become more competitive (i.e. to defeat the 'opposition', rather than produce products and services of greater and more lasting value) governments stimulate the very conditions that lead to football hooliganism, violence on the streets and labour disputes. Labour and management are guilty of the same attitudes reflected in their perpetual disagreements and 'in-fighting' rather than negotiating, settling their differences and coming to lasting agreements (a draw). Racial equality, peace, women's, gay liberation and other dissident movements, while demanding co-operation from everyone else, are equally dedicated to internal competition and conflict. Everyone wants to win something at someone else's expense. In the US this principle has been elevated to a religion.

Religion, in fact, is invoked everywhere in the name of winning. Eitzen and Sage quote a prayer delivered at a dinner given before the 1976 World [Ice] Hockey Association All-Star Game, one of the more vicious and lethal sports spectacles:

Heavenly Father, Divine Goalie, we come before You this evening to seek Your blessing . . . grant us the courage to skate without tripping, to run without icing, and to score the goal that really counts – the one that makes each of us a winner, a champion, and All-Star in the hectic Hockey Game of Life. Amen.[18]

Fifty-five per cent of US coaches and players insist that they pray to God before matches to allow them to win, reminding one of the claim that there are few atheists in foxholes. In our own as much as in primitive societies magic is invoked to assure success in various contests. Modern athletes commonly believe that 'lucky numbers', charms, and other superstitious practices help them achieve 'victory'.

This leaves only blood sports like cock-fights, dog-fights and bear-baiting, once popular and now mostly outlawed, yet still practised in some parts of the world. Others like fox-hunting and bullfighting fall within the law, but meet with opposition from animal lovers, who have an excellent case. But it is astounding that they limit their concerns to the animal world. They often turn what should be a legitimate protest against competitive winning and losing into a sectarian 'us against them' war fought on behalf of animals that mirrors again all the worst features of the evils they profess to abhor.

The same is true for hunting and fishing for sport, a subject to which Don Atyeo pays special attention. There is nothing wrong with hunting or fishing for the pot in a genuine survival situation, on a camping trip or safari. But to hunt in order to mount trophies on a living-room wall is psychologically damaging to the hunter even where game is plentiful. The hunter can be carried away by a feeling of participating in something bigger than himself, not dissimilar to that experienced by anyone caught up in a military parade. That is a deceptive and dangerous disorientation that some people find difficult to resist. They confuse it with 'co-operation', animal 'blood lust' and 'masculinity'.

The macho image of this kind of sport has been made respectable by people like Ernest Hemingway, Thomas Edison and Teddy Roosevelt – all of whom were dedicated winners – and by Hermann Göring, second in command to Hitler, who was a great hunter and collector of trophies. In valuative terms there is little difference between this kind of collecting and the trophies treasured by Ilse Koch, the female guard at one of Nazi Germany's concentration camps who specialized in collecting lampshades made of the skin of tattooed gas chamber victims.

Modern hunting on game preserves and farms, therefore, has nothing in common with the 'hunting for survival' it pretends to imitate. Tame game is driven in the path of the hunter sitting comfortably inside a blind or Land Rover, from which he blasts away, more or less at random, with a high-powered rifle, while refreshing himself with food and drink furnished by the management (and not by hunting and trekking to find a spring). The same is true for fishing for sport – deep-sea fishing especially. The 'amateur' fisherman is harnessed to a chair bolted to the boat's deck, armed with pre-baited tackle against which the hapless fish do not stand a chance. He is aided by strong-arm professionals who do the real work before and after the fish is hooked. A catch is virtually guaranteed and often mounted as a trophy. These sports are pathetic parodies of all they pretend to be.

Finally I turn to the biggest game of all – humans hunting other humans for sport. There is nothing new about this, except the 'harmless' and special form it now takes – the modern versions of medieval tournaments – and that there are usually no trophies except perhaps a certificate of merit and a bill.[19] Having played real killing games for profit all week at the office, on the stock-exchange or in government, many of today's executives 'relax' by doing the same on 'survival' weekends for 'fun'. A new kind of game farm has sprung up in the US and all over Europe where people may enjoy pretending to murder one another under conditions of maximum discomfort and for a stiff fee. You can do this and be paid for it by joining any army on a full- or part-time basis. The trouble with joining the army is that you cannot go home, take time out whenever you feel like it or argue with superior officers. The pay is far less than you could earn in the City, unless you become a mercenary, and you can get painfully wounded or killed when war is declared.

The regalia is real on these man-hunting expeditions – camouflage uniform, web belt, combat knife, helmet and boots, minimal rations, living rough, and identical weapons to those used by regular soldiers, terrorists and gangsters. Even the ammo is the same, except that the bullets are made of soft, red paint-filled plastic that burst on impact – all perfectly 'harmless'. Line up your victim in your sights, squeeze the trigger gently. Bang! Splat! You have made a hit. Your human game is covered with 'blood' and is dead for all practical purposes – a loser like all the others, killed off realistically or symbolically in all the competitive games we play. Your next quarry, by now alert, is already in your sights. You are a winner if you get him before he gets you. It is a kill or be killed game and a gamble, exactly like what you do all week long. But think of the satisfaction and sense of achievement if you succeed. Best of all, it does not matter if you make a mistake and become a loser. You can always become a better amateur expert killer next weekend – for an additional fee, of course.

11 Winning and Losing and The Dismal Science

> ... we wish to find out the mathematically complete principles which define 'rational behaviour' ... the discussion which follows will be dominated by illustrations from chess, matching pennies, poker, bridge, etc. ... [These studies] have their origin in the attempt to find an exact description of the endeavour of the individual to obtain a maximum of utility, or, in the case of the entrepreneur, a maximum of profit.
>
> von Neumann and Morgenstern[1]

This chapter follows the one on sports because business and sports pages are understandably adjacent in virtually all newspapers, and these subjects seem to have overlapping readerships. The wrong competitive and shady practices are often common to both, especially today.

I discussed the meaning of ideals and principles in the Introduction to this book and pointed out that everyone has ideals. However, the ideals held by would-be winners and losers differ radically from the ideals of those who opt for a drawn game between equals.

The principles of modern economics were formulated in the eighteenth and nineteenth centuries. Waves of industrialization, urbanization and the use of people as adjuncts to machines aroused concern among those who became aware of some of the difficulties that seemed to lie ahead. Writers of that time – Smith, Malthus, Babbage, Owen, Marx, Engels and others – attempted to distil economic principles out of the welter of possibilities. But none – not even Babbage, the inventor of the first modern computer who wrote extensively on economics – could foresee the twentieth century replacement of production line workers by computer-controlled robots. These eighteenth- and nineteenth-century thinkers, brilliant as they were, attempted to define economic principles for times to come, based on rationality. 'Rationality' was supposed to be derived from 'reasons' and 'beliefs' founded on facts, but the writers of that time did not consider the possibility that their reasons and beliefs might be the result of cultural conditioning, a concept that was not understood until the twentieth century.

A postulate frequently encountered in theoretical economics and elsewhere in social theory is that the behaviour of the individual or group can be described by saying that the individual or group is seeking to maximize some quantity. Thus, in the theory of the firm, the economist postulates that the individual seeks to choose that mode and scale of operation which will yield more profit than any other possible choice. In the theory of consumption, it is assumed that among all the combinations of commodities an individual can afford, he chooses that combination which maximizes his utility or satisfaction. Behaviour of this type is frequently referred to as rational.[2]

The emphasis on 'maximization of some quantity' is reflected in the work of von Neumann and Morgenstern who, as I have said, provided the mathematical and game theoretical foundations for twentieth-century economics,[3] although the mathematical modelling of economic behaviours had begun in the nineteenth century.[4]

The economic beliefs formulated 200 years ago did not alter to any appreciable degree in the twentieth century, although the nature of work underwent great changes. In the distant past when craft was the norm, the best, most durable and aesthetically pleasing product commanded the highest price. Those who possessed high skills were esteemed as 'artists' (as were, for example, eighteenth-century ship's carpenters and navigators) rather than as artisans. The producer/employee and the purchaser/employer stood to profit equally and proportionately. It was a relationship that defined a non-zero-sum, co-operative solution for the economic game, even when the reality did not always match the expressed ideals. It was far from a golden age of trade and economics. Piracy on the high seas and on land were still common, but they were called by their proper names and not gentrified as today.

All this changed with mechanization. The producer/purchaser relationship was transformed in principle if not always in practice from a co-operative exchange of valued goods and services into a

competitive one. Whereas in the past apprentice labour had been
traded for what was then considered a fair living until master
craftsman status was reached and the former apprentice set up in
business for himself, employer and employee were now in conflict.
The employer saw it as his function to keep wages as low as possible
and the worker to get as much for himself as the traffic would bear,
irrespective of the value of the work done. The employee also lacked
the promise of an eventual release from service to a master into
autonomous practice of his craft. Mass production, being purely
quantitative, was bound to lead to a zero-sum society and a
deskilling of labour. Capital, rather than making labour possible,
became its enemy. Each tried to 'maximize' something at the
expense of the other. 'More is better' became the norm.

The formation of defensive unions among workers was a perfectly
justified, and indeed essential, development in the face of vicious
exploitation by manufacturers and mine owners through the first
half of this century. But, not satisfied with an eventual if unconscion-
ably delayed living wage related to productivity and profitability,
the union leaderships saw it as their duty to do to industry what
industry had been doing to their members for as long as they could
get away with it. What should have been a co-operative enterprise
at least in principle if not always in practice, turned into a never-
ending economic war and zero-sum game. As in every war, only the
members of competing 'armies' co-operated with one another. As
Weintraub writes in *Conflict and Cooperation in Economics*:

Economics, to the extent that it deals with choices constrained by scarcity,
is a study in conflict ... The kinds of conflict situations of interest to
economists are almost never without some co-operative elements.[5]

Economists of our zero-sum societies support 'ideals' like 'free
enterprise' and the competitive principles of the 'free' marketplace.
They claim that supply and demand are self-regulating. It seems
incredible that anyone should believe them, living as we do in
economies dominated by mass production, planned obsolescence
and advertising, centralized bureaucratic managements of multi-
national corporations, conglomerates, cartels, monopolies and mon-
olithic states, all in conflict with one another, labour and the
consumer. Each is free to vie with the others for control and

domination of consumers (euphemistically called 'markets'). The consumer is far from free.

The ideal of competitive 'free' enterprise (the winning, 'us against them' principle) is the linchpin of capitalist economic belief. Another, equally absurd, is that a state-run communist economy, to which the individual's self-interest is subservient, supposedly serves the best interests of the people. Such an economy is devoid of incentives for qualitatively superior performance and delivers little to its citizens but conformity, scarcity, shoddy goods and bureaucratic domination. The capitalist, competitive 'us against everyone else' belief system is no better or worse than the myth that under an egalitarian regime everyone has equal rights, irrespective of the quality of the work that is done, service rendered, products produced, or position enjoyed in the hierarchy. Those who achieve least and perform worst (e.g. typical bureaucrats in government, industry and education) often reap the greatest benefit in both societies. This is not due, as is usually claimed, to imperfections in either system, but an inevitable product of the essentially competitive characteristics of both.

Not only have conditions changed since the formulation of modern economic theories of the left, right and centre, but the very words used to describe them have assumed entirely different meanings from what they meant when these principles were first articulated. In economics as much as in games, the meanings of words are generally interpreted without regard to causes, consequences or the operations that bring both about. Milton Friedman, the American champion of monetarist economics (the belief that manipulation of the money supply can control the rate of inflation while maintaining a 'right' level of unemployment, supply and demand), is fond of quoting Adam Smith without being aware that the words at the time the latter wrote them probably meant something quite different from what they mean today, even when used in the same context. Adam Smith wrote that: '. . . man must be [perfectly *free*] to pursue his own interest in his own way and [both his] industry and capital *in competition* with those of other men, or order of men.'[6] Friedman seems to have no idea as to what is meant by words like *freedom* or *competition*, nor does he suspect that his interpretation of their meanings and the context in which he uses them might differ from those that applied in Smith's day. According to Friedman, competition leads to co-operation, conditions that exist today mostly among allies and soldiers in war and in the temporary alliances common to anomalous co-operatively competitive economies. Freedom is always conditional and not, as Friedman implies, a licence to indulge in unlimited greed or power and a lack of concern for others. Friedman continues his garbled liturgy:

Scholars *co-operate* with one another because they find it mutually beneficial . . . *Co-operation* is world-wide, just as in the economic market . . . *Free trade* would not only promote our material welfare, but would also foster *peace and harmony* among nations and spur *domestic competition*.[7]

Friedman is either badly informed or wishes to fool his readers. Few scholars co-operate internationally today in subjects that matter (virtually all hard sciences and some of the 'soft' ones are enlisted in the service of the military), at the insistence of their various governments for reasons of 'national security'. By free trade, Friedman presumably means the lifting of all domestic regulation as well as trade barriers between nations. He believes that this somehow leads to international co-operation (i.e. peace and harmony), when it has only lead to escalating conflict, winning and losing, a race that is won by the few and lost by the many, except when binding agreements exist between exporting and importing governments. His statement that co-operation abroad would foster domestic competition is absurd, for the very opposite is true.

Domestic competitive free trading in a modern industrial state usually leads to monopolistic price fixing and other restrictive co-operative practices among a few centrally controlled competitors powerful enough to crush smaller rivals. They thrive on temporary alliances in order to compete more effectively with foreign companies in their markets, while conspiring against their domestic consumers by fixing prices at home in collusion with national governments. That is why British-made cars are far less expensive when purchased in Europe than in Britain, and Japanese-made telecommunications equipment sells for less in the US than in Japan.

All of this works in the short run, for some people at least. In the long run it leads to economic collapse. These collapses are repetitive, believed by economists to be indicative of 'business cycles'. But that, like most of economic theory, is nonsense. These so-called cycles do not follow a natural pattern like the weather. They are purely man-made and represent yet another instance of history repeating itself as it must, when competitive games of chance are played. It need never happen with strategic games intended to end in a draw; then only the best outcomes can be made to repeat themselves.

To summarize, periodic depressions and 'cycles' of unemployment are entirely unnecessary human inventions and not laws of nature. They are periods that are similar to the closure of gambling casinos during the off-season, when the managements leave for a long vacation to enjoy their profits. They know that while they are away the 'suckers' they have cleaned out will busily scramble to make more money so that they can take it away from them as soon as the sun shines again at home.

The Japanese, who believe fervently in domestic economic co-operation for the sake of more effective external competition, are past masters at the co-operatively competitive game. In the less disciplined West, where monopolies are theoretically frowned upon, combines designed for more efficient competition at home and abroad are usually arranged in secret, sometimes with governmental connivance.

Major industries in competitive economies demand that government exists only to co-operate with them at the expense of the rest of the society. When this occurs it enables them to compete more effectively against the consumer. Examples are legion. Privately operated aircraft transport is typical. Airline purchases of aircraft are government subsidized because transport planes are designed to be converted instantly for military use in the event of war. Subsidized in this manner by taxpayers' money and government contracts to carry the mails, they are monopolies that pay little attention to anything other than profits, even enlisting government help to guard the exclusivity of their routes against competition from foreign carriers.

Exactly the same conditions prevail in the shipping industry, in the privatization of defence industries and naval shipyards that depend entirely on government contracts, and in areas that affect the consumer directly – the subsidy of the automotive truck-building and highway transport industries at the expense of the taxpayer and public transport. It would take far too much space to detail the competitive practices that are currently bankrupting most nations, but they are common knowledge and can be discovered by reading any newspaper's business section, reliable books on economics, or any country's annual budget.

Meanwhile, the managements of these government-subsidized corporations campaign strenuously against government support of social and health services, aid to the poor, aged, ill or unemployed, or improvement of the infrastructure, through their trade associations and lobbyists. They consider such aid antithetical to the principles of free enterprise and competition, while their own government subsidies are claimed to encourage it. Large segments of US and European populations actually believe such nonsense.

Industry's conception of governmental co-operation (siding with it against everyone else) usually prevails because it can afford to support the electoral campaigns of candidates who promote its views. Unions (lacking the government subsidies that industry enjoys) have less cash to disburse and therefore suffer a severe handicap in influencing elections until things go sufficiently wrong to frighten voters. That is when a supposed (but not actual) 'anti-business' government is elected (the Democrats in the US and the Labour Party in Britain, for example) and former losers turn into winners. While there may be a changing of the guard, there can be no change in fundamental economic policy for as long as industry and labour are in competition. Politically this inevitably leads to perpetual confrontation or classical stalemates, but never to a co-operative draw (agreements-to-agree). Such clashes of interest – or lack of long-term self-interest on everyone's part (discussed below) – stand in the way of an evolution of rational, valuative judgements and a stable, peaceful, yet dynamic global economy.

In Adam Smith's time economic competition was far more qualitative than quantitative (i.e. representative of the draw, rather than winning in game terms). The craft ideal was still part of the production ethic. The object of industry was to produce durable goods that lay within the means of purchasers without going deeply into debt; to expand markets by filling needs rather than to create wants; to make the essentials of life available at a reasonable price; and to manufacture profitably so that innovative entrepreneurs accumulated sufficient capital to enable them to design new machines and build new plants. At the same time it was naïvely (or viciously) believed that wage rates (like products) were also governed by the laws of supply and demand, a credo that seemed to justify an inexcusable exploitation of a seemingly inexhaustible supply of adult and child labour. That belief was eventually laid to rest as a result of union organization.

Two other highly competitive ideas supported this last inhuman concept. First was the belief in the 'survival of the fittest' as a fundamental law of nature, the origins of which are discussed elsewhere. Social Darwinism was part of an even more pernicious myth – the belief in the innate inferiority of the poor, of races other than the Caucasian, of women in general, and the belief in the natural superiority of the top members of every establishment. As we saw, Darwin's cousin Galton, who also introduced statistics to the behavioural sciences, was the principal proponent of this theory. IQ tests, opinion polls and 'correlation' were his bequests to modern psychology and have these prejudicial beginnings in common.

Outdated and discredited nineteenth-century ideals are still deeply entrenched in our twentieth-century societies but are obscured by scientific jargon. The erroneous belief in the primacy of competition, to which co-operation is subservient, is still the central credo of today's social and biological sciences, justified by the curious belief that competition is the first and only law of behaviour, including economic survival.

What was not appreciated by Victorian manufacturers was that the lower and labouring classes constituted a mass of potential customers who only lacked money with which to buy their products. Workers remained at the periphery of consumption until Henry Ford realized, shortly after the First World War, that any substantial increase in demand could only come from them, provided their wages were sufficient for purchases beyond the needs of daily existence. Ford recognized (although he later forgot his own principles and fought unions tooth and nail) that workers represented a huge and as yet largely untapped consumer market.

Ford was a commonsense realist (at least in these respects and for a while) and certainly no altruist. He was viciously anti-union and a confirmed anti-Semite. But in the early days of his company he acted solely out of enlightened self-interest (the most sensible outlook in terms of long-range profitability) when he fixed his workers' earnings well above minimum wages after the First World War. Ford understood that in order to buy, those who constitute the largest market need surplus income. Such a surplus could be used for savings, investment or to consume. Advertising ensured that it was spent on consumption. Ford's wage policies became the US industry standard and contributed to economic expansion and growth of the Gross National Product (GNP) until the Great Depression of 1929.

After the Second World War, and with the huge increase in US production capacity it had brought about, new means were needed to generate a hoped-for annual increase in profits and GNP – both articles of faith in competitive economies. The answer to a decline in profits as a result of market saturation was a deliberately planned deterioration in the quality of goods and services and increased manipulation of consumer demand by means of massive advertising.

Planned obsolescence was introduced in post-Second World War years, and something new occurred in the history of manufacture in which competition played a leading role. Industry, instead of meeting the needs of consumers, figuratively declared war on them by creating wasteful expectations, wants and inferior products. It stimulated competition between consumers (e.g. keeping up with and exceeding the purchases of the Joneses) and then persuaded them that these artificially stimulated needs had to be satisfied by a constant increase in consumption of shoddy goods bought on credit.

The short-term profitability and long-term inflationary consequences of planned obsolescence are illustrated by the following example. A washing-machine can be designed so that it will be replaced long before the end of its useful life. That can be done in a variety of ways, even while an illusion of quality is maintained. For example, one or more essential parts can be designed to wear out sooner than the rest and made too expensive to repair or replace, so that it is cheaper for the consumer to buy a new machine long before the old one needs to be scrapped. Purely stylistic features can be introduced periodically and advertised as essential improvements; technological innovation can be held back and introduced piecemeal as inducements for consumers to get rid of their 'old' models well before they are worn out. These are the kind of dirty tricks that enable manufacturers to profit at the expense of consumers.

Such an economic approach inevitably stimulates levels of consumption that create ever-increasing personal, corporate and government debts. This leads to mounting pressure on everyone to increase earnings and profits in order to meet these debts and, at the same time, stimulates consumption further. Failure to meet such demands results in personal and economic depression. Every quantitatively competitive economy must eventually run out of steam. At that point all options for the punters lead to the same cul-de-sac, whereas a 'draw' solution provides new choices at every turn.

Playing to win in gambling casinos impoverishes most people while a very few lucky ones and the 'house' get rich. The same is true in today's societies, although with a difference: you can choose not to play games in gambling casinos. But you cannot opt out of society unless you are prepared to sleep on park benches. I should point out that I am all in favour of people getting rich as a result of qualitative competition – i.e. doing something better than anyone else. I am opposed only to greedy enrichment by default, by competing in the wrong way, cheating and winning in the conventional sense. Quite aside from all this, current practices tend to create levels of production and consumption that cannot be sustained indefinitely. As J. K. Galbraith wrote:

The individual serves the industrial system not by supplying it with savings and the resulting capital; he serves it by consuming its products. On no matter, religious, political or moral, is he so elaborately and skilfully and expensively instructed.[8]

Planned obsolescence brought about a systematic escalation of relatively objective, quantitative competition and qualitative decline. The craft principle of durability was relegated to toolmaking, but considered anachronistic in the production of consumer goods. Trade practices that were considered unethical in the past became the economic doctrines of the post-war era. These factors, coupled with union and management demands for ever-increasing wages, stock options, incentive bonuses and golden handshakes, entirely unrelated to value or performance, created an inflationary spiral, the end of which is not in sight.

Economists tend to blame mysterious forces of the marketplace or labour's greed for perpetual inflation. There are several core reasons for inflation and all have greed in common. Industry needed and encouraged the wage spiral. Escalating wages and planned obsolescence were the modern recipe for economic success. It also seemed as if costs could be reduced and profits increased further by introducing automation. But full employment, high wages, perpetual market expansion through massive advertising, wasteful packaging methods, decline in quality, increased profits and spreading automation are self-contradictory ideas.

They lead to unemployment, depressed wages, reduced consumption (because the unemployed consume less), and higher taxes for those who are employed (because the unemployed require at least minimal subsistence), and a general contraction of the economy, social services and repair and maintenance of the infra-structure. Whereas prices should fall due to reduced demand (if indeed the market were controlled by supply and demand) they rise because manufacturers, distributors and retailers insist on maintaining increases in their profits despite shrinking markets – a major cause of inflation. Other techniques of increasing profits and escalating inflation are to reduce the size, quantity or quality of the product while maintaining the same retail price, or to repackage the same product, selling it at a higher price because it is claimed to be 'improved' in some way and therefore 'new'.

Robotization – a final step in automation – complements obsolescence because it allows non-identical goods to be produced on a production-line basis. Whereas the old marketing technique encouraged conformity, the new stresses pseudo-individuality and a different kind of conformity to rapidly changing fashions. It escalates competition by constantly introducing an endless variety of superficially non-identical goods produced on an automated, computer-controlled production line. The 'individualized' Cabbage Patch Doll (no two are alike) was a typical example.

Such competitive production and marketing methods and the considerable amount of advertising needed to promote them further increase costs and profits (computed as a percentage of costs) and the rate of inflation. The additional profits enable manufacturers to manipulate consumer demands and to automate even further, thus increasing profits by reducing labour costs. These quantitatively competitive practices may seem like successful quick fixes for economic health and industrial expansion, but they are recipes for longer-term disaster. It is impossible to predict when such an economy will collapse. It may go up and down like a roller coaster, but all that can be predicted is that a gambling game played to be won will be lost sooner or later by most. Blaming our declining economies on contributing factors like the oil crisis explains nothing and only makes matters worse.

Robotization makes planned obsolescence possible on a scale that was unimagined by the most daring advertising executives of a few decades ago. But this will also stimulate further inflation which can no longer be blamed on wage costs because of the considerable reduction in the workforce it will create. Once fully roboticized, the only wages paid in automated industries will be to programmers, maintenance personnel and managements. Competitive industrial and government bureaucracies do not consider that inflation is boosted by the wages and inflation-proof pensions or stock options they dole out to themselves, or by prices that have no relation to costs or value, and which often rise in order to pay for these 'fringe benefits' in otherwise unprofitable or mismanaged enterprises.

Massive robotization may not be an immediate threat to most labour, but it will become one in time. It is already a factor to be reckoned with in Japan. Meanwhile Korea, Indonesia, the Philippines and China are beginning to furnish the 'cheap labour' that made Hong Kong, Taiwan and Japan attractive to US industry after the Second World War. The US toy industry was the first to discover that it could compete more effectively by manufacturing abroad. Not only was labour much less expensive, but entrepreneurial manufacturers in the Far East were willing to invest in moulds, dies and machinery, provided they got product ideas and blueprints free of charge plus large orders, reducing the capital investment required for production.

The greed of competitive US manufacturers, their exploitation of Japan's low-cost labour force in the 1950s and 1960s, and their investment in Japan's industry at the expense of US designers, manufacturing capacity and the workforce, were responsible for Japan's so-called post-war economic miracle. There was nothing miraculous about it. Goods as varied as toys, plywood, appliances, car parts and electronics were marketed as American products at a greater profit and at less cost when they were produced abroad rather than at home. All of this provided Japan's industry and labour with the skills, incentives and profits to build up its manufacturing base at the expense of US industrial development and employment.

The first few generations of electronic products made in Japan, based on Western discoveries and inventions, gave Japan an edge in the eventual manufacture of a wide range of goods and markets. The copying of US products was encouraged by unscrupulous American entrepreneurs. In the toy trade, for example, this was a widely accepted competitive practice in post-war years, known as 'knocking off' a competitor's designs. Company presidents and their representatives rushed to the Far East in the post-war era, bringing with them the products developed by their domestic American competitors to be copied without fear of litigation.

Patent and copyright laws are virtually non-existent in the Far East and impossible to enforce in the US unless the original designer has more money than the thief to defend his patents. Hence US-abetted Japanese piracy of American designs was safe from prosecution. Western industry financed and profited from Japan's cheap, docile labour and its co-operation in unethical trade practices – about which it now bitterly complains. The former US winners in the economic race are now losing. But they created their own difficulties, as is inevitable in every competitive economy.

Meanwhile, Japan has drawn on less industrialized nations round the rim of the Pacific basin for labour that costs even less than its own, creating precisely the same problems for itself as those from which the US suffers. Japan's current excess productivity and high rate of robotization help deepen the rest of the world's economic depression and, together with the inevitable increase in the value of the yen, will eventually cause the same problems in Japan as elsewhere and for the same reasons. Japan will join the world's losers, as is starting to happen now. Japan is beginning to experience the ogre of unemployment. What employees believed to be 'lifetime jobs' promised by paternalistic managements as cornerstones of their social and economic philosophy are no longer secure, sacrificed to the ideal of competitiveness. Britain, where the industrial revolution began and where it also deteriorated into a competitive 'game', was merely among the first to experience its consequences.

One other factor threatens Japan: it has the most success-driven, stress inducing, competitive educational and patriarchal system in the world, and operant conditioning methods are employed there perhaps more rigidly than in any other society. The authoritarian Bushido and Samurai concepts of competition in Japan provide a historic, cultural frame of reference and rationale for these attitudes and practices, although they conflict in significant respects with earlier Shinto and later Buddhist ideals. Japan has suffered from this internal philosophical contradiction for centuries. The co-operative Tao principles (inherited from China) that merged with a similarly oriented Buddhism (imported from India) were eventually absorbed and corrupted by Bushido, the cult of the Samurai and aggressive martial arts. These contradictions are embedded in Japanese culture as well as in its economy. Deconditioning may prove most disturbing for many Japanese and could be a major obstacle to the country's future social and economic evolution.

Ideas like planned obsolescence were foreign to Western engineering and quality-oriented entrepreneurs who founded major industries in the early days of industrialization. They were invented by second and third generation bureaucratic managements who were motivated by winning (i.e. by exploiting people, money and markets) rather than by dreams of qualitative achievement or even the accumulation of wealth as a result of qualitatively superior performance; by avoidance of responsibility rather than by its assumption; and rule by committee rather than by responsible individuals. Galbraith explains how this came about:

The real accomplishment of modern science and technology consists of taking ordinary men, informing them narrowly and deeply and then, through appropriate organization, arranging to have their knowledge combined with other specialized but equally ordinary men. This dispenses with the need for genius.[9]

Galbraith is wrong in one respect. The ordinary men of whom he speaks have the same potential as so-called men of genius. The difference between them is that the first allow themselves to be conditioned by the group, become competitive and thus never realize their potential. Men of genius are ordinary men who resist conditioning and play for a draw. Their independence enables them to step outside the system and see its problems and possible solutions clearly. The organization man (in government, industry and in the universities) creates the problems from which we suffer;

the independent thinker can solve them if given opportunities to do so. Anyone can be such a genius.

With the advent of conglomerates and multi-national corporations controlled by bureaucratic managements, the laws of supply and demand, made inoperative by Henry Ford as far as wages were concerned, were suspended without notice to consumers. Economists like Milton Friedman tried to keep these laws alive as articles of faith, attempting to delude themselves and their followers that we in the West live in free-market, free-enterprise and free-choice societies. Communist and socialist cultures suffer different but related and equally unfortunate delusions.

As Galbraith shows, the manipulation of consumer demand enabled large corporations to plan far ahead, grow and assure themselves of profits. The long lead time required for research and development of new products is given as one of the excuses for manipulating, rather than meeting, consumer demands. It also takes most of the gamble out of management decisions (exceptions like Ford's 'Edsel' disaster merely prove the rule). But there are two even safer and more certain ways of playing the game of ever-escalating profits and winning by making others (competitors and taxpayers) lose. One is by mergers and friendly or hostile takeovers engineered by managements greedy to enrich themselves quickly. The other is just as profitable if you have a few ex-admirals or ex-generals on your board of directors. The first method does away with risk-taking, research and development of any kind. The second limits them to what is underwritten by the military.

Corporations support the military and vice versa (as we saw in the air transport example), and provide the rationale for constantly increased defence budgets in a mutual back-scratching game. Industry's lobbyists and trade associations (aided by corrupt 'consultants' to and purchasing agents for the military) spend millions that come out of taxpayers' pockets to persuade legislators to increase spending on military hardware from year to year. Industry and its elected and bureaucratic spokesmen in government (you can always tell whose spokesmen they are, for they go to work for 'their' companies on 'retirement' from government), in collaboration with the military, provide statistics just before annual government budgets are allocated, purporting to show that the 'enemy' (whoever it happens to be at the moment) is far ahead in the production of offensive armaments. They try to influence public opinion and policies in this manner and they usually succeed.

Military spending in peacetime is independent of the laws of supply and demand as far as consumption is concerned, and is therefore far more profitable and dependable than catering to or even manipulating consumer demands. Old or new weapons that need 'combat testing' are given away (as foreign aid) or sold to support military adventures far from domestic shores or even to future 'enemies'. (It is quite amazing that certain manufacturers who boast of their patriotism happily sell lethal weapons abroad without compunction, and with the full approval of their governments. These very same weapons are often turned on their fellow citizens in a very short time as they were, for example, in Britain's Falklands war.) Other 'obsolescent' weapons are mothballed or periodically scrapped. *The Arms of Krupp*,[10] by William Manchester, details the history of this corrupt arms trade and economic game that has continued throughout the world for several centuries.

Recurring scandals and corruption are rife in the military, in intelligence agencies which foment small wars abroad with or without authorization, in research and development in industry, universities and in highly profitable over-run agreements that cause huge stockpiles of war materials to accumulate that no one needs or can ever use. When this comes to the public's attention, a few individuals are made scapegoats and things continue in their competitive way without change. In the US a favourite saying is that you don't throw the barrel away because of a few rotten apples. But what is not admitted is that the whole barrel is rotten – staves and all. Secrecy – essential in all forms of competition (after all, you don't show your cards to the 'enemy', even if they are your own citizens) – hides much of the corruption in the name of national security or loyalty to the service, nation or governing party.

Today's civil governments support military spending less for defence reasons and far more to stabilize stagnating economies suffering from the consequences of excess industrial capacity and automation. On top of this, government grants enable the larger defence contractors to research and develop robotization in their secondary role as producers for consumer markets, at the expense of the labour force. With exceptions like military vehicles, for which commercial robot production lines can be used, most defence contracts call for labour-intensive work, corrupting workers into believing that their future lies in defence production. The consumer (i.e. the taxpayer) pays for all of this, just as he pays for bureaucratic wastefulness, inefficiency, advertising, planned obsolescence, corruption, and the competitive methods that impoverish him. The consequences of these developments are two-fold.

The first is that the differences between State and privately managed economies have shrunk and keep shrinking. Corporate, labour, and government bureaucrats are all would-be winners dedicated to short- rather than long-term solutions (i.e. politicians and union leaders tend to think no further than the next election, company executives think only of this year's profits, stock options and golden handshakes, academics of research grants and tenure, factory workers of perks and the next pay packet, and bureaucrats of their grades and pensions). They do not want to reach agreement about anything, because they fear that this would be the end of what they consider their expertise in the games they play. They are wrong, because the draw solution could provide them with all the options there are, but they are too stupid (i.e. conditioned) to see that. They could all be captains of industry, statesmen, candidates for the Nobel Prize and most others could do creative and productive work and lead satisfying lives at least some of the time.

The second is that so-called free-enterprise economies are more efficient than communist ones because corporate bureaucrats are better at playing the competitive game within and outside the corporation than government ones. Capitalist game players know how to co-operate with their own governments who, in return, grant them relative autonomy to win in their war against one another and the consumer. In communist countries the bureaucrats want to be the only winners, are mostly concerned with internal battles and are disdainful of those who are 'outside' their system – especially dedicated craftsmen. Communist government bureaucrats who had and still have a large say in industrial management, tend to be isolated from any reality other than their own and, as a result, stifle economies wherever they dominate them even faster than their capitalist counterparts. The main difference between inefficiency and corruption in government and private enterprise seems to be a matter of visibility. It is always due to quantitative competition at the expense of qualitative superiority, whether it occurs in a capitalist, communist, or socialist society.

Until now in communist countries production managements were at the mercy of central government bureaucracies which insisted on solving logistic and engineering problems on an ideological and administrative basis. Their judgements advanced their own interests at everyone else's expense (a sign of competitiveness) without regard for quality control or consumer needs. Gorbachev seems to have recognized the dangers of bureaucratic control at government levels. He may end up with a more productive, but equally fatal, system if he copies the Western model of quantitatively competitive economics. Instead he should insist that Russian industry and commerce become qualitatively competitive; that they play for a draw rather than for victory.

The late President Kennedy in his inaugural speech suggested to the American voters that they 'ask not what your country can do for you, but what you can do for your country'. Kennedy's advice was good only for civil servants and politicians, and very bad for those whose jobs have disappeared as a result of governmental and corporate incompetence, greed, corruption, lack of foresight and subscription to competitive principles. Coming from the President of the bastion of individualistic free enterprise, this sounded remarkably like what Russian and Chinese communist leaderships have been saying to their people for years and it is wrong in all cases.

Nations like the USSR and the People's Republic of China are as yet far from meeting consumer demands other than those needed for survival, to say nothing of reaching industrial saturation. Therefore the problems of excess production capacity and technological unemployment are not yet serious. But these symptoms will crop up there, as everywhere else in the world sooner or later, as long as these countries seek to compete quantitatively.

The young, uneducated, minority groups, low-skilled workers and those closest to retirement age already suffer high and growing technologically caused unemployment in most industrialized countries. In Britain the cost of idleness is paid for, for the time being, by North Sea oil, a reduction in health, social and educational services (at a time when the whole workforce needs re-education rather than mere re-training), a virtual cessation of infra-structural maintainance and renewal (at a time when it is crumbling into ruin), and the selling off of national assets, euphemistically called privatization.

The United States maintains a relatively high level of employment by the expedient of ever-growing military expenditures and indebtedness, shored up by a competitive, paranoid military policy that serves to justify it. This is supported by cutbacks in social aid to those who need it most, as well as wildly fluctuating tax, interest and currency rates. Periodic spending cuts that supposedly affect military and social budgets are purely cosmetic, for military budget cuts are soon restored in various ways to keep the economic pump primed for a while. Similarly inappropriate stop-gap measures have helped delay the inevitable in most other Western countries.

One likely reason for Gorbachev's desire for peace is to expand Russia's consumer goods production capabilities, which lag behind those in the West. There is an additional bonus to Gorbachev's policies from the Russian point of view of which he is surely aware. A reliable peace between the superpowers could ruin US and European economies for a long time to come, because their deceptive economic health is largely dependent on huge defence expenditures. It may also be that Gorbachev, if he is a statesman rather than a politician, has come to understand that the co-operative principle to which the Soviet Union has paid lip-service for nearly three generations may be the only way out of the world's economic and other troubles. It is possible that he grasps the draw principle, as applied to domestic and international relations. In that case conventional communism and socialism, as much as conventional capitalism, will be in for considerable revisions.

It seems strange that economists of the left, right and centre have not worked out the non-zero-sum principle to any degree. Some of its aspects appear in the writings of John Maynard Keynes and, more recently, in those of Lester Thurow. Yet both miss asking the right questions and providing the correct answers. Being close to the truth does not seem to be good enough. It is rather like a marksman missing his target by a hair. A miss is as good as a mile.

Keynes showed that full employment, whether in private industry or in work commissioned by the government to improve the infrastructure, or a combination of both, makes for a far more stable economy than one in which no planning exists. The same should, of course, be true for international trade. Unfortunately such planning in most Western, so-called free enterprise societies is frowned on as far as consumers and workers are concerned, considered essential for industrial, business and military purposes, but only used as a last resort to save and restore a failing, unplanned, free enterprise, competitive economy.

By then there is usually no time for long-term planning (largely because most elected officials in government and in unions look no further than the next election). There is then time only for stop-gap measures like the US Community Conservation Corps (quasi-military 'made' work for youth) and the Work Projects Administration (useful but often hurried and wastefully conducted public works projects) initiated by President Roosevelt during the pre-Second World War depression. The Tennessee Valley electrification programme, fought tooth and nail by power companies as 'communist' (i.e. 'co-operative'), was the largest of these and one from which industry has benefited most ever since (the A-bomb development would have been impossible without it). But most other such projects (with exceptions like the Blue Ridge Mountain Drive) were too little and too late. Had it not been for the Second World War, the 1929 depression would have continued indefinitely, unless long-term planning had been employed to stop it.

Lester Thurow is an economics professor at the Massachusetts Institute of Technology. Two of his books, *The Zero-Sum Society*[11] and *The Zero-Sum Solution*[12] are of special interest. Both deal with US and world economics in the 1980s and 1990s. Thurow uses the term 'zero-sum' not only to describe the economic problems of our time but also to define what he considers the solution. In the *Zero-Sum Society* he writes:

A zero-sum game is any game where the losses exactly equal the winnings. All sports events are zero-sum games. For every winner there is a loser, and winners can only exist if losers exist. What the winning gambler wins, the losing gambler must lose.

But on page 214 he insists that:

. . . we are going to have to learn to play a zero-sum economic game. If we cannot learn, or prefer to pretend that the zero-sum problem does not exist, we are simply going to fail.

In other words he recommends a cure that consists of the disease.

In *The Zero-Sum Solution* he re-states this theme:

The Zero-Sum Solution is The Route to Economic Growth ... it will be painful for America to get back into competitive economic shape ... To fight a war successfully requires ... co-operation and teamwork ... The societies that win economically are the ones that pay attention to improving their social organization ... If America wants to be a market winner [in competition with Japan] it must organize itself to win ... To have a competitive team, it is necessary to have the best players working with the best equipment under the best managers.

In between these eulogies on the virtues of quantitative competition, increased production and consumption, the perennial growth in the GNP and the zero-sum game, Thurow stresses co-operation and the non-zero-sum game, without ever using this last term or acknowledging its existence and meanings. He seems unaware of the differences and contradictions in what he correctly identifies as the problem and recommends as the remedy, even when he is right:

Adversarial [i.e. competitive] relations can be eliminated only when there is a genuine community of interest. If no such community exists, then there is nothing to agree upon. Labour and capital are natural adversaries much as the viper and the mongoose, and the firm is simply the battleground upon which their economic warfare takes place. The capitalists may win, the workers may win, they may arrange a temporary truce [i.e. a zero-sum stalemate], they may fight each other into exhaustion [another kind of zero-sum stalemate], but there is no basis for co-operation [a draw].

None the less he continues:

The old system [of employment practices] makes America uncompetitive now, and it will make America only more uncompetitive as time passes ...

To be successful, every economy needs to be able to generate both new jobs and a healthy rate of productivity growth. New workers need new jobs if unemployment is not to rise continually, and everyone wants the higher standards of living that only higher productivity can bring ...

Thurow predicts the consequences of the winning and losing game as reflected in today's economies. He even pleads for co-operation on a national and international scale. But he also seeks a formula for perpetual quantitative growth, increase in the GNP, and quantitative competition between different enterprises and nations, while pleading for co-operative improvements in the quality of life on a global scale. It cannot be done – or rather, it has been tried for more than 200 years and it is leading us to long-term disaster. In other words, Thurow misses what a fuller penetration of the game metaphor can teach us. He uses some of the correct words, but he does not get their meanings right. At other times he defines the meanings correctly, but uses the wrong words. That is to say that he is not totally objective and his conclusions must therefore be incomplete and insufficient, something that he probably suspects.

None the less Thurow's books should be required reading for everyone interested in economics. Their flaws are minor compared to the misconceptions in the conventional economic literature, of which von Neumann and Morgenstern's *Theory of Games and Economic Behaviour*[13] is typical. Even so the latters' ideas are taken seriously except by rare critics like Norbert Wiener.[14] What, then, can be done?

The following defines some of the economic ideas that can be extrapolated from an analysis of the non-zero-sum game, including those that Thurow has missed. These are the ideals and principles on which any future economy must be based if it is to flourish and survive in the long term. It is not a question of achieving utopia, but improvement in the quality of life in an evolutionary manner and on a global basis.

The first principle of the draw or non-zero-sum economy is that it must be global in order to work. Co-operation between some players in the economic game in order to compete more effectively against others can never work in the long term. Limited or temporary co-operation and alliances define one aspect of the zero-sum syndrome from which we suffer. Co-operation to defeat others defines the competitive principle that is operative in war and modern economics. Economic agreements must be global in order to work, and there should be no secret agreements.

The second principle demands an international division of labour. At present every major country in the world seeks to become not only self-sufficient – in car production, for example – but also a competitive exporter. This leads to excess manufacturing capacity on a global scale, irresponsible competition, the subsidizing of inefficient industries and export, and economic instability.

Obviously the automotive or steel industries should not be concentrated in one place on earth, but they also do not need to be duplicated everywhere. This should be a question of agreement, allocation of resources on a rational basis relative to proximity to raw materials and markets, and similar considerations.

Such regional considerations already regulate production in agriculture to some extent. Unfortunately these agreements – like those among EEC members – exist primarily to enable farmers to raise food supplies that no one can use – a practice that creates grain, butter and meat mountains, wine and milk lakes that are not even used to subsidize the disabled, aged or unemployed. Only the farmers and owners of storage facilities benefit. These costly surpluses are the result of subsidies that encourage technological overproduction and greed on the part of factory farmers and warehouse entrepreneurs. They also show that the law of supply and demand does not work in a technological society even when it comes to food production because, while it is best to leave matters to work themselves out with minimal government interference (or support), it is essential for governments to intervene quickly and responsibly whenever any imbalance threatens.

Like all aspects of the draw solution, division of labour agreements – who produces what and in what quantity – need not be radical or inflexible, but should bring about gradual changes that limit excess production depending on time, place and circumstances, and periodic collective reconsideration of changing local and international conditions. The non-zero-sum draw solution (i.e. every one wins in proportion to qualitative effort and investment) also calls for individual and collective self-discipline and responsibility.

The third principle is that a non-zero-sum economy must be evolutionary, rather than revolutionary; voluntary, rather than forced; open, rather than devoted to secrecy – in other words the opposite of all things that turn strategic games into games of chance. A fair and sane non-zero-sum economy can only come about as a result of agreement through understanding. Economic, political, diplomatic or military force can impose such conditions in the short term, but they will not work in the long run.

The fourth is that individual, qualitative performance takes precedence over quantitative production, once the essentials of subsistence and public service are provided, subject to general agreement as to what constitutes subsistence. The provision of essentials and of accountable public services require a surplus and profit (earned either as a result of efficiency or gathered by taxation) for future contingencies and reinvestment, maintainance and improvement of the infra-structure. This must hold true not only for basic food supplies, health care, medical services, public housing, energy and water supply, policing and transport, but for all things that people are unable to do for themselves in highly industrialized and urbanized societies.

All other than essential services and industries can be privately operated and managed at a reasonable profit, related to value, durability and social cost. The relative mix of private and public enterprise is unimportant. But such a mixture should exist wherever appropriate for reasons of qualitative competition, guided by socially responsible self-restraint.

Fifth, equality among individuals and groups must be limited to opportunity and performance. Everyone must be provided with an equal opportunity to realize his or her potential if they choose to exercise it and demonstrate sufficient interest. Ability is not measurable if only because some people develop early and others late. No one should be denied the opportunity to make the most of his development whenever it occurs.

This principle does not eliminate inequalities among mature individuals, but these would be based on quality of performance and the social or aesthetic value of what is performed, rather than on quantity. Inevitably this type of subjective standard is likely to lead to mistakes in judgement. The object is not to create an ideal world but a less corrupt and corrupting economy than the present one. Besides, with sufficient safeguards against nepotism, empire-building and quantitative competition, any injustices can be corrected periodically, provided the necessary mechanism – like an ombudsman – exists for doing so and if there is general agreement on principles.

Standards in any field must be limited to mechanical performance (i.e. the 'best' electric plug becomes the standard so that incompatibility does not lock consumers into inefficient high profit, and rapidly obsolescent systems). But such standardization must never extend to aesthetic value judgements, for these are individual and ephemeral and can never be absolute.

The sixth principle of non-zero-sum gaming concerns the relationship between the individual and the group and a definition of freedom for both. Today, capitalist, free-enterprise societies claim that individual self-interest comes ahead of group responsibility. That is their definition of freedom. But despite superficial order, this is a form of institutionalized anarchy, no different than the 'no-rule' game described earlier. The promised freedom is reserved for the society's winners, while the losers are forced to conform.

In communist and socialist countries the emphasis is on a kind of equality – collective conformity in which the individual's goals are subservient to those of the State. Such freedom is different, but no more or less hypocritical than the belief system sponsored by capitalism. Both systems create zero-sum societies with certain exceptions, no matter what they profess. There are always more losers than winners and only the latter enjoy what is conventionally considered freedom. But even they are not free, for they are trapped by the closed system within which they operate. In both societies it is extremely difficult, and often impossible, for individuals to cut loose from the prevailing conditioning and to set their own goals. For those opportunities are the only forms of freedom that count.

The non-zero-sum society, in contrast to both capitalist and communist ones, would guarantee total freedom to all individuals provided they exercise it to reach a benign (i.e. everyone wins) individual or collective goal that does not harm anyone else. In other words, freedom is available to all provided no one is hurt (including feelings), what is done does not draw blood and, when involving others, is done only with their agreement and informed consent. Everyone would be free to do whatever he or she likes, individually or in groups, subject to these qualifications and conditions which define freedom itself.

The seventh principle concerns variety. The non-zero-sum society provides a maximum of options and allows a minimization of conformity in lifestyle, employment, management and production. It stimulates creativity in all walks of life and in every occupation, from the most ordinary to the unusual. It is therefore far more challenging than any zero-sum economy.

There can be no single answer as to which draw solution is best.

Some are better than others, but many are equally good, no matter how they are achieved. In other words, while there are relatively few ways in which competitors can win, the number of ways in which to co-operate with the self, with others and with nature are infinite. Competition – playing 'against' others and trying to win – breeds conformity and authoritarianism.

The eighth principle concerns learning. The draw solution shows that learning is something that each of us must do for him- or herself and that all that can be taught is method. Today, most forms of education involve operant conditioning with reinforcement (carrot and stick training) which makes people less intelligent than they naturally are.

The concept of learning by punishment or reward is self-defeating. This principle even extends to life's recidivists – those who refuse to learn and keep repeating the same mistakes over and over again. They can only be forgiven if they learn, and when they make good for whatever reversible damage they may have done. Those who do irreversible damage can only forgive themselves by trying to make it up to those who suffered because of their wrong doing to whatever extent they can and is allowed them.

The ninth, and perhaps most persuasive principle of the non-zero-sum solution is its relative inevitability. As in 'heads or tails', and even with mindless randomization, every game ends in a nearly even, balanced outcome in the longest run. An even better result can be brought about immediately by applying organic, systematic and ordered behaviour, craftsmanship and agreement. Human awareness, correct intentions and behaviour determine whether we actively bring about the gradual evolution of relative perfection at the earliest moment, whether we may have to wait for it to occur by chance or until all other possibilities have been tried and a perpetual draw comes about as a matter of course. The last is the Nirvana for which Buddhists wait. The differences between an earlier and a later realization of the inevitable are those of time, energy and skill. We can make a beginning now to end the winning and losing cycle, trust to luck, or delay until all systems have run down and the second law of thermodynamics rules supreme before people are willing to agree that the draw (the first law of thermodynamics applied to organic behaviour) is the best solution.

None of these are utopian ideas. Instead they are ideals and principles to which any reasonable individual or group can subscribe without surrender of autonomy. These are the ideals and principles that assure maximum and benign diversity (not differences achieved by perpetual conflict), freedom and evolution in our human cultural and gene pool. The object is not to manipulate people behaviourally, or by genetic or other intervention ostensibly designed to create a perfect human being. Instead such a being, if there ever were to be one, and like all principles and ideals, represents a distant goal towards which to strive, correcting mistakes as we go along. The goal is less perfection than perfectibility. That may be the best we can ever hope to achieve and it seems quite good enough from our current vantage point. It is or would certainly be superior to any social or other goal currently sought.

As shown earlier the non-zero-sum solution makes it possible for everyone to win in proportion to effort and performance. Everyone can be given an equal opportunity to be equally successful in all the games they play, but some will be more richly rewarded by playing and achieving draws in the most difficult games there are.

The non-zero-sum economy requires re-education and the opportunity for all to learn who want to learn; perpetual enlargement of the learning environment; and feedback at all levels of society. It will have to be an education that stresses interest-based learning of the actual meanings – the causes, consequences and operations that bring both about – of the very words we use and actions we perform – self-discovery rather than indoctrination. As I have said, meaning underlies the whole of our economic, and every other, aspect of existence, although that is not appreciated or perceived in our present-day, exclusively materialistic societies in which education stresses conformity and doing and believing as you are told.

To be prepared for the most promising and co-operative future, people of all ages will have to learn to think for themselves, rather than waiting to be told what to think or do; to work with little or no supervision; to become individually accountable; to know intuitively when and with whom to co-operate, when to refuse, or when to defend themselves aggressively, yet with minimal force. All these are essential components of the draw principle and an evolving non-zero-sum society. It is not a principle that will change the world, but each of us can use it to change him- or herself – which may change the world in time.

12 Peace or War – The Biggest Game of All

> We may say therefore War belongs not to the province of Arts and Sciences, but to the province of social life. It is a conflict of great interests which is settled by bloodshed, and only in that is it different from others. It would be better, instead of comparing it with any Art, to liken it to business competition, which is also a conflict of human interests and activities; and it is still more like State policy, which again, on its part, may be looked upon as a kind of business competition on a great scale.
>
> von Clausewitz[1]

How wars are won and lost and how peace can be preserved have been matters of dispute throughout history. Successful military leaders are praised for their genius, yet what such genius consists of has never been properly defined by any Western philosopher of war. Generals who lose wars are pitied or despised, although both winners and losers are usually depicted as heroic. In the eyes of historians and novelists, with the exception of writers like Tolstoy, the preservation of peace and the avoidance of war does not seem to rate as highly as the waging of battles. History, like plays and novels, thrives on drama (i.e. winning and losing) rather than on tranquillity and peace (the draw principle). Although writers like Tolstoy have represented war as anything but heroic, such views did not gain many adherents until fairly recently.

It is therefore interesting to see how people felt about war just three or four generations ago. Herbert Spencer, Darwin's friend and author of the multi-volume *Principles of Ethics*, wrote:

While social antagonisms continue to generate war, which consists in endeavours to inflict pain and death while submitting to the risks of pain and death, and which necessarily involves great privations; it is needful that physical suffering, whether considered in itself or in the evils it bequeaths, should be thought little of, and that among pleasures recognized as most worthy should be those which victory brings.[2]

It is unlikely that the multitude who fought at Balaclava, or in any other battle before or since that time, would have agreed with Spencer, writing in the comfort and safety of his Victorian study. Regrettably, the pleasures that victory brings were lost on those who were killed or who, maimed for life, were hidden away in some veterans' hospital. They were also lost on the veteran unemployed and hunger marchers of the 1930s, no matter how enthusiastically they may have marched into the trenches in 1914; and on the *gueules cassés* who, with most of their faces shot away in the First World War and before the days of plastic surgery, enjoyed the privilege of selling lottery tickets on the streets of Paris between the two world wars.

There is also no agreement about the benefits of war or what might be the best and most successful method for fighting defensive wars (as opposed to aggressive ones) or – far more important – for maintaining peace. In the absence of any such agreement, twentieth-century military leaders hope that knowledge engineers and game theoretical experts may discover short-cuts to victory and encapsulate them in artificially intelligent computerized systems like the Strategic Defence Initiative and so-called 'smart weapons'. They are evidently persuaded that these will relieve military staffs of the responsibilities of decision-making and command in any future war.

The concern of the military is real. Already the speed and complexity of fighter aircraft exceed the pilots' abilities to react. Advanced technologies do not allow them sufficient time to make decisions. The technologies of war on the ground and at sea are also beginning to outstrip human decision-making capabilities. It is therefore tempting for the military to turn over that responsibility to the technologies without appreciating that man is the ghost in the machine.

Frank George, former professor of cybernetics at Brunel University and an adviser to the Pentagon and Britain's Ministry of Defence, insisted that:

We are absolutely serious about constructing a machine-in-evolution or a machine species, and not just a machine . . . Suppose we decide to build individual machines to wage war for us. We would need to make them highly flexible, since they are *not* going to have a human controller, and without great flexibility they would be an easy prey to an enemy. What we have to do is build a great deal of human-like intelligence into the machine, and it is worth thinking carefully how this should be done; we are, in effect, building a robot soldier . . .[3]

That is just what the military establishments of the world have been doing for a very long time, using human, flesh and blood 'material'. Every soldier, through the ranks up to field marshal, believes that he obeys a higher authority. Some claim to derive their orders direct from God. That makes robots of all military men who do not think for themselves. Patrick Hayes defined the military ideal at a 1971 NATO conference on artificial intelligence, the as yet unrealized and unrealizable hope of the high command. His humour was apparently unintentional:

A robot is an intelligent system equipped with sensory capabilities, operating in an environment similar to the everyday world inhabited by human robots.[4]

The irony of that statement is that military commanders usually prefer the troops under their command to be as robot-like as possible and not to do their own thinking. A belief has been maintained that wars, like games, are won by expendable playing pieces that do as they are told; a combination of robot-like obedience on the part of the troops – the playing pieces – and superior precision, foresight, moral and physical force, logistics and scientific planning on the part of general staffs – the players. Military thinkers persuade themselves that the same intellectual processes apply to achieving success in games and wars as in art and science for as long as they win. When they lose they then insist that they were merely following orders. In other words they pretend to have been playing pieces rather than players, switching back and forth as convenient.

In Britain the meaning of 'playing the game' was interpreted in a number of different ways. To some it meant fairness and to others it meant winning by any means. To Baden-Powell, hero of Mafeking and founder of the Scout Movement, it meant an opportunity to drum 'winning', jingoistic patriotism and the competitive spirit into the working-class youths of his time who were, by definition, life's losers and destined to serve as cannon fodder to preserve the Empire.

Don't be disgraced like the young Romans, who lost the Empire of their forefathers by being wishy-washy slackers without any go or patriotism in them. Play up. Each man in his place and play the game . . .[5]

To those who sought to indoctrinate public school boys it meant:

> The playing fields of England
> All up and down the land,
> Where English boys play English games,
> How bright and fair they stand!
> 'Tis there in a friendly rivalry
> School meets with neighbouring school
> And English boys all 'play the game'
> And learn to keep the rule.
> There each one plays for side, not self,
> And strength and skill employs,
> On the playing-fields of England,
> The pride of English boys.[6]

US President 'Teddy' Roosevelt americanized these sentiments and enshrined them in his country's folklore. Similar patriotic clichés eventually misled millions of young and not-so-young Englishmen, Americans, Frenchmen and Germans into being impaled on the barbed wire of Ypres and Passchendaele. They went 'over the top' and to slaughter 'for the team', led by officers imbued with the public school (or the French *École Militaire*, or the Prussian *Junker*) spirit to whom all of this was simply another version of 'playing the game', of winning and of not letting down the side.

It was a lesson for which they had been prepared on the playing fields of Eton and Harrow, or whichever educational system had conditioned them. All were taught that winning is everything; that it is shameful to refuse to play the 'war game'; and that draws do not count. These were murderous lessons and many never knew that they were wrong – some because they died needlessly in battle, but many more because they had been so thoroughly conditioned that it was unthinkable to try to be anything other than a winner. That is how most of the survivors of the First World War became losers and the Second World War came about, a game played by similar rules.

Even the Second World War seems to have taught would-be winners nothing, for Christopher Evans, a psychologist who was one of the early British propagandists for artificial intelligence in the 1950s and 1960s, insisted that:

... the computer can handle and integrate a far greater amount of data than any human ... and the games can therefore be filled with more elaborate detail ... the permutations of possibilities can be predicted with great speed and accuracy, rival 'futures' are ranked and probabilities of their occurrence spelled out ... and most interesting of all, the computer's predictions, unlike those of a human, are objective and realistic, free from emotional biases and optimistic hunches ... War is a tactic for survival and he who strikes first and hardest has the greatest chance of success.[7]

Any mechanization of decision-making, by human or by mechanical robots, poses serious threats to world peace. It leaves no room for pity, compassion, a change of mind or giving anyone the benefit of the doubt. Every radar blip, even when caused by freak atmospheric conditions (and sometimes a civilian plane), is perceived by human or mechanical robots as an enemy attack or a hostile invasion from outer space (depending on whether the programmer believes that 'the Russians', 'the Americans', 'the Iranians', or 'the men from Mars' are coming). Additionally, the systems analysts' game-derived prejudices (e.g. that winning is achieved by superior strategy or intelligence, that draws do not count, and that he who strikes the first pre-emptive blow enjoys a tactical advantage) are embedded in 'artificially intelligent' expert systems and reflected in the computers' output. Many of the decisions that entrapped the US in Vietnam were computer-derived and based on such false premises.

It is interesting to compare what infantry soldiers (and not aviators or staff officers, who never come face-to-face with the 'enemy') feel about war, to militarist rhetoric, Fourth of July and Armistice Day speeches, or pacifist sentiments usually expressed by people who were never 'there'. Combat soldiers are a small minority even in war. For example, in the Second World War no more than 10 per cent of all US soldiers ever heard a shot fired in battle. The remainder were involved in supply, administration and other support services far from the firing line. A similar ratio of combat to non-combat troops holds true for most modern armies. The minority that do the fighting provide the combat casualties; they bear the brunt of war's monotony and degradation, its brutalization and immunization of feelings. By some, on their return to squalid peacetime lives, the camaraderie of the barracks or in the field is seen through distorted lenses. Those who enjoy the specially privileged life in rear echelons naturally prefer the unsettled state of war where they can get away with nearly anything. They look back on those privileges with nostalgia once peace is declared and a more humdrum existence becomes the order of the day. Even frontline soldiers suffer a related kind of psychological disorientation as a result of their 'co-operative' war experiences:

Many soldiers – tired of the rigidities of normal life – look back at violent moments of their war experiences despite the hunger and terror, as the monumental culminating experience of their lives. There is the Brüderbund of fighters, they felt happy for the first and only time in their lives.

. . . There is in many today as great a fear of a sterile and unexciting peace as of a great war. We are often puzzled by our continual failure to enlist the united effort, cheerfulness in sacrifice, determination and persistence that arise almost spontaneously in the pursuit of war.[8]

To kill under orders from superior officers, without restraint, and to be threatened with punishment if they do not obey blindly, to be in league with like-minded and supportive fellow countrymen (who are thoroughly competitive in civilian life) can be intoxicating to weak-willed, authoritarian young soldiers who are well-indoctrinated in the myth of the superiority of the winner. It is even harder, once subject to often needlessly brutal military discipline, to evade (rather than simply refuse – which could mean a firing squad) carrying out an inhumane or a degrading order. It can be done, but it requires a draw orientation and a willingness to be an individualist heretic in the true sense of the word (see Appendix C for the proper definition). This also means that you must be prepared to take your punishment if you fail to resist in an intelligent manner.

Captain Medina's briefing to his men before the massacre of My Lai as recalled by one of the soldiers who was present:

'Our job is to go in rapidly, and neutralize everything. To kill everything.'
'Captain Medina? Do you mean women and children, too?'
'I mean everything.'[9]

Obviously people who lead uneventful, yet competitive peacetime lives with nothing to look forward to except more of the same, cherish the irresponsibility and co-operation of war, even with its boredom, spit-and-polish barracks and hurry-up-and-wait routines, the arrogance of superiors and dangers in the field. That was war as it used to be.

But any future conventional or even nuclear war will not be limited to relatively few soldiers and unfortunate civilians. The civilian casualties of the Second World War, Vietnam and the war between Iran and Iraq will seem minor by comparison. Directed largely by computers programmed with what are believed to be winning strategies, the loss of life and damage to the ecology will be so great that the consequences will affect everyone and might be irreversible for centuries. The chances of survival will be problematic, given laser-guided pin-point targeting that destroys everything up to whatever horizon is visible to airborne sensors. Area targets can be saturated by missiles beyond those ranges. The illusory pleasures of soldiering will disappear. On and beyond the battlefield an overwhelming firepower can saturate every inch of ground. There will be no rear echelon for rest and recreation, and no place to hide for soldier or civilian except in command bunkers deep below ground. But then those always were the safest if not the most exciting places to be in modern wartime.

Given these likely conditions in any future war, to rely on military expert systems or supposedly intelligent computers is irresponsible in the extreme and poses a threat to the future of mankind. As Ward Just points out, to mechanize decision-making creates: '. . . a mechanization of responsibility as well, taking judgements farther and farther away from the minds, and therefore the ethics of men.'[10]

Military expertise, even when it leads to victory, is not what it is believed to be. None the less most military writers and historians feel that there is a scientific approach to warfare, based on their belief that any victory – in games or in war – is the product of a superior intelligence and that it is predictable.

Alfred Vagts, a pacifist war historian who fought in the German army in the First World War, makes a legitimate distinction between the military (a defensive necessity) and 'militarism', something no society with a claim to liberty and humanitarian concerns can safely tolerate. However, even he convinced himself that there is a military 'science', an intellectual discipline and humanitarian method, that underlies strategy and tactics. It is a common error among the military, militarists and even some pacifists:

Every war is fought, every army is maintained in a military way and in a militaristic way. The military way is marked by a primary concentration of men and materials on winning specific objectives of power with the utmost efficiency, that is, with the least expenditure of blood and treasure . . . Militarism, on the other hand . . . is so constituted that it may hamper and defeat the purposes of the military way . . . Rejecting the scientific character of the military way, militarism displays the qualities of caste and cult, authority and belief . . . It is not militarism, in this sense, therefore, when armies call for and make efficient, rational up-to-date, and to a certain extent, humane use of the materials and forces available to them . . .[11]

Another pacifist of the pre-First World War era, William James, the psychologist and brother of Henry James the novelist, rephrased Aristotle's 'catharsis theory', echoed more recently by Konrad Lorenz and his followers. James believed that human nature leaves us no choice except to do battle and that, if war is to disappear from the earth, man will need a harmless substitute:

So long as anti-militarists propose no substitute for war's disciplinary function, no *moral equivalent* of war, analogous, as one might say, to the mechanical equivalent of heat, so long they fail to realize the full inwardness of the situation. And as a rule they do fail. The duties, penalties, and sanctions pictured in the Utopias they paint are all too weak and tame to touch the military-minded.[12]

H. G. Wells, another pacifist of that period, believed in the virtues of military conformity in preference to messy civilian life (like most philosophers of war Wells's recipe would seem to apply to everyone but himself, given his rather chaotic lifestyle). Wells saw a resemblance between the communal ideal and the parade ground, a common confusion of values and one reason why socialism has not worked so far anywhere in the world, tending to subordinate the rights of the individual to the group, relieving him of responsibility and autonomy. Wells wrote in 1908, six years before the First World War:

In many ways, military organization is the most peaceful of activities. When the contemporary man steps from the street of clamorous insincere advertisement, push, adulteration, underselling and intermittent employment into the barrack-yard, he steps on to a higher social plane, into an atmosphere of service and co-operation and of infinitely more honourable emulations.[13]

It is doubtful whether any but the most hidebound militarist would agree with this definition of society's goals after spending a few days in the trenches at Passchendaele, in the Battle of the Bulge, in Vietnam, at Goose Green or in Afghanistan. Men in combat may cling to and cover for one another out of fear and necessity and display what passes for loyalty and co-operation, and occasionally these friendships continue in peacetime. Most do not, because wartime soldiering does not consist of free and voluntary associations of independent men for purposes other than the most desperate survival in circumstances that are not of their making.

Wars are seldom started by combat soldiers. They are initiated by civilian or military leaderships who remain far away from the battlefront except for propaganda visits, ostensibly to cheer the troops, but actually for homefront consumption and reasons of political opportunism. Formerly they watched these massacres from hilltops beyond artillery range. Today, with pin-point missile accuracy over long distances and nuclear weapons, they hope to survive in underground bunkers, furnished with all the conveniences needed for a long siege. The above-ground reality will be beamed down to them via robot-guided TV monitors – a horror show no more real than the nightly TV films that acclimatize us to what may lie ahead if militarists have their way.

There is a legitimate need for self-defence against ruthless and unprovoked attack and here the military fulfil an essential function. However, we must take care that such provocations are not manufactured by the military themselves, as they have frequently been in the past, to provide an excuse for offensive war disguised as defence. The Gulf of Tonkin incident provided the rationale for US intervention in Vietnam: it was engineered by the Pentagon. A similar sham was perpetrated by Hitler in 1939 when he invaded Poland in response to a supposed provocation by the Poles.

The claimed attack by Polish soldiers and civilians consisted of German soldiers disguised in Polish uniforms, carrying stolen Polish weapons. On 31 August 1939 these German soldiers attacked three

German border posts from which the guards had been partially withdrawn and who 'defended' themselves by firing into the air from a distance so as not to injure the 'attackers'. The make-believe Polish soldiers then left behind four German concentration camp inmates whom they had brought along and executed on the spot, after dressing them also in Polish army uniforms. Hitler's war started the next day, using the fraudulent Polish provocation as an excuse. It had been planned for months by Heydrich and Naujocks of the Sicherheitsdienst, one of Germany's two infamous secret services, with Hitler's knowledge and approval. The details of this raid are found in reputable German and allied sources.[14]

Eibl-Eibesfeld, Lorenz's successor at the Max Planck Institute in Germany, rightfully deplores such tactics which have been used as an excuse for territorial aggrandizement, unprovoked invasion and criminal aggression of every kind. Unfortunately Eibl-Eibesfeld, after expressing humanistic concerns like his mentor, demonstrates once again that cultural conditioning is stronger than logic or reason. He repeats an ethological and biological truism on page 37 that he claims later to be a natural law that applies only to animals:

A popular misconception about wild animals is that when they fight, they fight to kill. That is true of a predator and its prey, but it is certainly not the rule in intraspecific fighting between vertebrates.[15]

But on page 123 of his book, Eibl-Eibesfeld would make his readers believe that thanks to lethal wars and indiscriminate killing we, the human species, have evolved from our less successful and relatively pacific animal ancestors and reached our exalted cultural, intellectual and altruistic position on the evolutionary ladder. The following sounds like something straight out of *Mein Kampf*:

The important point to bear in mind is that destructive war is a result of cultural evolution. Furthermore, it is not, as is sometimes maintained, a pathological phenomenon, but performs important functions, as we shall see later. It also accelerates biological and cultural evolution by the intensification of selective pressures. This applied both to the rapid development of the brain and to the development of altruistic behaviour.[16]

The explanations of the causes and consequences of war given by other experts in various fields of expertise may differ but are no better than those provided by Eibl-Eibesfeld. One psychological expert on conflict, Sigmund Freud, addressed himself to this subject in a letter he wrote in 1933, responding to an enquiry from Albert Einstein concerning his explanation of the causes of war.

Conflicts of interest between man and man are resolved, in principle, by the recourse to violence. It is the same in the animal kingdom, from which men cannot claim exclusion; nevertheless, men are also prone to conflicts of opinion, touching, on occasion, the loftiest peaks of abstract thought, which seem to call for settlement by quite another method.[17]

Freud was quite wrong about the 'animal kingdom' and the social Darwinist stance he adopted, and he seems to have been unable to conceive of the draw principle or an agreement-to-agree in diplomacy or in academic discussion. (The latter is born out by his bitter feuds with former colleagues like Jung and Adler, against whom he conducted intellectual warfare for their audacity in disagreeing with his views.) In his answer to Einstein, Freud described what he believed to be the history of the evolution of human society, dependent on peace imposed by force. The unification of the world and an imposition of peace by superior force has been the ambition of emperors, military rulers and dictators from Alexander the Great to Hitler, and the professed aim of empire from the Pax Romana to the Pax Britannica. All were achieved by invasion, war, murder and colonization; conditions that could never lead to a lasting peace but must end in eventual collapse, as do all strategic games that are played to be won.

Freud continues in a vein that is reminiscent of every dictator in history:

Our logic is at fault if we ignore the fact that right is founded on brute force and even today needs violence to maintain it.

. . . you [Einstein] surmise that man has in him an active instinct for hatred and destruction . . . I entirely agree with you . . . In this connection may I set out a fragment of that knowledge of the instincts, which we psychoanalysts, after so many tentative essays and gropings in the dark, have compassed? We assume that human instincts are of two kinds: those that conserve and unify, which we call *erotic* . . . or else 'sexual' . . .; and, second, the instincts to destroy and kill, which we assimilate as the aggressive or destructive instincts.[18]

Freud defined peace, like love and art, as a sublimation of sexual gratification, and competition and war as the 'death wish'. The pseudo-intellectuals of the West, steeped in Victorian hypocrisy, stared in wonder and no one seemed to notice that the emperor wore no clothes, as it were, given Freud's personal history and his anti-humanistic and self-contradictory views.

Freud ends his letter to Einstein with:

The upshot of these observations ... is that there is no likelihood of our being able to suppress humanity's aggressive tendencies. In some happy corners of the earth, they say, where nature brings forth abundantly whatever man desires, there flourish races whose lives go gently by, unknowing of aggression or constraint. This I can hardly credit; I would like further details about these happy folk ... From our 'mythology' of the instincts, we may easily deduce a formula for an indirect method of eliminating war.

... How long have we to wait before the rest of men turn pacifist? ... But by what ways or bypass this will come about, we cannot guess.[19]

Freud, like the militarists of his or any other day, did not understand peace or war any better than he understood most other human behaviours. In war, the huge losses of life and property are usually caused by military stupidity. What passes for expertise is questioned by N. F. Dixon, a psychologist with considerable military experience, who quotes a psychiatric profile of the conventional military mind in his book *On the Psychology of Military Incompetence* that is far more accurate than Freud's:

The militarist is a relatively prejudiced and authoritarian person. He is emotionally dependent, socially conformist and religiously orthodox. His interest in the welfare of others is relatively low. He is extremely distrustful of the new and the strange ... uncreative, unimaginative, narrow-minded, security seeking, prestige-oriented, parochial, ultra-masculine, anti-intellectual ... lacking in aesthetic appreciation, complexity of thinking, independence, self-expression and altruism, and relatively high in anxiety ... [and] lower in self-esteem than any other professional group.[20]

Another military writer, R. B. Asprey, points out quite correctly[21] that only guerrilla fighters intuitively understand the principles of war. In modern armies that understanding seems to be restricted to special units like the SAS. The successful guerrilla is highly motivated, relies on himself and on constant deception, trickery and deceit, befriends the local population and lives off the land – tactics that win wars with a minimum of risk to the self and with as little destruction as possible. The regular soldier and militarist tend to look for orders from a superior, for orderly methods of combat, systems and routines for maximum destructiveness – conceptions dear to the conventional military mind. Thus the possibility of expert systems and a superior mechanical intelligence that issues the right orders at the right time tend to appeal to it.

It never occurred to any except rare independent thinkers to question the game-derived assumptions on which conventional military strategies are based. Most believe that warfare is comparable to physical science or art or, as von Clausewitz would have us believe, that it is one of the social sciences. For as long as such thinking predominates, in the midst of peace we are perpetually at war. War, once it is believed to be the norm, is equated with human nature, brute force and a 'survival of the fittest'. But if you look at the question of survival holistically and with total objectivity it becomes obvious that survival depends on the maintainance of peace rather than on war, brains far more than brawn, co-operation rather than conflict; human subjective, rather than mechanical and relatively objective, values and principles. Successful warfare, even in defence against an unprovoked attack, can only depend on a succession of dirty tricks, deception, lying, cheating, murder and what would be considered reprehensible behaviour in peacetime. That is how war – and every game – is won, but not the peace.

Having misunderstood how games are won and lost, and never having discovered the meaning of the draw, game theorists and Western philosophers of war like von Clausewitz provided the military and politicians with a 'Dobuan' rationale for the constant escalation of hostility, threat, counter-threat and armament, leading to wars based entirely on false beliefs that defy all logic, reason and facts. The mechanization and computerization of game playing in general and war-gaming in particular have blinded politicians and the military even more to the true principles that govern games, war, peace and human behaviour.

The first modern war-game used by the military was designed in 1780 by a German. The board was divided into 1,666 squares, fought over by two armies of more than eighty-five battalions each. One country after another adopted this method of war-gaming and the Kriegspiel, as it became known, was elaborated throughout the nineteenth and twentieth centuries. A set of *Rules for the Conduct of*

War-Games was published in Britain in 1872, yet war-gaming did not play a significant role in British military strategy until the Second World War.

Naval war-games had similar beginnings. By the 1870s they had found favour in the United States with the encouragement of Captain (later Admiral) Mahan, who influenced the conduct of war at sea until the Second World War. One of the most disastrous war-games was a naval one, played aboard the Japanese battleship *Tamamoto* during the Second World War as a dress rehearsal for a major assault on US forces. It resulted in the naval Battle of Midway, a decisive US victory and a turning point in the war. The Japanese had adopted the German Kriegspiel prior to the Second World War and elaborated it at Tokyo's Total War Research Institute with an enthusiasm similar to that with which they have more recently embraced the idea of artificial intelligence.

War-gaming was widely used by the German General Staff between the two world wars. It seemed attractive because Germany's army was limited to 100,000 men by the Treaty of Versailles. These games were conducted under the direction of General Erich von Manstein before and after the rearmament of Germany in violation of the treaty of Versailles.

After Germany's defeat in the First World War, the Allies insisted that Germany be prohibited from building warships, other than corvettes for coastguard duty, or military planes and tanks. Some of these restrictions were evaded by secret co-operation with the Soviet Union that permitted German officers and non-coms to participate in Russian 'war-game' manoeuvres from time to time during the days of the Weimar Republic. Like the Allies, who effectively financed Nazi Germany and Hitler as a bulwark against Soviet Russia, the Soviets hoped to use the Germans as a shield against capitalist paranoia. Nevertheless, the Soviets offered France and all other former Allies an *entente cordiale* in the early 1930s in order to isolate Germany and prevent the Second World War. That offer was refused. All of this makes the Soviet-Nazi pact far more understandable than it seems on the surface, because it was obvious even then that the Soviets were merely buying time.

Meanwhile, the German military, playing one side against the other, held annual 'war-games' in Germany as well, during which lorries served as symbols for tank and armoured infantry battalions, and gliders (later used effectively by the German army's airborne divisions) as simulated bombers and fighters. Many of Germany's Second World War pilots got their first formal flight training as glider 'hobbyists' from former Luftwaffe officers in this elaborate and highly deceptive 'war-game'. The German General Staff played actual table-top war-games as well, preparing for the Second World War and 'revanche' almost as soon as hostilities ceased in 1918.

War-gaming, simulation, modelling and operational research (all based on game-derived principles) came into their own on the Allied side during the Second World War. Britain, the US and Russia used such games to test military strategies in the air, on land, at sea and especially in combined operations. It was believed that war-games could provide useful models for an eventual assault on Europe, although they were not relied upon. Operational research succeeded, for example, in minimizing convoy losses due to German submarine attacks in the North Atlantic. But they failed to provide a winning strategy for the war at sea or anywhere else for exactly the same reasons that a knowledge of probabilities and statistics can help reduce losses in poker, but cannot predict a winning hand.

The development of nuclear weapons, supported by rapid advances in computing and automation, provided a great impetus to a revival of war-gaming after the Second World War, especially in the US. It was felt that an entirely new set of assumptions needed testing in theoretical situations because they could not be tried out in the field. Nuclear weapons were exploded in the atmosphere (until that proved too dangerous) and underground, but they could not be tried out under combat conditions. Computer simulations provided a way of testing various scenarios for which the cold war offered the inspiration. However, the outcomes of such war-games depend very much on the presumptions and prejudices programmed into military computers, and even more on the realities left out of specified conditions as a result of wishful thinking, blindness and stupidity.

Generally, the assumptions programmed into such games were and remain wrong, like the unsinkability of US aircraft carriers and the failure of nuclear war-game players to include the possible effects of a nuclear winter, not only on a presumed enemy but also on themselves. Lord Zuckerman, a leading science adviser to the

British Government during the Second World War, predicted that in Britain there:

> ... would be an immediate death toll of ten million, with another ten million wounded, and with all major hospitals of the country destroyed ... rail and road communications would be totally disrupted, there would be no food supplies ... and there would be no major telephone exchanges. I doubt if the United Kingdom would or could ever recover from such a blow ...[22]

However, Edward Teller, father of the H-bomb, views such weapons from a different perspective. In 1980 he compared the likely results of nuclear war to the damage done by Genghis Khan during his invasion of Persia in 1219 where he instructed his troops to kill every living soul. '... there is no example of greater havoc in history. Yet at least 10 per cent of the Persian population survived.'[23]

Teller seems to be perfectly happy with a 90 per cent global death rate which he considers to be an 'acceptable' cost of war. He could only do so if he considered such destruction within the context of a game in which he was one of the few survivors after most playing pieces (everyone else) are swept off the board. But Teller, like other nuclear war-game players (including those who view the nuclear threat as a peace-preserving stalemate), ignores the most likely scenario: that the surviving bunker elite (bureaucrats, politicians and military leaders and their servants – one cannot help but wonder what they have in mind for their wives and children) must eventually emerge to fight the final battles against the above-ground survivors. Whoever fought those would be the ultimate loser, for surely the first job should be to co-operate in order to grow food, rescue and safeguard essential informational, educational, medical and raw material resources, and restore some semblance of civilization.

The escalation of the arms race during the 1950s and 1960s led to computerized political/economic/social/military conflict scenarios acted out in the form of game simulations in the United States and by NATO. According to Wilson[24] and Allen[25] they were 'played' at the highest military and civilian levels, including the State Department, the CIA and the White House. A Joint War Games Agency was set up within the Pentagon in conjunction with DARPA

(Defence Advanced Research Projects Agency) which organized these games and sub-contracted some to think-tanks like the RAND Corporation, SRI (Science Research Institute) and the Hudson Institute; corporations like Raytheon, IBM and Bendix; Universities, including MIT and Stanford; and organizations specializing in game simulations like Abt Associates. Many of these were also centres for research into artificial intelligence and it is largely thanks to a belief in the 'expertise' of the war-game players that the concept of 'expert systems' was born.

Initially the professed purpose of computerized war-games was less to predict the outcome of particular strategies in war, and more to encourage participants to become aware of the complexities involved in conflict management. The chief lesson learnt should have been that wars are best avoided. Instead, these war-games were used as scenarios for the Bay of Pigs, the Vietnam War, the nuclear stalemate, and a clandestine support by the US of wars in the Middle East, Central America, Africa and Afghanistan which have taken the place of its foreign policy.

The rules and conditions under which such games are still played perpetuate the prevailing dogma. Successive US Presidents have firmly believed that victories on the battlefield, on the stock-market, in politics, over gaming tables or on the football field are won by superior tactics, strategies, intelligence, free enterprise, Truth, Justice, belief in God and the American Way. It is therefore difficult for them to accept that on those occasions when they win they do so solely by chance and because they do not know what they are doing; or their dirty tricks were dirtier than those of their opponents; and that the basis of victory is always error inadvertently made by the 'enemy' or induced by the would-be winner and not material, spiritual, ideological or intellectual superiority on the part of the victor. Perhaps they know this already, but cannot discover any other way to play.

Some of the Pentagon's war-games became incredibly elaborate and required rule books that took months to prepare. They fell into categories that Wilson and Allen describe. One kind of game might be played for weeks; another for a few days. Some required the participation of large numbers of military decision-makers; others only a handful. Certain games needed months of evaluation after their completion; others, like the Canadian 'Landing Force Game', were played for years.

Similar war-games were developed by the UK Defence Operational Analysis Establishment at Byfleet, some in co-operation with NATO and US forces. One of these involved a 100-page rule book and cost £50,000 per year to run. War-gaming on this scale permitted scenarios to be enlarged beyond anything that was possible in pre-computer days. Military game experts persuaded themselves that the level of realism of these games approached combat conditions.

Modern war-games are either deterministic (strategic) or probabilistic (games of chance). Deterministic games are based on fixed assumptions like given 'kill ratios' relative to fire power. Probabilistic war-games involve random 'Monte Carlo' elements that have the same effect as a throw of the dice. Deterministic games are similar in principle to noughts and crosses, chess and go, whereas probabilistic ones are pure games of chance like craps or roulette. The war-game players seem quite unaware that any game, including pure games of strategy, are turned into pure games of chance as soon as they are played to be won.

The 1960s provided a fertile soil for computer war-gaming inspired by Vietnam, the East/West conflict, recurrent Arab/Israeli wars and the ever-present nuclear threat. Defence departments of major nations could consider every combination of allies, enemies and conflict possibilities. These war-games provided the players with an incentive to test their assumptions, on the basis of which they could increase their bureaucratic powers, perpetuate the arms race and pretend economic health for as long as they kept the world on the brink of war.

The dangers of conventional war-gaming were reflected in a series of such games played by the Pentagon between 1960 and 1963 that convinced US military and government leaders that a war in Vietnam and a nuclear war waged against the USSR could be won – both dangerous assumptions. The code-name of the nuclear war-game was STAGE (Simulation of Total Atomic Global Exchange) and its outcome still affects the attitude of military and political leaders on both sides of the Atlantic.

The defeat and withdrawal of US forces from Vietnam, and the failure of war-game-derived tactics, brought about a temporary hiatus in the employment of operational research methods to warfare. But war-games returned to favour during the Carter Administration and by 1978 they were played with renewed enthusiasm under the aegis of a revitalized Pentagon war-games bureau, the Strategies, Analysis and Gaming Agency (SAGA), headed by General Scott.

Allen brings the history of US war-gaming up to date[26] and tells of the latest developments in these respects in the Pentagon, State Department and White House. War-gaming and artificial intelligence form the cornerstone of the Strategic Defence Initiative, popularly known as 'Star Wars'. The current escalation of war-gaming, modelling, simulation and operational research has resulted, according to Allen, in a Rand Corporation game developed for the US Government that is entirely computer controlled and does not involve any human decision-makers. 'Artificial intelligence' now provides the metaphorical finger on the nuclear button because, as Allen states, no US war-games player has yet been able to bring himself to push that button even in play.

Presumably the conditions programmed into this 'artificially intelligent' computer could without hesitation release the nuclear missiles from their silos, bombers, submarines and satellites. This allows the White House and Pentagon war-game players to pretend that they are henceforth free from all responsibility as far as a declaration of nuclear war is concerned. As we have seen in wars ranging from the Crimea to Vietnam (and earlier among Madagascan natives), the strategic games played by the military tend to turn into real-life conflicts sooner or later. The 1988 crises in the Persian Gulf were also first played some years ago as war-games in the Pentagon. The reality turned out exactly as predicted because such games tend to turn into self-fulfilling prophesies sooner or later.

Some of the most questionable applications of the technologies are attempts by the military and their civilian advisers to build computer models that encapsulate what they believe to be simulated human intelligence. As I said earlier, the capability already exists for mechanizing decision-making so that computers could initiate and conduct warfare based on game-derived strategic perceptions with or without minimal human participation or intervention. A large part of the US 'Star Wars' programme hinges on just such a computerization of decision-making. The danger lies in the fact that many scientists, politicians and the military believe that the computer 'thinks', when it merely follows pre-programmed commands (the film *War Games* is a good example of an imaginary artificial intelligence approach to military decision-making by machine, except that even there the writer or director confused a draw with a stalemate as far as noughts and crosses was concerned).

Military computers match patterns, resulting from war-game-derived conclusions, implanted by human decision-makers to whatever information is given them in the future. In other words, the military play computer war-games based on wrong assumptions. They come to the wrong conclusions. These conclusions are then programmed into supposed decision-making computers that institutionalize those misconceptions. The computer works out all possible variations via its conditional branching network relative to new input. The programmers, knowledge engineers and generals delude themselves that it is thinking and that it produces new and creative solutions, thus relieving them of the need for human decision-making.

But these are variations based on the original prejudices of the systems analysts, programmers and generals. Artificial intelligence and expert systems provide the illusion of absolving human decision-makers of responsibility because any unforeseen or disastrous result can be blamed on computer rather than human error or failure, or so it is believed. The military would then be able to blame a 'higher authority', as they have in the past. The 'buck' would no longer stop with them, with elected civilian officials or even with God. It would stop with the most recent generation of super-fast, parallel-linked, mainframe computers.

Conventional game theorists, such as Abt, Schelling, Newell and McCarthy (the last two being deeply committed to artificial intelligence), derived their military thinking from von Clausewitz. His works are the favourite reading of political and military leaders throughout the West. Von Clausewitz's misconceptions, coupled with a misinterpretation of Darwin's theory of evolution, have turned modern war into an instrument of offensive policy on a scale that was inconceivable in the past. These ideas provided the rationale for the false belief that conflict is the mainspring of nature – and human nature especially – an ill-willed principle elevated into a prevailing philosophy in the biological, social, economic and military sciences and now also in computing.

Von Clausewitz compared war to business competition and diplomacy (see the quote that heads this chapter) and considered all three activities akin to games that are won by 'superior' players and those most fit to rule. Militarists and game theoreticians still subscribe to these unfortunate and quite erroneous ideas which are also corner-stones of the twin concepts of artificial intelligence and expert systems.

Von Clausewitz had a profound influence on war-gaming. But he did not understand human nature any better than the principles that govern games, diplomacy, commerce, peace or war. He was an officer/observer, an arrogant theorizer who never commanded men or participated in combat. His ideas have had a disastrous effect on Western thinkers from the Napoleonic to the present era, irrespective of ideological differences. Marx and Engels were as enamoured of von Clausewitz's strategic concepts as were Bismarck and the generals on all sides who led millions to mindless slaughter in both world wars. Von Clausewitz did not just reflect the spirit of his time; he was instrumental in elaborating and perpetuating it. Like Hitler, most twentieth-century military and political leaders remain avid subscribers to misconceptions that are summed up in the following quotes taken from von Clausewitz's writings:

The destruction of the enemy's armed forces is the means to the end . . . For victory it is necessary that there should be a battle between the enemy's principle forces and our own . . . Victory as a rule, springs from a preponderance of all physical and moral power combined . . . War is nothing but a continuation of political intercourse, with a mixture of other means . . . If War belongs to policy, it will naturally take its character from thence. If policy is grand and powerful, so will be the War, and this may be carried to the point at which War attains its absolute form . . .[27]

It is also the point at which peace becomes indistinguishable from war. Von Clausewitz adds: 'No one subject to the Word of Command has any will of his own.'

Just how powerful such ideas are, how easily they can be applied to subjugate and control, and how they have influenced and confused the thinking of computer experts is illustrated by the writing of Edward Feigenbaum who states in *The Fifth Generation*:

'The superior technology usually wins the war – whether that war is martial, entrepreneurial, or cultural. The superior intelligence . . . always does.'[28]

Feigenbaum's statements are extraordinary in the light of the loss of the war in Vietnam to an enemy whose technology (but not culture) was decidedly inferior to that of the US. He also erroneously attributed these ideas to Sun Tzu, a pre-Christian Chinese philosopher of war who was the earliest dissenter from conventional military wisdom and whose tactics were followed faithfully by the Vietmin. He said exactly the opposite of what Feigenbaum claimed he had written – a standpoint that is significant in view of an increased reliance on expert systems by the military of most nations. Sun Tzu's ideas on experts, expressed 2,000 years before the age of computers, defines military competence precisely: 'To triumph in battle and be universally acclaimed "expert" is not the acme of skill.'[29]

Sun Tzu identified war as the opposite of peace, a failure of diplomacy, rather than its extension. To him the object of war, when unavoidable, was not to win battles or destroy an enemy, but to restore peace at the earliest opportunity. His tactics aimed to achieve this while minimal damage was suffered and inflicted. According to him, when his strategies are applied the would-be enemy defeats himself, a principle reflected in aspects of Taoist and Buddhist thought, in Tai Chi and Oriental martial arts.

Sun Tzu was aware that a response more unexpected and hurtful than any unprovoked violence is appropriate provided it serves to stop or end a physical or psychological attack. Only that or evasion, when possible, can end a war.

To Sun Tzu, war consists of ceaseless deception, secrecy and unpredictability on and off the battlefield, taking advantage of the enemy's every error and inducing mistakes by tactical and psychological ploys – all the strategies that win games. Intelligence (in the informational sense) played a vital role in all of this, as did the recruitment and rewarding of spies and turncoats, the suborning and corruption of the enemy's officials and the destruction of his alliances. Warfare could thus be described as a de-systematization process (i.e. the perpetual, random shuffling of the deck and the maximization of chaos and chance), whereas peace depends on systematization (i.e. the arrangement of the cards systematically and the limitation of chance to a minimum).

As Sun Tzu realized, 'intelligence' in a military sense is a crucial tool in war as in any competitive game played to be won. The same is true of secrecy. Therefore one essential condition of peace (or a draw) is the opposite: absolute openness and the sharing of information.

There are several kinds of useful 'military intelligence', consisting of information about technological developments, military strength and disposition, intentions, and covert actions. Technological information is best obtained by direct contact with academic and industrial workers, and by reading academic, research and trade journals where most of what is pretended to be 'secret' information can be obtained, either directly or by reading between the lines. Much the same is true for discovering a government's intentions. Spies and undercover agents are not much use in such intelligence-gathering, for they do not possess the skills needed to sift what is new and valuable from what is common knowledge among academics and technologists in various fields.

Most governments only pay lip-service to the idea that scientific and technological advances should be shared openly in times of peace. They also do not admit that secrecy, diplomatic and military espionage, 'destabilization' and 'defection' efforts of their peacetime intelligence services are hostile, provocative and war-like acts. They are the strategies and tactics of 'winning' and trying to make the other side lose. None can ever lead to a draw, an agreement to agree, or to peace. Only the Chinese used to concentrate exclusively on gathering technological information in times of peace. Their 'intelligence headquarters' abroad are centred in Chinese bookshops and distribution centres for their publications, rather than in embassies or consulates. Their peacetime intelligence operatives are intellectuals and technicians rather than 'spooks' disguised as embassy attachés. There is nothing covert about these activities because they are above board and legitimate.

There should not be any secrets between scientists and academics of different nations in times of peace unless they are dishonest and seek to claim credit for the work of others, or if they are in the pay of the military.

In the West, as much as in the Soviet Union, science has been suborned and become a tool of war even in times of peace. Attempted secrecy, usually futile and of the shortest-term value, is government policy to which academics subscribe whether they like it or not. American and Soviet science have become adjuncts to the military, and scientists are vetted for their reliability in keeping their work secret. Until now Russian scientists required special permission to travel and meet colleagues abroad and were accompanied by government minders. A US scientist cannot receive research funding unless he agrees to submit any innovations to the government and may not publish them if his discoveries have any military application. American universities and individual academics abide by this policy 'voluntarily'. They know that research funds would suddenly dry up if they did not do so. In other words they allow themselves to be effectively blackmailed by their own governments. Like all willing victims, they 'co-operate' with their blackmailers and are equally responsible for the consequences.

The difference between the Soviet Union and the US, in this as in most other matters, is less between the carrot and the stick, but how either is wielded, when, and by whom (during the McCarthy days the stick was used widely in the US to ensure that scientists and intellectuals did as they were told). In general, and perhaps even now, Soviet scientists are punished if they do not conform; US scientists are rewarded when they do. The sciences, kept in check by their governments' operant conditioning, are the handmaidens of the military in both countries. In Britain this is only partially true because the Thatcher Government has cut back funds for fundamental research (except weapons development). The US Administration has taken a leaf out of the Prime Minister's book and done the same in the US, generating howls of anguish from academics who do not wish to be deprived of their carrots.

What is interesting about this is that true 'fundamental research' is nearly always a labour of love, done by 'outsiders' like Einstein who are forced to finance their original work themselves (Einstein worked in the patent office in Bern). They are only rewarded after at least theoretical results have been achieved – and often not even then. But because they are outside the system they think more independently and critically and that is why they succeed where 'insider' academics, who depend on the system, fail. The military, elected officials and government bureaucrats take advantage of this by only funding research in practical applications based on the original research of the outsiders. They do not appreciate the value of original research except in times of actual war because they do not understand learning and the creative process symbolized by the draw principle.

The military and covert action branches of every country's peacetime intelligence establishments are at perpetual war with one another. Peace is a hollow pretence when secrecy, dirty tricks, murder, the suborning of allies and arming of dissident groups, to say nothing of the destabilization of governments with whom they may disagree are daily events. There can be no peace when these activities are instruments of diplomacy and foreign policy. But, as we have seen all too often in the case of the CIA, MI5 and the KGB, secret intelligence agencies are not only at war with other governments in times of so-called peace. They and the various branches of their own military and intelligence establishments battle one another. The selection processes for, and the conditioning of, military and secret service personnel in 'us-against-them' gaming is such as to foster severe forms of paranoia.

An intelligence cabal tends to arise in countries that sustain large peacetime espionage and destabilization establishments. It is often a law unto itself, made up of some of the most devious and secretive individuals determined to sustain a constant state of war (except for temporary alliances) against 'enemies' at home and abroad, including domestic government agencies and citizens who may differ from the highly competitive belief system with which every intelligence community is infected.

Worst of all is when a government supports an independent intelligence establishment within its ranks and shares its paranoia. It will try to conceal and keep secret every crime; even those committed against its own citizens. It will try to prevent the airing, publication or prosecution of any wrong-doing and hide behind 'official secrets' acts and conditions of employment agreements that are legally void in the event of the witnessing of a crime according to international law. The Nuremberg war crimes trials established this law and the precedent to which all governments of civilized countries are supposedly subject, although most pretend that it does not apply to them.

Richard Nixon (who achieved original fame by riding on Senator

Joseph McCarthy's 'anti-communist' coat-tails) tried desperately to hide behind 'national security' in order to cover up and keep the story of the Watergate break-in from reaching the public. The Peter Wright *Spycatcher* and John Stalker cases are further examples of disclosures that the British Government is trying to cover up. People who make these and similar disclosures and not those they accuse are often put on trial. Thus precedents established at the end of the Second World War are flouted everywhere today.

German and Japanese 'war criminals' were gaoled or executed for committing or condoning unethical acts in wartime. They were punished for failing to disclose and stop horrendous crimes committed in the name of national security and in order to 'win the war'. They insisted that they had merely followed orders or acted as they did because of loyalty oaths sworn to their governments. The German and Japanese leaders were found guilty in varying degrees. Are British, American and other countries' military and civil government leaders and employees exempt from these obligations?

It is an absurdity to believe that the same kind of intelligence and strategies used to maintain peace also win wars. The characteristics of peace, like those of a game played to be drawn – systematic strategies, sound economics and the open pursuit of science and art – demand fair dealing, openness, trust and reliability, mutual error correction and a sharing of information. The processes of peace are therefore totally predictable and the very opposite of those that govern war. Success in war depends on secrecy and the creation of ever-increasing chaos – the strategies and tactics needed to win games of strategy and chance. According to Sun Tzu:

All warfare is based on deception . . . there has never been a protracted war from which a country has benefited . . . Where the army is, prices are high; when prices rise the wealth of the people is exhausted . . . Generally in war it is the best policy to take the state intact; to ruin it is inferior to this . . . To capture the enemy's army is better than to destroy it . . . For to win one hundred victories in one hundred battles is not the acme of skill . . . Thus what is of supreme importance in war is to attack the enemy's strategy . . . Next best is to disrupt his alliances . . . Next best is to attack his army . . . The worst policy is to attack his cities . . . Thus those skilled in war subdue the enemy without battle . . . Your aim is to take All-under-Heaven intact. Thus your troops will not be worn out and your gains will be complete. This is the art of offensive strategy.[30]

Machiavelli was aware of some of these truths, although his writing is far less succinct than that of Sun Tzu. The following is outstanding for its simplicity and convergence with the principles of game playing, and explains just how wars are provoked:

The cause of war . . . consists of some incident which is brought about . . . by those who are desirous of provoking a war . . . if I want to make war on some Prince . . . rather than attack him, I shall look for some justification and ground for attacking one of his allies, knowing full well that, if his ally be attacked, either he will resent it and I shall get what I want in that war will arise, or, if he takes no notice, he will disclose either his weakness or his unreliability in that he does not defend a dependent state.

Although to use fraud in any action is detestable, yet in the conduct of a war it is praiseworthy and glorious.[31]

Sun Tzu realized that war is an admission of failure by governments to coexist peacefully. But should this happen, the object of war should be to restore peace at the earliest moment rather than to indulge in an orgy of destruction. The latter has been the tendency of generals and war departments who subscribe to the von Clausewitz philosophy, which is deeply embedded in the mechanization of warfare. N. F. Dixon describes some of the consequences of the application of von Clausewitz's principles by the US military in Vietnam:

. . . the Vietnam war . . . cost the US 300 billion dollars; the US released 13 million tons of high explosive (more than six times that dropped by the US in all theatres of war throughout World War II); delivered 90,000 tons of gas and herbicides; delivered enough energy to displace 3.4 billion cubic yards of earth – ten times that required to dig both the Suez and Panama canals; wasted 20,000 square kilometres of forests and destroyed sufficient crops to feed two million people for a year; made 26 million craters and used enough raw materials and fuels to keep several major industries supplied for years.[32]

Approximately 1.9 million people were killed, 4.5 million wounded and 9 million became refugees.

The war in Vietnam was conducted by the US with maximum mechanization and computerization in many strategic aspects of decision-making. The results were an enormous expenditure of materiel, great loss of life and property on both sides, and the loss of the war and prestige by the US. Because the Vietcong applied the principles of Sun Tzu – guerrilla warfare in various guises – it defeated the US.

R. B. Asprey sums up conventional military thinking and incompetence as reflected in the von Clausewitz philosophy, in Vietnam and more recently in Afghanistan, Central America, Iran and Iraq and in computerized, artificially intelligent, military expert systems:

From Darius onward, we find commanders cursed with an arrogance of ignorance often compounded by arrogance of power . . . and we find their soldiers and people paying a heavy cost in consequence . . .[33]

Asprey has no illusions that war is a social or any other kind of science or an art. He shows that it is never heroic and contradicts the myth of the feudal code of chivalry, a murderous creed elevated to honourable status by sycophantic bards, troubadours and jingoists of the past and present. He cites the example of Charlemagne who murdered 4,600 unarmed Saxons, and of the Byzantine Emperor Basil II (976–1025) who returned 15,000 men he had defeated in battle to their master, the Bulgarian Tzar, blinded except for one hundred to serve as their guides. Asprey also quotes Colonel B. Griffith, a former US marine who understood warfare better than most: 'Guerrilla warfare [i.e. warfare by trickery and deception] is more scientific than a bayonet charge.'

War-games played along conventional lines, and the assumption that they could lead to strategic and tactical expert systems or artificially intelligent decision-making, are not only counterproductive and a waste of the taxpayers' money, but they endanger the peace. They reinforce the erroneous belief that wars are won by scientifically determined strategies and superior force, as proposed by von Clausewitz, instead of the deceptive tactics detailed by Sun Tzu. No computer could suggest a never-ending catalogue of dirty tricks that would induce and take advantage of an enemy's mistakes. Nor could it suborn his supporters, allies and soldiers and corrupt his spies. That is the intelligence and those are the tactics that can enhance the probability, but could never guarantee the certainty of success in war.

Military textbook answers – the only ones that could be programmed to serve as expert systems – lead to inevitable defeat because they can be foreseen by any potential enemy. The military tend to prepare for and fight the next war on the basis of strategies used in the last. But improvisation and a constant change of tactics are the recipes for success in war. What is significant in the context of this book is that such unreliability cannot be programmed.

Untrustworthiness, irrationality and unpredictability are the characteristics of successful warfare. In peacetime these are the characteristics of the insane and those who are criminally inclined. The qualities that imbue a general or war leader with the highest intelligence are his awareness of the need for constant treachery towards any aggressor, to know when to stop, and to distinguish between the behaviours that maintain peace and those that restore it in the event of an unprovoked attack. Such a leader can afford to resort to what would amount at other times to criminal or insane behaviours, temporarily and within defensible limits in times of war, and a nation is safe in his hands in times of peace, for he knows how to behave appropriately in both circumstances.

Small wonder that conventional war-games turn into military disasters when the tactics that allowed them to be won are misunderstood, misinterpreted and applied in actual war, in the prevention of war and in peacetime. Robert McNamara, US Secretary of Defense during the Kennedy and Johnson Administrations, later regretted his reliance on war-game models that had predicted that the Vietnam war would be won by the mid-1960s. Quite aside from any ethical issues that were involved, McNamara and the Pentagon did not realize that it was not the game analogy that was wrong, but their understanding of how games and wars are won and lost. No expert system or computer could have helped them achieve that understanding for as long as their premises were wrong from the start.

The obsession with war-gaming by governments and the military had other peacetime consequences. It generated a constant growth in the commercial market for war and other competitive games, arcade and computer game addiction, a proliferation of TV shows dedicated to the winning spirit in all its forms, and a growing acceptance of hostility in public and private behaviour. All reinforce one another and the compulsion to win, to defeat a symbolic enemy whether represented by an arcade machine or computer, or a business or other rival. The dividing line between fiction and reality becomes blurred when people can no longer distinguish between a fictional film or TV drama 'baddie' and someone overtaking them on the road in a car. All of these 'encounters' incite obsessive 'winning' and tend to heighten irritation and conflict rather than an awareness of how social situations can be made to work smoothly.

The progression from John Wayne and Sylvester Stallone to do-it-yourself violence is an inevitable and predictable consequence. Like all conditioned behaviours it becomes addictive and is bound to escalate perpetually. We have progressed from brutal comic books and violence watched passively on TV [34] to the world's first living DIY video game: Planet Photon – a franchised game centre, of which there were thirty in the US, fifteen in Canada and more planned there and in Europe:

Three dollars later, equipped with a Photon phaser . . . and £118-worth of Photon helmet, Photon control module, and power pack, you become a Photon warrior. Two teams of ten Photon warriors . . . then spend six minutes roaming around a 10,000 sq ft play area – an extra-terrestrial planet-scape of strange lights . . . and battlements. Object of the game is to score as many points as possible by shooting (or as they say in Photon lingo 'disrupting') members of the opposing team . . . [35]

A more recent US expression of this trend is 'interactive TV', the 1987/8 toy fad:

The [laser simulation gun] toys are activated by light pulses from the TV . . . 'Captain Power and the Soldiers of the Future' is shown on 96 American TV stations and is billed as 'a dynamic entertainment vehicle for the whole family' . . . 'the most violent children's television programme ever produced', with 130 acts of violence per hour, an attempted murder every 30 seconds, and a killing every minute . . . [36]

The trouble is that (like the gradual increases in death and paralysis caused by school rugby between 1977 and 1984) these developments are not noticed by most people, especially if they only live in the present and have little or no interest in history. Thus they believe that things have always been this way and are not aware of the erosion of values that generate friendliness in favour of those that stimulate violence and competitiveness including, of course, the self-defence required by provocative aggression.

Nearly every amusement arcade, computer shop, classroom, comic book, film or TV drama now fosters the idea that we live in a hostile universe. Perpetual competition forms a closed feed-back loop that reinforces the paranoia and lack of human consideration already rampant in today's societies. Increasing football hooliganism, violence in the classroom, on the street and in the home are provocations for a necessary increase in violent defensive responses by individuals and the police; symptoms of a society addicted to the principles embedded in all games played to be won rather than drawn.

It has been said that war is too serious a business to be left to the experts. That is equally true for peace-keeping. The myths of computerized expert systems and artificial intelligence demonstrably heighten the danger of yet another major war, irrespective of agreements between superpowers to limit their nuclear or conventional arsenals. These are token gestures for as long as there is no serious change in political, military and especially psychological orientation among world leaders and people of all ages and in every walk of life.

Limiting nuclear weapons and scrapping a few obsolete ones does not guarantee anything: it is a politically expedient 'winning' ploy designed for home consumption. It was Ronald Reagan's bid to be remembered in the history books for more than Irangate and the bankrupting of the US economy. It was also probably Gorbachev's ploy to divert attention from the internal reforms he tried to initiate against stiff opposition.

We have seen that despite the experiences of the First World War, where poison gases were used by both sides, and despite implicit agreements between the major powers not to use them again (observed even by Hitler), chemical weapons are used once a stalemate or a defeat threatens, as they were in Vietnam by the US and by both sides in the war between Iran and Iraq. There is no reason to suppose that nuclear arms limitation agreements would fare differently in similar circumstances, given the current military and political orientation everywhere in the world. For as long as nuclear weapons exist, once conventional war is declared between the so-called superpowers and it begins to look as if one or the other side may lose, the chances of nuclear war will be considerably increased, especially if we leave the decisions to use these weapons to human or mechanical robots. We have seen the consequences of such decision-making at the Nuremberg and Tokyo war crimes trials after the Second World War, and at the My-lai courts-martial during the Vietnam war.

A machine that thinks like a human being is an absurdity; a human being who thinks like a machine in critical situations is an obscenity.

Conclusions

This book deals in part with a powerful method of systems analysis (see Appendix B) that has enabled me to define every possible form of learning within any defined environment. Because learning applies to anything we can know, whatever method provides an analysis of the learning process applies to everything else, by definition. Using this method I have presented some of the options for our possible individual and collective future evolution, more in cultural than in genetic terms. The most important of these concern the re-definition of terms that have been persistently misinterpreted throughout most of human history. The findings on which this book is based place the study and understanding of inorganic and organic behaviour, learning and human nature on a far more rational basis than heretofore. They provide the basis for extracting the factually based meanings of human behaviour, which were considered to be matters of opinion for far too long (see Appendix C).

This does not mean that our everyday behaviours and relationships ought to be turned into another pseudo-science or that we all must turn into saints. Quite the contrary. The creative and essentially subjective aspects of life, nature, love of self, of other human beings, art, science, worthwhile work and goals of any kind are far too complex to be regimented – and they should not be, even when this seems possible. Only the relatively objective and mechanical operations in any field of endeavour can ever be mechanized successfully. The subjective ones can be considered systematically, but only to a point at which we can extract principles. At the same time none of these vital concerns should be thought of as value free, for then our existence remains meaningless and a matter of chance and uncertainty.

Despite the fact that we must accept that our knowledge will always be incomplete, an understanding of the fundamental principles on which nature operates allows us to distil any truth we seek from the welter of possibilities. We then discover that one of the underlying rules of existence is that ethics are the products of natural law and not matters of opinion or religious dogma. However, we must also accept that an ethical individual is not one who is always ethical, but one who knows when he has been unethical; that a truthful person is one who knows when he is lying and does not lie to him- or herself; and that all of existence is conditionally deterministic.

But before we can apply any of this, the principles of learning and of behaviour must be understood in a self-disciplined, systematic and totally objective (i.e. scientific) manner, if only to protect those who understand from attempted inroads made into their freedom and autonomy by those who are immune to love, friendship, compassion and foresight. These are insights dramatized perhaps better by the game metaphor than by any other.

Another and obvious conclusion is that the future matters far more than the past. None the less, the past is interesting if only for purely historic and aesthetic reasons and so that we can admire the work of those who built on co-operative principles which, while perhaps not articulated and often misunderstood, lie at the core of all human, creative achievement. With these exceptions, our forebears who acted on the wrong competitive principles appear to have little to teach us, except to allow us to learn from their mistakes. Given the history of mankind, we enjoy a superfluity of crass and horrible examples.

The future does seem full of promise for it opens far more doors than it closes. There can be something in it for everyone, either as active explorers of the vast and perpetually growing number of creative 'draw' options in any field of endeavour, or as more passive beneficiaries of the infinite number that are yet to be discovered. Each of us has the option of participating either as a player or as an observer.

Only those individuals and groups of both sexes who have a vested interest in trying to victimize their fellows, or who may consciously or subconsciously attempt to benefit from such victimization, are likely to feel themselves threatened by what I have written. But even they can learn if they want to.

It does not matter whether these ideas are or are not applied at this time. But it is vital that they be discussed. I am certain that they or variations on them will evolve and gain in credence, dominance and perfection sooner or later, for our understanding of many processes that are now only half-understood – like the functioning of our very genes – is at stake. For example, it is now planned to tag every gene in terms of its functions in order to intervene more successfully in the future in animal husbandry, hybrid plant development and human health. This will be a gigantic task that, facilitated by the fastest parallel-linked computers, may still take a decade to complete. However, it may turn out to be a waste of time and money, for the answers to the questions being asked do not lie in individual genes but in the combinatorial relationships between the gene structures themselves and the larger environment within which they exist – a level of complexity so vast that we will never be able to catalogue the sum of all those combinatorial possibilities.

Even so, the classification of combinatorial possibilities for gene and chromosomal relationships (using exactly the same mathematics as those given in this book) should enable experts in this field to reach conclusions in areas that matter most, without attempted encyclopedic knowledge or pretended omniscience. Here, as always, (e.g. the causes and cure of enuresis), the question is one of method and an understanding of meanings.

The analytic principles on which this book is based have been discovered and forgotten repeatedly in history. In modern times quantification was attempted by Anatol Rapoport[1] (who miscalculated and believed the combinatorial sum of all possibilities to be $2^{n(n-1)}$). This mathematical error was copied by von Bertalanffy,[2] Stafford Beer[3] and others, and has stood in the way of classification, understanding and discrete application of the combinatorial sum of all possibilities in diagnostics and prediction. Even at $n = 4$, Rapoport's miscalculation generates 2^{12} possibilities – far too many to be examined or tested in detail. Ashby,[4] who tried to quantify an $n = 4$ directed graph, arrived at 20 possibilities – fewer than the number of permutations. Buckminster Fuller also miscalculated. Recent 'simplex' methods (see Appendix B) have come closer than any of these.

The earliest Taoists seem to have worked out the combinatorial sum of all possibilities with precision up to $n = 3$ and $n = 4$ in the form of the I Ching. Certain Hindu, Sufi, Pythagorean, Druid and other sects discovered the same or similar methods for themselves and applied them in various ways. Ramon Lull, Giordano Bruno and Leonardo da Vinci, as well as 'alchemists' and medieval mathematicians, possibly calculated and used these methods successfully, but were disbelieved or discredited as heretics, or kept their discoveries secret.

Some were side-tracked into metaphysical or religious dogma, or formed or joined cults that violated what is essentially the celebration of autonomy and self-discovery – the discovery of the self by the self without self-effacement. For still others the time was wrong. I believe that the time for the generalization of this idea has come or else it would not have found a sympathetic publisher. Still, I may be wrong, in which case it will have to wait until some other era.

For all these reasons there is no cause to worry about the future of the world. It will certainly survive, perhaps not as we know it. I do hope, however, that it will be spared the miseries that predictably lie ahead for a considerable period of time if we do not heed nature's laws. Each of us creates his and her own fate or allows it to be created by others. Our collective future, far from being in the hands of chance, lies in our own. Which future prevails is a matter of choice for everyone individually and for all of us together.

Appendices

Appendix A shows the *geometric method* used to analyse and classify the sum of all causal and consequential combinatorial possibilities for the game of noughts and crosses, and the operations that bring them about. The given conclusions are based on a three dimensional, domain-defined analytic model that displays all possible strategic and tactical choices for both players (see diagram 2) as well as the reasons for making them, including won, lost, drawn and stalemated games, errors and intentions. This method provides the basis for deducing the feelings and beliefs of the players (i.e. the psychological factors). Obviously the sums involved are too great to permit more than a few representative games to be considered. The accompanying text provides the criteria needed to interpret the model.

This same modelling technique can be used to analyse other transactional relationships in any given context. In order to understand the differences between games that are won, lost, drawn, stalemated or incomplete, it is necessary to refer both to the text and to the classification system in Appendix B wherever indicated. Most words for which meanings may be in question are defined in Appendix C.

Appendix B consists of a *mathematical model* that makes it possible to consider the sum of all combinatorial possibilities and, at the same time, to reduce that sum to essentials (i.e. radical data reduction, equivalent to a 'jump to conclusion'), irrespective of subject matter or context, as a result of an infinite set of classification algorithms shown in the tables. The modules, all of which are shown for $n = 4$ and one for $n = 5$, can be combined in a number of ways to make up any three-dimensional model (like that shown in Appendix A for noughts and crosses), which provides perfect causal and consequential foresight and hindsight within any domain-defined environment. This is, therefore, a syntactic (order and arrangement) and semantic (meaning) decoding mechanism; a neural-network representation that provides deep insights into relatively objective and subjective processes of learning, thought and behaviour.

Today's computers are excellent syntax manipulators (i.e. they can shuffle letters, words, numbers or other symbols in all permutations with maximum speed and efficiency, limited only by processing time and programming). But until now, to my knowledge, no genuine aid to semantic (i.e. meaning) decoding has existed.

The semantic and syntactic/sequential decoding mechanism provided by the classification of the sum of all combinatorial possibilities generates all the choices there are – past, present and future – and classifies them into categories, groups, families and individually unique states. The time it takes to do this, given the fastest, modern, parallel-linked mainframe computers, depends on the number of factors the user wants to consider and the method used to winnow them down to essentials. I suggest that the methods shown here are the fastest and best super simplex mathematical and hence mechanical ones that are possible at this time. Given this method, it is still up to human beings to·select their goal in advance (as to which portion of the sum of all possibilities they wish to consider), and to make the value judgements required to choose the most appropriate out of the sum of residual possibilities. Any computer can generate these as a result of the classification method shown in Appendix B and facilitate the kind of semantic analysis that provides the meanings given in Appendix C.

What I have discovered and developed seems to be, therefore, a model of how we think, up to the point of valuative decision-making both before and after significant portions of the classified sum of all combinatorial possibilities have been considered. This faces us with the fact that only we can make the required value judgements before and after the purely mechanical sifting process involved in data-processing of any kind. This same model is also an analogue of how intentions, goals, feelings and beliefs can be analysed and understood. The decision as to how and to what to apply this method is up to the user. It is certainly 'user-friendly', to use a modern cliché.

But it also provides the limits imposed by nature on what it is possible to model mechanically.

Appendix C consists of a *glossary of defined terms* used throughout this book. Many differ from those given in standard dictionaries, but their new meanings have been extracted by means of a causal-consequential-operational analysis of games, using the modelling methods described in Appendices A and B. The definitions are limited by space considerations. Words and phrases that are defined in the text of this book are not duplicated in the glossary. All words defined in the text and in the glossary can be found in the subject index.

If nothing else, the glossary provides the parameters of meanings within which this book was conceived. These meanings are internally and externally consistent and, barring error in detail, they are totally objective (i.e. causal and consequential, seen from outside any system under consideration and including subjective and relatively objective vectors of choice).

Appendix A – Geometric Analysis of Games

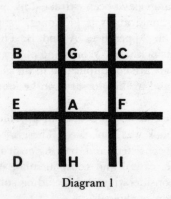

Diagram 1

Diagram 1 is a conventional noughts and crosses game diagram. The first moving player uses O and the second X in all following demonstrations. Only three-in-a-row combinations of the symbols XXX or OOO placed horizontally, vertically or diagonally, and no others (e.g. OXO), define 'winning' in the conventional sense. The letters A, B, C, etc. are coordinates that remain constant and in place on this game diagram and in the analytic models shown below.

Diagram 2 represents the possible relationships between both players and the game diagram for noughts and crosses in an unconventional manner. It is a three-dimensional analytic model that generates the brute force sum of all combinatorial possibilities for two players in their relationships to one another, to the game diagram and the symbols used in play. In other words, this model makes it possible to analyse all games begun by either player from any one of the nine squares of the game diagram. The arrows that indicate the data flow are left out here for the sake of clarity, but are shown in following analytic diagrams.

Close attention must be paid to each arrow's direction and the meanings assigned to it in order to understand this method of behavioural analysis. The arrows indicate the state of play, define

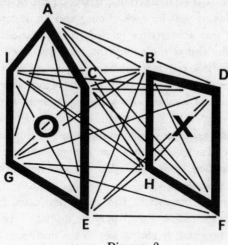

Diagram 2

the individual players' goals, intentions, strategies and tactics, and provide clues to the feelings and beliefs of both. This is so because the arrows indicate all possible options for playing this game and the sum of all turns, goals and intentions for past and future choices as well as outcomes, end states and consequences about which the players can only have feelings and beliefs, unless they know exactly what they are doing, why and how. In that case they need not be guided by feelings or beliefs.

Thus in diagram 2, two arrows, each pointing in an opposite direction (i.e. providing a binary 'yes' or 'no' choice), would be found on every line, including the heavy ones that define the players' respective domains. Every arrow indicates one possible direction of the data flow options. Taken together they provide all the choices there are within this finite representation of noughts and crosses. No other directions (i.e. choices) are available for reaching whichever objective a player may select (win, lose, draw or stale-mate), even if he plays at random. In practice, of course, there can only be one arrow per line in each analytic diagram because only one binary choice is possible at any one time.

This directed graph technique enables the analyst to deduce his own and the other player's intentions (i.e. the causes) and likely feelings (i.e. good, bad or indifferent), based on his or her beliefs concerning the chosen goal (or lack of one) and an understanding of how or why it was achieved or missed (the operations) at any stage, including the end of the game (the consequences). In other words such an analysis provides considerable insight into the self, the psyche of other players and the multiplicity of available options. Essentially this model enables the analyst not only to discover 'how', but also 'why'. The latter is the question – and answer – modern science has tried to evade for the same reasons as it has closed its mind to all subjective ones – an abrogation of responsibility. In time this method, or any other like it, could help bring about more responsible attitudes.

The analytic model consists of two parts (indicated by heavy lines) – a five-pointed figure (the O player's domain – because he has five turns if the game is played out to the end) and a square (the X player's domain – consisting of only four turns). Generally it is believed that 'more is better' because five turns are more than four; and that therefore the player who goes first (i.e. the O player or 'white' in chess) has a considerable advantage as far as winning is concerned because he can take advantage of the other player one turn earlier. Some people even believe that the first moving player can dominate and force a draw (i.e. agreement) on the other. But this again shows that the 'bigger bastard' principle holds true for all forms of behaviour based on the wrong beliefs. (See page 334 for a fuller explanation of why the belief in any first turn advantage is an error.)

In other words all beliefs based on anything other than facts are wrong, and this is where analyses based on the classified sum of all possibilities can help make the distinctions between right and wrong no matter what people believe – unless a reader is convinced that there is no such thing as right and wrong.

The sum of all combinatorial possibilities for noughts and crosses (when n = 9):

$$=9 \times 2^{36}$$
$$=9 \times 68{,}719{,}476{,}736$$

The first turn possibilities:

$$= 9 \times 268, 435, 456$$

The reason for these huge sums is that every one of the nine possible first moves is defined by the combinatorial sum for future possibilities. The second turn future possibilities are reduced substantially and no real hindsight and only limited foresight are possible at that stage of the game unless players are totally aware. Therefore the second turn options are relatively limited compared to the first and all following turns:

$$= 9 \times 16,777,216$$

The possibilities for succeeding turns can be calculated by multiplying by 9 the sums given in Appendix B, table 9, for n = 9. The sum of all combinatorial possibilities for the last turn (i.e. the first moving player's fifth turn) at which only past, but no future options exist:

$$= 9 \times 66,296,291,072$$

This model therefore provides perfect hindsight and foresight (i.e. total awareness) as far as this game is concerned. It can be equally precise when used to predict the relationship possibilities for any other subject, provided they are modelled in a similar manner and when a sufficient number of facts are known. The mathematical principles and criteria for predictions of any sort based on them are described in Appendix B.

Underlying all of this are very simple principles concerning operant conditioning, programming and learning that are defined and elaborated in Appendix B, diagrams 1 and 2.

INTENTIONS, FEELINGS AND BELIEFS

This model is *totally objective* (i.e. it permits *inductive* and *deductive* analyses to be made based on internally self-defined and externally verifiable criteria (see Appendix B), seen from outside the universe of discourse represented by the game. It includes both players and the *relatively objective* and *subjective* components that are involved in play, i.e. their goals, intentions, feelings and beliefs. Their relationship can be seen in a relatively objective context (in which each treats the other as an object, seeks to defeat him and 'feels successful' if he succeeds); and/or in a *subjective* one (e.g. co-operating with actual or potential equals to achieve the earliest draw, an agreement-to-agree, and feeling happy when that outcome is in sight or has been achieved); and/or viewed in a *relatively subjective* way (e.g. arriving at a stalemate and having your feelings hurt because you did not win).

It is equally possible that you do not care. You may believe that it does not matter which direction you take, which goal to choose, or that you do not know how to choose (i.e. you are depressed). For not caring, being unable or unwilling to choose or try out a new direction is equivalent to having no choice at all. This leads directly to a limited, perpetually recurrent, closed feedback loop, which manifests itself in depression and mental disorder (i.e. disordered thought). See Appendix B, diagram 4, and table 2, n = 4, category III, coordinates D1 and A8.

The approach to behavioural analysis demonstrated in this book demands only that the reader lets go of past conditioning. The best way to test my assertions is to play noughts and crosses with different people (i.e. by *induction*) and to keep track of their and your own reactions no matter what the outcomes may be. Or you can study the problem by *deduction*, using the illustrations given below and in Appendix B. Either way you will be able to predict outcomes and consequences with increasing precision as time goes by. To all intents and purposes you will be able to read your own and other people's minds as far as this game is concerned. Eventually you can transfer these new powers to other games, subjects and people who interest you.

To reiterate, the 'intentions' of the players are modelled in the analytic diagrams by the direction of the arrows (see diagrams 4, 5, 6, 8, 10 and 12). Any reversal of even a single arrow literally represents a 'change of mind'.

Diagram 3 is a conventional noughts and crosses diagram of a game that has ended as a stalemate because both players believe that this outcome is worthless. This belief is, of course, impossible to deduce from the game diagram, but the analytic one (diagram 4) shows why. This is not a draw for the reasons given below. The numbers in the squares (1, 2, 3, etc.) designate moves relative to

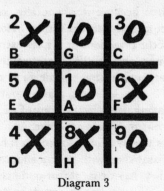

Diagram 3

each player's turn as shown in diagram 4 and in following ones. These numbers change position within both the game and the analytic diagrams for each different game. The odd numbers represent the first moving player's move on each turn, and the even ones those of the second. (The meaning of the letters of the alphabet on this and following diagrams were explained in the text accompanying diagram 1.)

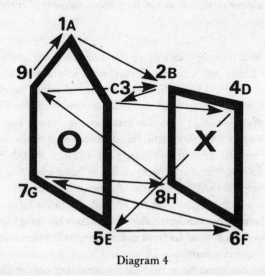

Diagram 4

Diagram 4 represents the analytic model that matches the game shown in diagram 3. As stated, this is a mutual stalemate (an agreement to disagree) because it is a totally conditioned system with wrong feedback to both players within a closed environment. This is indicated by the directions of the arrows (from 9I, the last move, to 1A, the first, and to 2B, the second player's domain, leading to endless repetition of the same or a similar game). In other words there is feedback to both players, but it leads to wrong conclusions – i.e. playing again in the hope of winning in the belief that this stalemated outcome does not count.

Each player thinks that he would have won if he had not made a mistake. Both are dissatisfied with such a supposedly meaningless outcome, because they have run out of options and believe that there is no possibility of extending this game to any larger universe of discourse. They are likely to be depressed. So they keep repeating that game out of boredom and in the hope that one of them will win (one form of addiction).

This is also equivalent to a marriage where both partners perpetually fight, which becomes habitual so that they cannot leave each other alone. The fact is that they do not know how to co-operate – come to a binding agreement about staying together or separating – either of which would be a good way out of their closed feedback loop.

Diagram 5 is a different stalemate demonstrated by the analytic model – one arrow has changed direction in relation to all others (that from 1A to 9I). This indicates a 'change of mind' on the part of the first moving player. The situation is exactly the same as in diagrams 3 and 4, except that the first moving player knows that 'there is no way to win' this game (his arrow points to the last turn conclusion), but the second one insists on a return match because he hopes to do better and win (perpetual feedback from his point of view). However that will be a waste of time unless the first moving player makes a bad mistake and the second one takes advantage of it. He may then be jubilant. But what has he won? A more important question should be 'how did he win?' Was there anything 'superior' about his strategy?

What is most interesting is that the first moving player also does not understand what all of this means, because he thinks that this outcome has only come about because noughts and crosses is trivial

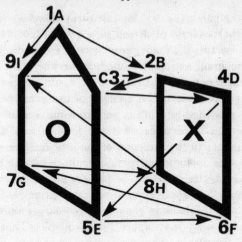

Diagram 5

and still believes that winning is all that counts in chess and other more complex games and sports.

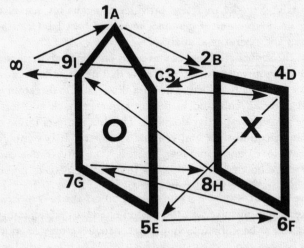

Diagram 6

Diagram 6 represents an analysis of a draw (an agreement to agree) – the best possible outcome played out to the last turn – because neither side has made any mistakes. The arrows point from the *conclusion* of the game (i.e. 9I, the last turn) to *infinity* (i.e. any enlargement of the universe of discourse, e.g. an 11 × 11 game, with 5-in-a-row counting as a victory), with the right kind of feedback (i.e. perpetual learning) to both players (i.e. the arrows that point from infinity to 1A and 2B).

This is perhaps the most useful analysis of the game played in diagram 3 and modelled previously in diagrams 4 and 5. The outcome is superficially identical, but the implications differ as shown by the changes in the direction of the arrows. The result is perfect in all respects, including perpetual feedback to both players. They agree that no better game can be played. But there is also an extension to infinity (i.e. application of the same principle to more difficult games) and feedback to each from any larger universe of discourse to which both may apply this principle. That is the equivalent of a friendship, happy marriage, business or other relationship in which both partners share the same interests and values and learn perpetually together.

The psychological subtleties remain invisible as far as the actual game diagram is concerned, but they become visible on the analytic one. The analytic model therefore provides a means for semantic decoding – i.e. extraction of genuine meanings based on causal, consequential and operational analyses.

Note that the sequence of moves and turns on this analytic model (diagram 6) are equivalent to a tennis rally that never ends because both players are equally skilled. The data flow (i.e. the direction of the arrows) moves evenly and in perfect sequence back and forth between the players' respective domains. This is a representation of perfect balance, equilibrium and genuine symmetry. It is symbolic of agreement, love, understanding, sharing, equality, order and peace. There are only two better games that can be played, one of which is shown in the next diagram.

Diagrams 7 and 8 are respectively a game diagram and an analytic model of one of the best games that can possibly be played. Both players can predict, after the first two turns, what the outcome will be. There is only one better way to play: if both really understood what is involved they would not need to play this game. They would know and agree to the outcome in advance of play and save time and energy applying the draw principle to more important subjects

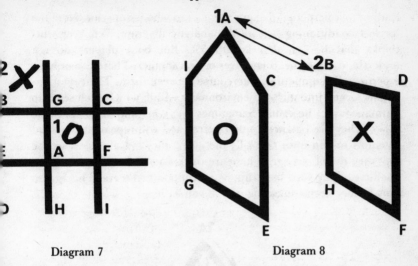

Diagram 7   Diagram 8

that interest them individually or together, as I have tried to do in this book. From then on they would only play noughts and crosses for fun, to teach others or to make a point. It would be pointless to play for any other reason.

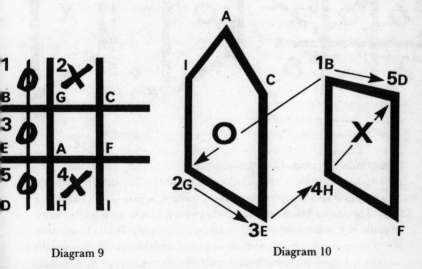

Diagram 9   Diagram 10

Diagrams 9 and 10 are examples of one of the worst games that can be played – the earliest victory for the first moving player, leading to a perpetual disagreement as to who is superior. Note the 'perfect conditioning' within the analytic diagram. Whoever wins thinks that he (or she) is superior. But both players do not understand the game, themselves or one another. There can only be a perpetually competitive intercourse between them. Their relationship is locked into a closed environment within which each seeks to outmanoeuvre the other. Sometimes one wins and sometimes the other. They are balanced only in error and will repeat their stupid attempts to win until one kills the other, they get divorced, or the day they die of old age. These are the *conditions* for disagreements, conflicts of any sort, bankruptcy, corruption and wars. This is also how history keeps repeating itself if you let it.

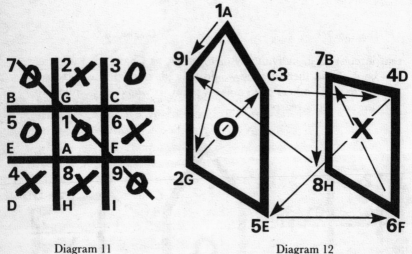

Diagram 11   Diagram 12

Diagrams 11 and 12 represent an even worse game than that shown in diagrams 9 and 10 – one won on the last turn by the first moving player. The utter confusion within the analytic diagram is representative of that in the minds of both players. Neither understands the game or what is being achieved. Both have tried everything to frustrate and defeat one another until one finally makes a big enough mistake spontaneously or one player induces his partner to make a mistake, of which the other then takes advantage. What has he won? This is what must eventually occur in chess championships, wars and other disagreeable human relationships that are played to be won by default rather than ended by agreement.

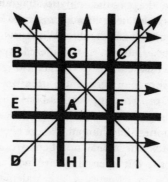

Diagram 13

Diagram 13 demonstrates how misleading any superficial analysis of the game diagram can be. It suggests that there are twenty-four ways to win by actual count (3 × 8), starting from each square in turn. When these victories will occur is anyone's guess because there is no way to predict them. The earliest 'victory' can occur on the first player's third turn as shown in diagrams 9 and 10, and by either player on any turn thereafter. The second moving player can take advantage of his partner one turn later by trading on his spontaneous or induced errors (i.e. by being the 'bigger bastard'). None of this can be predicted, except in principle.

However, draws can be predicted before the game begins and at any time thereafter, yet they seem to be unpredictable to most conventional players. They usually do not discover that 'no one can win' (a very big error) until the last-but-one turn. Less conventional, independent and more experienced players know much earlier what will occur, but often do not understand what any of this means.

However those players who become or remain unconditioned, think for themselves and look at the facts without prejudice, know that they will 'win' as soon as they see another player make a mistake, but help him correct it and then achieve a draw on the last-but-one turn. Others reach the same conclusion together, early or late in the game. But only the most foresighted are able to extend the draw principle to other matters and behaviour (inorganic and organic) in general.

The mathematical tables shown in Appendix B can enable anyone to learn, generalize and apply the analytic, diagnostic and forecasting method shown here for noughts and crosses to any other subject. The possible precision is considerable. When the classified sum of all combinatorial possibilities is considered systematically and mechanically (i.e. without any advance or *post facto* value judgements, and in the absence of deliberate, attentive human players – i.e. mathematically or by computer), about 97 per cent of all noughts and crosses games are inevitably drawn or stalemated. With valuative awareness any human players should achieve a 100 per cent success rate. The actual numbers are arrived at by the following calculations, but even they are not absolutely correct because some games in category I are stalemates that are not isolated here:

About $9 \times 66,634,697,304$ games are draws and stalemates [categories II and III plus $y = 1 + 2$ in category I]; see Appendix B, table 9; $n = 9$.

$9 \times 66,634,697,304$ divided by $9 \times 68,719,476,736$ (the combinatorial sum of all possibilities for $n = 9$), multiplied by $100 = 96.966$

Therefore about 97 per cent of all noughts and crosses games should be draws and stalemates and about 3 per cent would be won and lost when all possible games are played out mechanically (i.e. mindlessly and without thought) as a finite series.

THE SYMMETRIES OF THE GAME

Diagrams 14 and 15 represent a game and an analytic diagram demonstrating the so-called symmetries of noughts and crosses, used by conventional game theorists to 'prove' their beliefs and prejudicial value judgements. According to conventional game theory, these symmetries restrict the possibilities for the first few turns. They preclude starting wherever you wish in successive games and limit the players' choices. That is why many insist that 'no one can win this game'. But starting in any one of the nine cells is one of the few techniques that can confuse an inexperienced or inattentive player and one that makes it possible to win the game by being a 'bigger bastard' – a principle that applies to all games of strategy played to be won and to all games of chance.

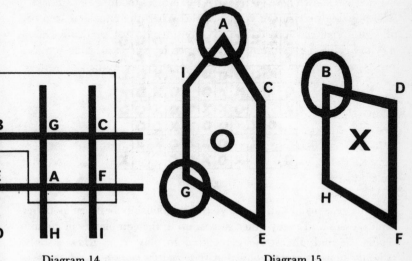

Diagram 14   Diagram 15

This absurdity is matched by the open-ended 'decision tree', an inconclusive and arbitrary model that analysts use to rationalize their beliefs and prejudices. Small wonder that they have come to the wrong conclusions about noughts and crosses and other games and when their interpretation of the game metaphor is applied to real-life strategies and behaviours.

The restrictions imposed by game theorists make it impossible to gain any insight into this game, the orientation of the players, or to analyse why and how games are won, lost or drawn. Further, when these so-called symmetries are taken into account, the permutational sums that are generated ($3 \times 2 \times 7 \times 6 \times 5 \times 4 \times 3 \times 2 \times 1$ *or* $3 \times 3 \times 2 \times 7 \times 6 \times 5 \times 4 \times 3 \times 2 \times 1$) make no sense at all and become numerical absurdities (see *Permutations* below).

EXTENSION TO A LARGER UNIVERSE OF DISCOURSE

Diagram 16 shows a game diagram of noughts and crosses played to one of the earliest draws on an 11×11 field, with five-in-a-row as the 'winning' requirement. As pointed out in Chapter 9, this game is actually played in a number of cultures. It is interesting for

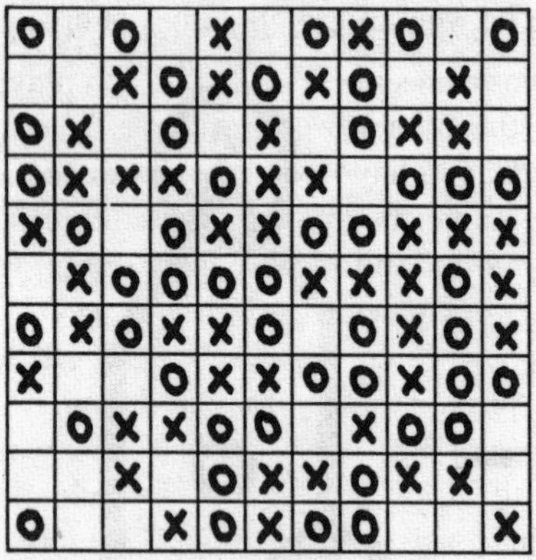

Diagram 16

various reasons. First, it shows the relationship between noughts and crosses and many other games, up to the complexity of go and chess. Second, the strategy required to play for a draw is only slightly more complex than that required for noughts and crosses, and yet some people have difficulty in discovering just what it is. Third, it also demonstrates that the conditions inevitably change with any enlargement of the universe of discourse (i.e. the 'winning' requirement of five-in-a-row). The three-in-a-row winning require-ment for the 3 × 3 game cannot apply here because, if it did, the game would nearly always end on the first moving player's third turn.

This example demonstrates that the whole idea of 'symmetries' is absurd, as I showed earlier, especially with this enlargement of the universe of discourse. With any complexity greater than noughts and crosses, the decision tree concept falls apart because it would take a twenty-four-sheet poster to develop it to any degree, and even then the players would have no idea as to what the 'best' moves should be. Finally, it also shows that ideas like symmetries, decision tree models and all the needlessly complex game theoretical jargon are academic smokescreens designed to hide the fact that those who use them have no idea what they are talking about.

The amount of attention needed to play the 11 × 11 game is only slightly greater than for play on a 3 × 3 field. As before, the key to a perfect outcome between equals is aggressively defensive, rather than offensive play; to challenge the other player, rather than to defeat him or to let him defeat you; and to pay careful attention to his and your own moves at every turn. Each player's main objective is not to allow the other to obtain three occupied cells in a row, open at both ends; you have lost the game by default if he does. The player who tries to get five-in-a-row, while neglecting to watch his game partner's moves and to play defensively, will lose every time unless, with luck, he achieves a stalemate.

The object of the game thus becomes a challenge for an active and aggressive pursuit of peaceful and benign goals, exciting in themselves – to spar but not to hurt; a creative learning situation that engages both players deeply for the sake of the thing itself, in which perfection consists of balance, harmony and peace, rather than the defeat of one by the other – the principle underlying the Oriental arts of self-defence.

THE CONVENTIONAL DECISION TREE MODEL

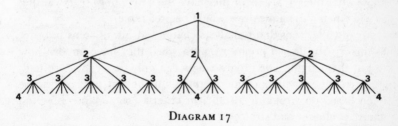

DIAGRAM 17

Diagram 17 is a conventional decision tree model for noughts and crosses, limiting it to the so-called symmetries of the game (i.e. one of the first three moves of the game without considering other possibilities). Such a representation is insufficient, inconclusive and non-predictive even for this trivial game. A huge sheet of paper would be required to model just the conventional permutational possibilities (to say nothing of the greater than two times sum that is required for a proper display of all permutations of this game). See *Permutations* below.

The combinatorial sum would probably require a sheet of paper large enough to wrap up the world and it would be meaningless, unless the generated patterns were classified, as they now are, and only a representative sum were displayed. It might then be possible, with more time and effort than anyone could afford, to extract the best and most successful and the worst strategies that I have isolated here on a few sheets of paper by jumping to the best and closest to perfect, or worst and most flawed conclusions, without needing to consider everything.

Yet this decision tree model is used for today's flow-charts, preparatory to writing computer programs for 'relational data bases' and other analytic or supposedly predictive and diagnostic software. As a result, many of today's computer programs – and especially those dealing with data bases, conceived on the basis of open vector flowcharts, decision tree models or statistical analyses – contain so many 'bugs' as to be virtually useless. No general analytic standard has existed until now, and the analyses that did work were usually the result of inspired intuition rather than systematic analysis. Most analysts make guesses while pretending to be knowing. Users can only complain. But they are also at fault because either they do not know what their goals are or they have the wrong ones (e.g. wanting to win when a dynamic draw would be preferable).

Meanwhile, consultant analysts charge exorbitant sums in order to tinker with flawed programs, even when they have no idea how to put them right. The programmers can only do as they are told. As a result, systems analytic methods taught and used today are often based on wrong or insufficient criteria (see Chapters 6–9 on games of chance and strategy).

Given this new method of classified combinatorial possibilities, analysis can be far more precise than it has ever been with a consequent drastic reduction in programming errors. One flaw in today's systems analysis concerns the conventional view of permutations and the rules that govern them.

PERMUTATIONS

The conventional permutation sum for $n = 9$

$$= 362,880$$

However, this sum only holds true for all noughts and crosses games played out to the last turn. It excludes the earliest draw (e.g. before and after the first or any following turn) or any so-called victory achieved earlier than the last turn. The sum that accounts for all possible permutations, from first move to last:

$$= n! \times >2<3$$

When n = 9

$$362,880 \times 2.718278777$$
$$= 986,409$$

In other words, the permutational sum of all games that can be played is more than twice and less than three times the conventional 9! sum, given in every maths textbook with which I am familiar. This is not a calculation error; it is an error in principle and concept, illustrated by the current infatuation with fractals.

For example, and as shown, the earliest victory for the first moving player can occur on his third turn. That game outcome, and every early draw or victory, are excluded from the conventional permutational sum. More significant is that all psychological and semantic factors – attention, intentions, goals, feelings, deception, understanding, agreement or error – are excluded even from the sum of all permutational possibilities as amended here.

When the so-called symmetries are taken into consideration, the permutational sum shrinks to a point at which it is useless for any analytic purpose. Depending on where the first moving player goes, the permutational sums for a 'symmetrically' reduced game of noughts and crosses are:

$$30,240 \text{ or}$$
$$45,360$$

FRACTALS

Fractals are one of the more recent fads in physics and computing. They consist of pretty repeating patterns (like wallpaper) that appear in full colour (or in black and white) on a computer's screen, generated by a mathematical program. One characteristic of such programs is that you can 'zoom' in or out in order to see more and more detail or obtain an overall view. This has given rise to a speculation that the universe and all things in it may be reflected by these patterns. That is true to a certain extent, for any mathematical formula will do the same (e.g. the generation of prime numbers and their composites). Were we to know and assemble all of them (numerically and graphically) we would have collected all the patterns in the universe. That is a futile, brute force exercise in pseudo-aesthetics, if only because there are too many patterns ever to be collected.

Meanwhile, it has been found that the number of 'pixels' (i.e. the dots that make up such designs on the computer screen) and the number of fractal designs themselves constitute a sum that is larger than 2 and smaller than 3 times some very large number. This remained an unanswered mathematical question until now. It is related to the noughts and crosses problem in an interesting manner. There, as we saw earlier, the concept of permutations was never properly understood, because the conventional n! permutation sum accounts only for all games played to the last turn and does not include any that end earlier for any reason. The *greater than 2 and smaller than 3 times n! sum* was therefore never considered or understood, and seemed like a strange anomaly when computer scientists began counting the component particles that make up fractals. They found this to be a puzzling number. They were computing all permutational possibilities without realizing it.

THE PRESUMED FIRST TURN ADVANTAGE

The question of the first turn's relative advantage or disadvantage in any purely strategic game or in games of chance can be demonstrated quite simply. It is a question of options and of how we perceive and understand them.

In noughts and crosses played on a 3×3 field, the first moving player enjoys nine choices on his first turn, the second eight, and so on. The sum of all choices for both players considered in this simplified form can be represented as $9 + 8 + 7 + 6 + 5 + 4 + 3 + 2 + 1 = 45$. The numbers would increase substantially if we considered the classified sum of all combinatorial possibilities, but the principle would remain the same.

The first moving player enjoys the sum of all odd numbered turns, starting with 9 ($9 + 7 + 5 + 3 + 1 = 25$). The second moving player enjoys the sum of all even numbered turns (8 + 6 + 4 + 2 = 20). Superficially it would seem that:

a. more is better and that

b. the first moving player enjoys an advantage because he has five more choices than the second moving one (either to win or to force a draw).

But this is wrong. For in fact more is needed only by those who understand less. Less suffices for those who understand enough. Five more choices for the first moving player can only mean that he or she can make five more mistakes than the second moving one. That is a serious disadvantage. All the second moving player needs to do is pay attention, follow the first moving player's lead and an error-free game (a draw) is guaranteed, provided the first moving player does not blunder. Therefore:

a. The first moving player enjoys a severe numerical disadvantage in conventional winning terms in as much as he can make as many mistakes as the number of turns he enjoys if he does not know what he is doing, tries to win playing against a knowledge-able player, or plays at random. All three conditions amount to the same thing.

b. The first moving player can first take advantage of the second moving player's errors, if any, on his third turn. This is one turn earlier than is possible for the second moving player, and may therefore seem like an advantage. But it is no advantage if considered in its true light. It is equivalent to the 'advantage' enjoyed by any two-legged person who spreads a banana peel in front of a one-legged, blind old lady on crutches. Any other player can do the same to him at a future turn. Whatever advantage accrues to either is not caused by superior or more intelligent play, but is a result of the other player's error due to age, ignorance, inexperience, inattention or disability. It defines the 'bigger bastard' principle inherent in all competitive winning.

c. If the first moving player knows how to play perfectly and the second does not, he can only win by keeping the method of perfect play to himself (i.e. secrecy). He refuses to teach what he knows to others to prevent their becoming his equals. In that case he is far from perfect because the 'bigger bastard' principle again holds true.

The outcome will be a perpetual draw if the 'knowing' player teaches the other to be his equal. Secrecy is therefore an important component in playing competitively in the conventional, relatively objective sense in both games of strategy and chance. (This suggests that any government official who keeps secrets from the electorate in times of peace is playing a competitive game *against* voters and taxpayers.)

d. If the second moving player knows how to play perfectly and the first does not, then the same criteria apply as in *c*. above.

e. If either player knows how to play perfectly and the other does not, and the one who knows tries to correct the other's errors and that other refuses to learn, and in the absence of any mental disability, that other deserves to lose. The player who knows is playing with a fool. That can be a serious disadvantage in critical situations.

f. If both players understand the game then they are equals and neither suffers any advantage or disadvantage on the first or any other turn. Neither will take advantage of the other's inadvertent error caused by inattention in situations that matter.

These generalizations hold true for all relationships that are symbolized by purely strategic games and games of chance, as discussed in the various chapters of this book.

Appendix B – Combinatorial Neural-Networks

COMBINATORIAL SUMS AND NEURAL NETWORKS

Periodically new buzz-words appear on the computing horizon – like 'artificial intelligence', 'expert systems', 'general systems', 'fractals' or the more recent 'neural networks'. Some of these words and phrases are nearly meaningless because they are inadequately defined. In other instances they are substitute words for old ideas (e.g. 'forward- and backward-chaining' is simply computer jargon for 'induction and deduction' – concepts in logical analysis as ancient as the classical Greek philosophers).

Neural networks describe the not-so-startling discovery that the human central nervous system is inter-connected – some portions totally, others partially (e.g. the brain has no 'feeling'). A fully integrated wiring diagram connected to a good memory system can, therefore, mimic brain processes up to a point short of 'thinking'. If this were not possible, then computing would be impossible. However, a computer does not think. It merely does what it is told, plus one other thing: it can generate and shuffle all permutations, options, and combinatorial variations of what it has been told within a comparatively short time. These are purely mechanical processes that can be expressed mathematically. Within these constraints, a computer can find 'shortest-path' journeys rapidly (i.e. *jumps to a conclusion*) within one of three categories (see tables 1–9), if given the correct program. It cannot do better than that.

SHORTEST-PATH ANALYSIS

The so-called 'four-colour map' and 'travelling salesman' problems are typical of what are considered in mathematics to be shortest-path problems. The same principle of analysis can be applied to

Rubik's cube or, for that matter, to any problem for which a shortest-path solution is sought. Shortest-path procedures are, in effect, jumps to conclusions, reducing iteration to a minimum or, seen in terms of classified combinatorial sum data processing, the most efficient form of radical data reduction.

A number of different shortest-path analyses exist: that of Khachian, a Russian mathematician, is elliptical.[1] Another recently developed method by Karmarkar[2] at Bell Laboratories in the US appears to be similar to my own method, but seems more complex. So far it does not seem to have led to any substantial discoveries or innovations. The classified combinatorial sum method used here is a linear, digital, three-dimensional, circular form of shortest-path analysis that may be faster and more efficient than other known ones.

Shortest-path methods of any description fall into the 'simplex' category of mathematical procedures, which differ from conventional ones. None the less, all are mechanical rather than organic data processing methods.

One of the most important non-mechanical acts that the human brain does – and that a computer cannot do – is to make value judgements. The criteria for making value judgements can now be modelled on a computer, dividing the options into categories, groups, families and individually unique states. But even given these criteria the computer can still not come to any decision. It can only generate a minimal number of the best options by the shortest route, derived from the original choices the analyst/programmer made (i.e. which category, family or criteria the computer is commanded to consider by the programmer or systems analyst).

For example, one value judgement that only human beings can make consists of being able to tell (including telling a computer) the difference in game playing between a victory (achieved by default and error) and a draw (achieved by error-free or error-corrected play). If an analyst wishes to generate the earliest, latest or any other kind of draw, the computer will provide a choice. If, on the other hand, the computer is instructed to select only won and lost games based on systematic, non-random and non-deceptive procedures, it will be at a loss. It cannot tell how to achieve such an outcome in this manner, nor could it, even after it has scanned all permutational or combinatorial possibilities. It certainly cannot select disconcerting methods of play required to win. It can only play at random or, if given patterns to follow or specific criteria for matching winning and losing, draw or stalemate situations, it can 'recognize' them when they occur. But no machine can do any of this autonomously. (Some human beings are also unable to do so and thus use their brains only mechanically, part of the time at least. They are human robots.)

This principle applies to many human activities and so we sometimes think and act mechanically (i.e. as if we were nothing but machines) and at others in an organic manner (i.e. when we do make value judgements in advance and state our conditions and goals; think for ourselves and choose the best options to reach them out of the vast sum of combinatorial possibilities).

In order to make value judgements in this way, the human brain must be able to consider the sum of all possibilities with great speed or jump to a conclusion – right or wrong – without considering everything in its memory store. At the very least the brain requires a mechanism that is capable of generating a matrix of the sum of all possibilities so that it can jump to conclusions without considering everything. The central nervous system is the wiring diagram for that binary matrix.

Clearly, any process that models a sum of all combinatorial possibilities, including intentions, feelings and beliefs (see Appendix A) is analogous to the human central nervous system – i.e. it models any universe of discourse globally (or to use another contemporary buzz-word 'holistically'). Such a modelling method is totally objective (it represents a three-dimensional map of reality seen from outside the system itself, and therefore includes both subjective (e.g. co-operative) and relatively objective (competitive) options. It is, you might say, a geometric model of a neural network.

Such a neural network (the unclassified, brute force sum of all combinatorial possibilities) can be represented in a number of ways. The classification method that permits any practically realizable portion to be isolated did not exist previously and is detailed in the tables on following pages. The sum of all possibilities can now be categorized, grouped, sieved out, boiled down or shrunk to manageable proportions. That can be done via the classification method I have discovered (see tables 1–9). This method enables us to 'jump to conclusions' in a manner similar to what the central nervous system does *preparatory* to thinking.

In other words, the human brain first selects the category, group and family that is most germane and then data reduces this residual sum of all possibilities further and to an absolute minimum number of alternate options between which a choice must be made. This last step, like the first – i.e. making a value judgement – is a human responsibility that no machine can match, as these findings clearly demonstrate. All the machine can do is to generate portions of the total sum of possibilities and to shuffle them at random or systematically as per our programming instructions. The machine, of course, has no idea what any of this *means*.

While this proves the impossibility of artificial or machine intelligence, it does provide a useful model of how human beings use or fail to use their native intelligence. It would also appear that this provides us with the basis for a most efficient computer model to assist human thinking, analysis, diagnostics, forecasting and decision-making.

The calculation required for generating the unclassified brute force sum of all possibilities has existed for a very long time, but was not recognized for what it was or for what it could be used except for very limited purposes like brute force encoding and decoding of secret messages. Only the classification method is new and it is essential before the brute force calculation can become useful in practical terms.

When n = the number of factors that are involved (i.e. in the memory), that sum $$= n \left[2^{\frac{n(n-1)}{2}} \right]$$

This holds true for noughts and crosses (n = 9) as we have seen. It is also true for a pack of fifty-two playing-cards:

$$52 \times \left[2^{\frac{52 \times 51}{2}} \right]$$

Prior to the discovery of a classification method these sums were of relatively little value because all that was known about them was that they included many permutational redundancies – i.e. permutations that keep repeating again and again in a seemingly chaotic manner – although why this should be so, whether or not there was any way of distinguishing between them, or whether any systematic order could be discerned in such vast sums was unknown. This has caused great problems in brute force methods employed to decipher secret codes for instance. The same meaningless and sometimes meaningful combinations kept recurring for seemingly inexplicable reasons.

Now that a classification system exists, these huge sums can be subdivided and analysed systematically as far as small systems are concerned, and the findings generalized, applied to larger sums and tested by computer. Additionally, huge systems can be analysed by isolating small portions and examining them to see whether principles and generalizations extracted from the smaller systems apply to larger ones. That is equivalent to jumping to a conclusion – something our brains do every day. They can do no better because omniscience is impossible. Some qualifications exist, many of which have been discussed in this book in considerable detail as far as game playing, psychology and other subjects are concerned.

This appendix shows how the classification system works, what the criteria are on the basis of which the classification is achieved, how our brains jump to conclusions, and how all of this permits syntax (arrangement) and semantics (meanings) to be extracted (instead of being imposed, as now). There is not enough space to go into all the details; therefore a general overview must suffice. The game analogy is useful because it shows how the subtlest psychological meanings can be deduced in considerable detail in what superficially appear to be simple, yet are actually highly complex situations (see Appendix A). Among other things this method relates the simplest solution (i.e. shortest-path analysis) to organic complexity (e.g. the intentions, goals, feelings and beliefs of the players).

The unclassified brute force sum algorithm works from $n = 2$ to infinity. However, at less than $n = 4$, and when this is modelled geometrically, the results are two-dimensional and can be misleading. The first three-dimensional result is achieved at $n = 4$ (see diagram 4). It generates 4×64 possibilities. By $n = 5$ the combinatorial algorithm generates $5 \times 1,024$ patterns. At $n = 6$ it grows to $6 \times 32,768$ – too large to be analysed in detail. $n = 4$ is therefore a useful sum with which to begin. It is small enough to be manageable and large enough to be representative of larger three-dimensional systems. At and below $n = 3$ all systems are two dimensional and remain invisible in reality, although, like language or other symbolic representations, they can be modelled.

Since $n = 4$ generates the same number of patterns regardless where and at which node (i.e. point) you begin (e.g. like the first move in noughts and crosses), it suffices to classify only 64 of all 256 possible patterns that establish the sum of all possible relationships and options between any four facts, starting out from any one of these (e.g. 'a' in diagram 1), expressed as a number, letter of the alphabet or any other symbol.

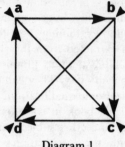

Diagram 1

Diagram 1 shows one of the sixty-four possible patterns when n = 4. 'a' is the starting point for the sake of simplicity. Reversing one arrow at a time in relation to all others generates a finite sum of sixty-four combinatorial possibilities, each of which is unique in so far as options, relative to permutational sequence, are concerned. These sums can be increased in several ways: *a*) by using the other three letters of the alphabet (b, c and d) as additional starting points, thus generating a finite sum of 256; *b*) by enlarging the system and adding additional letters – e, f, g . . . – or numbers up to infinity; *c*) by adding additional modules two-dimensionally to one or more nodes; or *d*) by building a multi-domain, three-dimensional model to which as many two-dimensional slices or domains can be added as required (see analytic diagrams for noughts and crosses in Appendix A).

This system therefore offers an infinite continuum of finite series; a definition of the meaning of infinity that emerges from an analysis of this systems representation.

For practical purposes, e.g. application to games, it is useful to consider the meanings inherent in this method of analysis so that it can be related to the game of noughts and crosses (or anything else involving organic behaviour) as shown in Appendix A:

a = the self;
b = a letter, word, sentence, paragraph, book or a whole subject;
c = the same as *b*, except that this is a different letter, word . . . etc;
d = the conclusion, outcome, end state or consequence.

Obviously, if you go from 'a' to 'b' to 'c', reach 'd' (the conclusion), without feedback to the self, you have learnt nothing and have not profited from your experience. This is therefore a *concluded* situation or pattern – equivalent to winning and losing (see diagram 4, coordinate A1).

Space does not permit a detailed analysis of all sixty-four patterns shown on diagram 4, yet they define all possible methods of operant conditioning, training and computer programming involving four facts or groups of facts. Valuative selection enables us to choose the most appropriate pattern for any given analytic or programming purpose. Learning is something else again.

LEARNING VS TRAINING AND PROGRAMMING

As just stated, diagram 1 is one of sixty-four patterns that can be used to analyse all possible forms of operant conditioning, training or programming for any task involving four subjects – the learner ('a'), two contributing conditions, states or subjects ('b' and 'c'), and a result, conclusion or outcome ('d'). Diagram 4 shows all of the possibilities when n = 4 (i.e. when we are dealing with four facts). For example, it is possible to model and trace what occurs with total freedom (category III, family 1, coordinates A8 and D1) and how this leads to a limited and totally conditioned feedback loop from which no escape is possible. Another pattern (category II, family 3, B2) shows that goal definition leads to perfect and repetitive performance within any finite environment (as in a programmed computer or trained – but not educated – individual), yet precludes learning in the true sense.

Central to the discoveries on which this book is based is the difference between operant and other conditioning. The first defines programming of any sort (of human beings or computers), and the second, learning to be autonomous yet co-operative with the self, nature, the environment and all like-minded human beings, and defending yourself vigorously against all others, to stalemate or allow them to defeat themselves when you are attacked (i.e. to be no one's willing victim) – this is the definition of what it means to be truly human and humane.

Diagram 2 shows a perfect, goal-defined learning circuit ('d' and from there to infinity), within which the learner can choose whichever route he wishes to achieve the best result, depending on sensory/motor strengths, interests and, especially, appropriateness. This is only one of several 'best' learning modules. Here the option

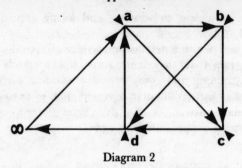

Diagram 2

patterns are maximized from the start and generate feedback from goal 'd' (and from further goals to infinity) back to 'a'. There is a gradual decline of options until the goal is reached, whatever it might be, at which point they increase maximally until a new goal is defined, and so on.

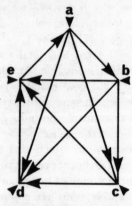

Diagram 3

Diagram 3 shows one of 5 × 1,024 combinatorial possibilities when n = 5. Note that this module, combined with the n = 4 module (see diagram 1) forms the analytic model for noughts and crosses. It is useful to compare this present diagram to the O player's domain in the analytic noughts and crosses diagram shown in Appendix A. It matches and shows all possible internal moves and turns within that player's domain, unrelated to that of the X player. The X player's domain is n = 4. Linked three-dimensionally, both sub-systems form n = 9, demonstrating another truism – that the whole is greater than the sum of its parts, i.e. n = 4 (256 option patterns) times n = 5 (5,120 option patterns) generates only 1,310,720 possibilities. But n = 9 as an integrated network generates 618,475,290,624 possibilities.

Diagram 4 shows all sixty-four possibilities at n = 4, beginning at 'a', based on the rotation of one arrow in relation to all others.

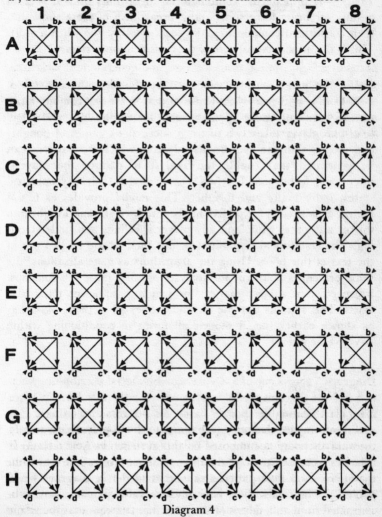

Diagram 4

Tables 1–3: show detailed analyses from n = 3 to 5. Table 2 consists of a full analysis for n = 4 of the sixty-four patterns shown in diagram 4 above, according to given test criteria. No vector geometry is shown for n = 3 (see table 1) or for n = 5 (see table 3). Only a summarized analysis is shown for n = 5.

Tables 4–7: provide the combinatorial algorithms from n = 2 to infinity for brute force sums and a breakdown of these sums into their constituent component ratios (e.g. x = 6, y = 3 when n = 9). This is the mathematical core of the classification system.

Tables 8–9: give the sums generated by the algorithms in tables 4–7, from n = 3 to n = 9. Those at n = 9 are the combinatorial turn-by-turn and move-by-move sums for all the *legal* and *illegal* (e.g. one player takes two turns in succession) games of noughts and crosses that can ever be played, from which the patterns can be generated that enable the analyst to deduce the players' intentions, feelings and beliefs. They model their psychological states, individually and together. This model provides as fine a matrix as is needed for perfect hindsight, foresight and insight into this or any other game and any player's feelings and understanding. The conditional limitations of this method are spelled out in the text of this book. Using the algorithms as generalizations, the same principles hold true for analyses of other finite relationships, irrespective of subject matter, for which a sufficient data base exists. This systems analytic method defines all methods of *learning* as shown earlier (i.e. it models all forms of conditioning within any given context).

CLASSIFICATION

The classification method is based on a number of criteria that emerge from the geometry (see diagram 4 – e.g. feedback to 'a'), and are therefore not imposed on this systems analytic technique. The first consideration are the three main categories into which the geometric data flow patterns can be divided (see diagram 4 and table 2). The tables show how advance value judgements can be extracted from an analysis of the three main categories, groups and families for any value of n. Note that groups do not emerge and cannot be isolated or identified until n = 5 (see table 3).

1. Category I: consists of closed or concluded pattern families and individually unique states, equivalent to winning, losing and certain stalemates when applied to game playing.

2. Category II: consists of pattern families and individually unique states within which there is perpetual feedback to the starting point 'a', equivalent to draws and stalemates that are merely imperfectly understood draws played out to the last or last-but-one turn in game terms. However, when such draws are understood and extended to infinity (see Appendix A, diagram 6), then some of the patterns in this category can be turned into perpetual learning circuits and represent perfect outcomes for every game or other relationship.

3. Category III: consists of pattern families and individually unique states similar to those in category II, except that feedback is always to a terminal other than 'a'. This is yet another kind of stalemate (see Appendix A, diagram 5) and it can have a variety of different meanings, depending on context.

TEST CRITERIA

Table 2 provides a detailed analysis of n = 4 (see diagram 4), starting from 'a'. n = 4 is divided first into the three categories defined above. Each category is further subdivided into families. The coordinates given in the first column relate the analyses to diagram 4. The patterns in each family that are not defined by a set of coordinates are sub-routines, equivalent to '*jumps to conclusions*'.

Each family is grouped according to the one characteristic that every individually unique permutation has in common – the same option pattern. The option pattern is generated by the data flow (i.e. the number of different branches at each point or node and the possible number of directions for continuance, defined in table 2 as convergences).

Every individual member within each family is defined by given test criteria that consist of the following, and that are clearly labelled on table 2:

a = *Alphabetic and numerical sequence* (i.e. permutation):
    1 = correct sequence (a: b: c . . . or 1: 2: 3 . . .)
    0 = incorrect sequence (a: c: b . . . or 1: 3: 2 . . .)

b = *Inclusiveness*
    1 = includes all factors (a: b: c: d in any sequence when n = 4)
    0 = includes fewer than all factors (e.g. a: b when n = 4)

c = *Feedback*
    1 = feedback to 'a'
    0 = no feedback or feedback to other than 'a'

d = *Conclusion* (considering everything or jump to conclusion)
    1 = correct conclusion ('d' when n = 4)
    0 = wrong conclusion (any other than 'd' when n = 4)

Note: In certain category I instances (see table 2, n = 4, category I, family 2), feedback to the causal trigger or node 'a' can occur, but it is always a less than all-inclusive sub-routine and one that is equivalent to operant conditioning.

OTHER CRITERIA

Tables 4–9 involve additional criteria that require definition:

1. *Groups*: Tables 4–9 show nine values for 'y'. The value of y is limited to the value of n for any given system. This means that the value of y establishes one parameter of an x : y ratio for every value of n, from x = n − 1, y = 1, to x = 0, y = n. x is implicit on tables 4–9. Each such x : y ratio, except y = 1, x = n − 1 constitutes a group that includes a given number of families, characterized by one and the same option pattern that differs from all others. All members of a group share the same x : y ratio – usually (n − 1)! or, in some instances, [(n − 1)!/3] permutations per family.

2. *Internal affect*: (see tables 4–9). It is obvious from an examination of the various patterns that in some cases one or more circuits involving 'a' are isolated from the rest. So, for example in

diagram 4, patterns C3, E6 and four others consist solely of traffic flow between two terminals, starting from 'a' (a–b and a–c). This is *internal* traffic flow. In the given cases c–d and b–d are *external* or environmental states. Internal affect is enlarged as systems grow bigger (i.e. with increase in the value of n), but it is always limited to those terminals that feed back to 'a' or other internally affective nodes.

3. *External affect*: (see tables 4–9) is limited to the relationships within the external environment as defined in 2. above, and by its affect on internally affective nodes. The variations in external affect create internally affective and effective, unique permutational redundancies.

4. *Effect*: (see tables 4–9) is equivalent to possible outcomes, goals, end states, conclusions and consequences as a result of a combination of internal and external affect and the possible relationships between them.

5. *Time*: The interval between cause and effect, relative to the route taken to reach a conclusion (concluded or feedback), depends on relative processing speed, complexity of the data flow (i.e. the number of nodes), conditional branching, possible feedback or concluded states and whether data processing involves all possibilities within the system or shorter 'jumps to conclusion'. It is here that the classified combinatorial method saves a considerable amount of time, irrespective of computer processing speeds.

As shown in Appendix A, a combination of n = 5 and n = 4 produces the analytic diagrams needed for a combinatorial analysis of noughts and crosses. Similar combinations of domain structures can be developed to analyse any other set of relationships within and outside the game frame of reference. One other application – general forecasting and prediction – deserves mention in the context of this book.

FORECASTING CRITERIA

Diagram 5 (see also tables 8-9) shows what is involved in prediction, based on the criteria used for the classification of the

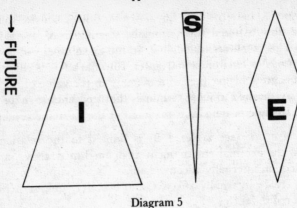

Diagram 5

sum of all combinatorial possibilities, relative to evolutionary time. They are marked E (effect, goals, end states and consequences), I (internal affect) and S (external or environmental affect) on the various tables and represent a geometric equivalent to the given numbers (for $n = 5$, in this instance). Further meanings can be extracted from the geometry these state-defined conditions generate for systems of different size and in various frames of reference (e.g. $n = 9$ for noughts and crosses).

Effect (E) is diamond-shaped and consists of two joined 'Pascal' triangles. As can be confirmed from experience, a single cause and effect (or related clusters of causes and effects) can always be found when a system comes into being. The number and variety of consequences are greatest in the middle game in noughts and crosses ($y = 5$ and $x = 4$) when the $y : x$ ratio is nearly equal, and least at the start (e.g. when $y = 1$ and $x = 8$ at $n = 9$) and at the absolute horizon of any future (when $y = 9$ and $x = 0$ at $n = 9$). In other words, the environmental affect is maximal (e.g. at the start) and minimal (with maximal internalization of the sum of all possibilities on the last turn in any game or relationship, when the external, environmental affect $= 0$), and when causes and consequences are reduced to 1. But where external and internal affect are nearly in balance, the number of optional possibilities, causes and consequences is greatest.

Internal affect (I) is more or less triangular in principle over the full evolutionary development for any value of n. It is 1 at the start and progressively maximized to include the whole external environment (S) at the horizon of any future (e.g. when y = 5 in diagram 6).

External environmental affect (S) assumes the approximate shape of an inverted triangle in time. It is maximal at the start and diminishes to 1 when y = n−1 and x = 1 (e.g. the last-but-one turn in any purely strategic game).

These criteria and conditions define the evolution of systems over periods of time which differ depending on whether organic or inorganic processes are involved. They provide predictive powers limited by the available information and as defined below.

THE PAST AND FUTURE PARADIGM

The three geometric shapes defined in diagram 5 superimposed on top of another provide a schematic structure that models the evolution of systems, depending on the number of factors that are involved. When n = 9 the shape of past and future (i.e. the classified sum of all combinatorial possibilities), expressed geometrically, requires more space than is available on this page.

Diagram 6 is a representation of all past, present and future options generated 'holistically', based on a superimposition of E, I and S, and the numbers shown in table 9, n = 5. This representation of time is based on the classification of the combinatorial sum of all possibilities when n =5.

A = the sum of all *relatively objective* (i.e. category 1 – closed, winning and losing, stalemate, inorganic, mechanical) options.

B = the sum of all *relatively subjective* (i.e. category III – stalemate, feedback to the wrong starting point, totally conditioned) options.

C= the sum of all *subjective* (i.e. category II – draw, perpetual feedback) options.

Numerals 1 − 5 on diagram 6 represent values of y when n = 5 (see table 3).

No other possibilities exist, because this is a finite system. Any enlargement of this universe of discourse, just as that from the 3×3 game to 11×11, involves changes in the configuration, but the same principles apply to infinity, irrespective of subject matter.

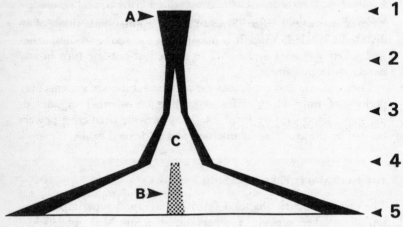

Diagram 6

Diagram 6 includes all classified combinatorial possibilities for an $n = 5$ universe. Note that towards the finite horizon of the future (i.e. the bottom line, when $y = 5$), the relatively objective aspects of behaviour within the system are reduced to a minimum. That proportion shrinks significantly with every increase in the value of n, but never disappears entirely and is representative of the second law of thermodynamics, seen in a behavioural context.

The same principle holds true for any value of n, except, of course, that the configurations change somewhat, as they must. None the less, all smaller representations of this infinite continuum of time fit inside the next larger one, and all have the same proportionate beginning.

This representation of the evolution of systems in time seems also to clarify the three laws of thermodynamics relative to behaviour in the largest – inorganic and organic – sense, regarded in a totally objective manner from a vantage point outside whatever system is under consideration.

As stated earlier, the geometry for $n = 3$ (see table 1) is not given here. To understand the classification systems of the combinatorial sum of all possibilities and its meanings for any value of n, it is best first to become familiar with diagram 4 and to relate it to table 2, before considering the other tables. Tables 3 to 9 extend the principles and the classification method detailed earlier in diagram 4 and table 2 according to the enumerated criteria, and generalize them and the data reduction system by means of algorithms that appear to hold true to infinity.

TABLE 1
CLASSIFICATION OF COMBINATORIAL SUMS

n = 3

Category I: Concluded – relatively objective

Family 1: All-inclusive.
    In game terms these are games that are won and lost.

Coord.	Alphabetic sequence	Numeric sequence	Convergence at each node	Options at each node	Test criteria abcd
A4	a:b:c	1:2:3	1:2:3	2:1:0	1101
A3	a:c:b	1:3:2	1:2:3	2:1:0	0100

Family 2: Reflexive; binary.
    In game terms these are games won before the last turn.

| A2 | a:b | 1:2 | 2:3 | 1:0 | 1000 |
| B4 | a:c | 1:3 | 2:3 | 1:0 | 1001 |

Family 3: Blocked; maximum environmental affect; minimal internal affect.
    In game terms these are games that end on the first turn for any reason (e.g. mother calls time for dinner).

| B1 | a | 1 | 3 | 0 | 0000 |
| B2 | a | 1 | 3 | 0 | 0000 |

Category II: Feedback to 'a' – subjective

Family 1: All-inclusive; totally conditioned (one choice at each node).
    In game terms these include games drawn on the last turn. However a game with only three nodes or cells is impossible; therefore when n = 3 this definition is symbolic rather than real.

| A1 | a:b:c...a | 1:2:3...1 | 2:2:2...2 | 1:1:1...1 | 1111 |
| B3 | a:c:b...a | 1:3:2...1 | 2:2:2...2 | 1:1:1...1 | 0110 |

TABLE 2

CLASSIFICATION OF COMBINATORIAL SUMS

$n = 4$

Category I: Concluded – relatively objective – 0 choice at last node.

Family 1: All-inclusive; maximum choice at 'a'; systematic decline to 0.

Coord.	Alphabetic sequence	Numeric sequence	Convergence at each node	Options at each node	Test criteria abcd
A1	a:b:c:d	1:2:3:4	1:2:3:4	3:2:1:0	1101
	a:b:d	1:2:4	1:2:4	3:2:0	1001
	a:c:d	1:3:4	1:3:4	3:1:0	1001
	a:d	1:4	1:4	3:0	1001
A5	a:b:d:c	1:2:4:3	1:2:3:4	3:2:1:0	0100
	a:b:c	1:2:3	1:2:4	3:2:0	1000
	a:d:c	1:4:3	1:3:4	3:1:0	0000
	a:c	1:3	1:4	3:0	1000
A4	a:c:b:d	1:3:2:4	1:2:3:4	3:2:1:0	0101
	a:b:d	1:2:4	1:3:4	3:1:0	1001
	a:c:d	1:3:4	1:2:4	3:2:0	1001
	a:d	1:4	1:4	3:0	1001
D4	a:c:d:b	1:3:4:2	1:2:3:4	3:2:1:0	0100
	a:c:b	1:3:2	1:2:4	3:2:0	0000
	a:d:b	1:4:2	1:3:4	3:1:0	0000
	a:b	1:2	1:4	3:0	1000
D5	a:d:b:c	1:4:2:3	1:2:3:4	3:2:1:0	0100
	a:b:c	1:2:3	1:3:4	3:1:0	1000
	a:d:c	1:4:3	1:2:4	3:2:0	0000
	a:c	1:3	1:4	3:0	1000
D8	a:d:c:b	1:4:3:2	1:2:3:4	3:2:1:0	0100
	a:c:b	1:3:2	1:3:4	3:1:0	0000
	a:d:b	1:4:2	1:2:4	3:2:0	0000
	a:b	1:2	1:4	3:0	1000

TABLE 2
CLASSIFICATION OF COMBINATORIAL SUMS

$$n = 4$$

Family 2: All-inclusive; equal choice at first three nodes.
Note: Feedback to 'a' in first sub-routine only.

Coord.	Alphabetic sequence	Numeric sequence	Convergence at each node	Options at each node	Test criteria abcd
B1	a:b:c:d	1:2:3:4	2:2:2:4	2:2:2:0	1101
	a:b:c...a	1:2:3...1	2:2:2...2	2:2:2...2	1010
	a:b:d	1:2:4	2:2:4	2:2:0	1001
	a:d	1:4	2:4	2:0	1001
A6	a:b:d:c	1:2:4:3	2:2:2:4	2:2:2:0	0100
	a:b:d...a	1:2:4...1	2:2:2...2	2:2:2...2	1011
	a:b:c	1:2:3	2:2:4	2:2:0	1000
	a:c	1:3	2:4	2:0	1000
E4	a:c:b:d	1:3:2:4	2:2:2:4	2:2:2:0	0101
	a:c:b...a	1:3:2...1	2:2:2...2	2:2:2...2	0010
	a:c:d	1:3:4	2:2:4	2:2:0	1001
	a:d	1:4	2:4	2:0	1001
D3	a:c:d:b	1:3:4:2	2:2:2:4	2:2:2:0	0100
	a:c:d...a	1:3:4...1	2:2:2...2	2:2:2...2	1011
	a:c:b	1:3:2	2:2:4	2:2:0	0000
	a:b	1:2	2:4	2:0	1000
H5	a:d:b:c	1:4:2:3	2:2:2:4	2:2:2:0	0100
	a:d:b...a	1:4:2...1	2:2:2...2	2:2:2...2	0010
	a:d:c	1:4:3	2:2:4	2:2:0	0000
	a:c	1:3	2:4	2:0	1000
C8	a:d:c:b	1:4:3:2	2:2:2:4	2:2:2:0	0100
	a:d:c...a	1:4:3...1	2:2:2...2	2:2:2...2	0010
	a:d:b	1:4:2	2:2:4	2:2:0	0000
	a:b	1:2	2:4	2:0	1000

TABLE 2
CLASSIFICATION OF COMBINATORIAL SUMS

$$n = 4$$

Family 3: Instinctive; maximum options at 'a'; descending to 0.

Coord.	Alphabetic sequence	Numeric sequence	Convergence at each node	Options at each node	Test criteria abcd
D6	a:b:c	1:2:3	2:3:4	2:1:0	1000
	a:c	1:3	2:4	2:0	1000
B4	a:b:d	1:2:4	2:3:4	2:1:0	1001
	a:d	1:4	2:4	2:0	1001
D7	a:c:b	1:3:2	2:3:4	2:1:0	0000
	a:b	1:2	2:4	2:0	1000
E1	a:c:d	1:3:4	2:3:4	2:1:0	1001
	a:d	1:4	2:4	2:0	1001
C4	a:d:b	1:4:2	2:3:4	2:1:0	0000
	a:b	1:2	2:4	2:0	1000
E5	a:d:c	1:4:3	2:3:4	2:1:0	0000
	a:c	1:3	2:4	2:0	1000

Family 4: Reflexive; binary.

Coord.	Alphabetic sequence	Numeric sequence	Convergence at each node	Options at each node	Test criteria abcd
C3	a:b	1:2	3:4	1:0	1000
C7	a:b	1:2	3:4	1:0	1000
E6	a:c	1:3	3:4	1:0	0000
H6	a:c	1:3	3:4	1:0	0000
F1	a:d	1:4	3:4	1:0	0001
F4	a:d	1:4	3:4	1:0	0001

TABLE 2
CLASSIFICATION OF COMBINATORIAL SUMS

$$n = 4$$

Family 5: Blocked; maximal environmental affect; minimal internal affect.

Coord.	Alphabetic sequence	Numeric sequence	Convergence at each node	Options at each node	Test criteria abcd
F2	a	1	4	0	0000
F3	a	1	4	0	0000
F6	a	1	4	0	0000
F7	a	1	4	0	0000
G2	a	1	4	0	0000
G3	a	1	4	0	0000
G6	a	1	4	0	0000
G7	a	1	4	0	0000

TABLE 2
CLASSIFICATION OF COMBINATORIAL SUMS

n = 4

Category II: Feedback to 'a' – subjective

Family 1: All-inclusive; 2 options at first two nodes.

Coord.	Alphabetic sequence	Numeric sequence	Convergence at each node	Options at each node	Test criteria abcd
A2	a:b:c:d...a	1:2:3:4...1	2:2:3:3...2	2:2:1:1...2	1111
	a:b:d...a	1:2:4...1	2:2:3...2	2:2:1...2	1011
	a:c:d...a	1:3:4...1	2:3:3...2	2:1:1...2	1011
B5	a:b:d:c...a	1:2:4:3...1	2:2:3:3...2	2:2:1:1...2	0110
	a:b:c...a	1:2:3...1	2:2:3...2	2:2:1...2	1010
	a:d:c...a	1:4:3...1	2:3:3...2	2:1:1...2	0010
A3	a:c:b:d...a	1:3:2:4...1	2:2:3:3...2	2:2:1:1...2	0111
	a:b:d...a	1:2:4...1	2:3:3...2	2:1:1...2	1011
	a:c:d...a	1:3:4...1	2:2:3...2	2:2:1...2	1011
H4	a:c:d:b...a	1:3:4:2...1	2:2:3:3...2	2:2:1:1...2	0110
	a:c:b...a	1:3:2...1	2:2:3...2	2:2:1...2	0010
	a:d:b...a	1:4:2...1	2:3:3...2	2:1:1...2	0010
C5	a:d:b:c...a	1:4:2:3...1	2:2:3:3...2	2:2:1:1...2	0110
	a:b:c...a	1:2:3...1	2:3:3...2	2:1:1...2	1010
	a:d:c...a	1:4:3...1	2:2:3...2	2:2:1...2	0010
H8	a:d:c:b...a	1:4:3:2...1	2:2:3:3...2	2:2:1:1...2	0110
	a:c:b...a	1:3:2...1	2:3:3...2	2:1:1...2	0010
	a:d:b...a	1:4:2...1	2:2:3...2	2:2:1...2	0010

TABLE 2

CLASSIFICATION OF COMBINATORIAL SUMS

$$n = 4$$

Family 2: All inclusive; 2 options at first and last nodes.

Coord.	Alphabetic sequence	Numeric sequence	Convergence at each node	Options at each node	Test criteria abcd
D2	a:b:c:d...a	1:2:3:4...1	2:3:3:2...2	2:1:1:2...2	1111
	a:c:d:b...c	1:3:4:2...3	2:3:2:3...3	2:1:2:1...1	0100
	a:c:d...a	1:3:4...1	2:3:2...2	2:1:2...2	1011
B8	a:b:d:c...a	1:2:4:3...1	2:3:3:2...2	2:1:1:2...2	0110
	a:b:d:c...b	1:2:4:3...2	2:3:3:2...3	2:1:1:2...1	0100
	a:d:c...a	1:4:3...1	2:3:2...2	2:1:2...2	0010
A7	a:c:b:d...a	1:3:2:4...1	2:3:3:2...2	2:1:1:2...2	0111
	a:b:d:c...b	1:2:4:3...2	2:3:2:3...3	2:1:2:1...1	0100
	a:c:b:d...c	1:3:2:4...3	2:3:3:2...3	2:1:1:2...1	0101
	a:b:d...a	1:2:4...1	2:3:2...2	2:1:2...2	1011
H1	a:c:d:b...a	1:3:4:2...1	2:3:3:2...2	2:1:1:2...2	0111
	a:d:b:c...d	1:4:2:3...4	2:3:2:3...3	2:1:2:1...1	0100
	a:d:b...a	1:4:2...1	2:3:2...2	2:1:2...2	0011
C1	a:d:b:c...a	1:4:2:3...1	2:3:3:2...2	2:1:1:2...1	0111
	a:b:c:d...b	1:2:3:4...2	2:3:2:3...3	2:1:2:1...1	1100
	a:b:c...a	1:2:3...1	2:3:2...2	2:1:2...2	1011
E8	a:d:c:b...a	1:4:3:2...1	2:3:3:2...2	2:1:1:2...2	0111
	a:d:c:b...d	1:4:3:2...4	2:3:3:2...3	2:1:1:2...1	0100
	a:c:b:d...c	1:3:2:4...3	2:3:2:3...3	2:1:2:1...1	0010
	a:c:b...a	1:3:2...1	2:3:2...2	2:1:2...2	0011
	a:c:b...d	1:3:2...4	2:3:2...3	2:1:2...1	0000

TABLE 2
CLASSIFICATION OF COMBINATORIAL SUMS

$n = 4$

Family 3: All-inclusive; one option at first and last nodes.

Coord.	Alphabetic sequence	Numeric sequence	Convergence at each node	Options at each node	Test criteria abcd
B2	a:b:c:d...a	1:2:3:4...1	3:2:2:3...3	1:2:2:1...1	1111
	a:b:c...a	1:2:3...1	3:2:2...3	1:2:2...1	1010
	a:b:d...a	1:2:4...1	3:2:3...3	1:2:1...1	1011
B6	a:b:d:c...a	1:2:4:3...1	3:2:2:3...3	1:2:2:1...1	0110
	a:b:c...a	1:2:3...1	3:2:3...3	1:2:1...1	1010
	a:b:d...a	1:2:4...1	3:2:2...3	1:2:2...1	1011
E3	a:c:b:d...a	1:3:2:4...1	3:2:2:3...3	1:2:2:1...1	0111
	a:c:b...a	1:3:2...1	3:2:2...3	1:2:2...1	0010
	a:c:d...a	1:3:4...1	3:2:3...3	1:2:1...1	1011
H3	a:c:d:b...a	1:3:4:2...1	3:2:2:3...3	1:2:2:1...1	0100
	a:c:b...a	1:3:2...1	3:2:3...3	1:2:1...1	0010
	a:c:d...a	1:3:4...1	3:2:2...3	1:2:2...1	1011
G5	a:d:b:c...a	1:4:2:3...1	3:2:2:3...3	1:2:2:1...1	0110
	a:d:b...a	1:4:2...1	3:2:2...3	1:2:2...1	0010
	a:d:c...a	1:4:3...1	3:2:3...3	1:2:1...1	0010
G8	a:d:c:b...a	1:4:3:2...1	3:2:2:3...3	1:2:2:1...1	0110
	a:d:b...a	1:4:2...1	3:2:3...3	1:2:1...1	0010
	a:d:c...a	1:4:3...1	3:2:2...3	1:2:2...1	0010

TABLE 2
CLASSIFICATION OF COMBINATORIAL SUMS

$$n = 4$$

Family 4: All-inclusive; one option at first two nodes.

Coord.	Alphabetic sequence	Numeric sequence	Convergence at each node	Options at each node	Test criteria abcd
C2	a:b:c:d...a	1:2:3:4...1	3:3:2:2...3	1:1:2:2...1	1111
	a:b:c:d...b	1:2:3:4...2	3:3:2:2...3	1:1:2:2...1	1101
	a:b:c...a	1:2:3...1	3:3:2...3	1:1:2...1	1010
B7	a:b:d:c...a	1:2:4:3...1	3:3:2:2...3	1:1:2:2...1	0110
	a:b:d:c...b	1:2:4:3...2	3:3:2:2...3	1:1:2:2...1	0100
	a:b:d...a	1:2:4...1	3:3:2...3	1:1:2...1	1011
E7	a:c:b:d...a	1:3:2:4...1	3:3:2:2...3	1:1:2:2...1	0111
	a:c:b:d...c	1:3:2:4...3	3:3:2:2...3	1:1:2:2...1	0101
	a:c:b...a	1:3:2...1	3:3:2...3	1:1:2...1	0010
H2	a:c:d:b...a	1:3:4:2...1	3:3:2:2...3	1:1:2:2...1	0110
	a:c:d:b...c	1:3:4:2...3	3:3:2:2...3	1:1:2:2...1	0100
	a:c:d...a	1:3:4...1	3:3:2...3	1:1:2...1	1011
G1	a:d:b:c...a	1:4:2:3...1	3:3:2:2...3	1:1:2:2...1	0110
	a:d:b:c...d	1:4:2:3...4	3:3:2:2...3	1:1:2:2...1	0100
	a:d:b...a	1:4:2...1	3:3:2...3	1:1:2...1	0010
F8	a:d:c:b...a	1:4:3:2...1	3:3:2:2...3	1:1:2:2...1	0110
	a:d:c:b...d	1:4:3:2...4	3:3:2:2...3	1:1:2:2...1	0100
	a:d:c...a	1:4:3...1	3:3:2...3	1:1:2...1	0010

TABLE 2

CLASSIFICATION OF COMBINATORIAL SUMS

$$n = 4$$

Family 5: Instinctive; total conditioning; 1 option at each node.

Coord.	Alphabetic sequence	Numeric sequence	Convergence at each node	Options at each node	Test criteria abcd
C6	a:b:c...a	1:2:3...1	3:3:3...3	1:1:1...1	1010
B3	a:b:d...a	1:2:4...1	3:3:3...3	1:1:1...1	1011
H7	a:c:b...a	1:3:2...1	3:3:3...3	1:1:1...1	0010
E2	a:c:d...a	1:3:4...1	3:3:3...3	1:1:1...1	1011
G4	a:d:b...a	1:4:2...1	3:3:3...3	1:1:1...1	0010
F5	a:d:c...a	1:4:3...1	3:3:3...3	1:1:1...1	0010

Category III: Feedback to node other-than-'a' – relatively subjective.

Family 1: Total freedom at 'a' without goal definition; total conditioning because the data flow is entrapped in a closed feedback loop (e.g. b:c:d...b) from which there is no escape.

D1	a:b:c:d...b	1:2:3:4...2	1:3:3:3...3	3:1:1:1...1	1101
	a:c:d:b...c	1:3:4:2...3	1:3:3:3...3	3:1:1:1...1	0100
	a:d:b:c...d	1:4:2:3...4	1:3:3:3...3	3:1:1:1...1	0100
A8	a:b:d:c...b	1:2:4:3...2	1:3:3:3...3	3:1:1:1...1	0100
	a:c:b:d...c	1:3:2:4...3	1:3:3:3...3	3:1:1:1...1	0101
	a:d:c:b...d	1:4:3:2...4	1:3:3:3...3	3:1:1:1...1	0100

TABLE 3

CLASSIFICATION OF COMBINATORIAL SUMS

$n = 5$

y	Category	Family	Option pattern	No. of members
1	I	1	0	64
Group $y = 1$				Total $= 64$
2	I	2	1:0	32
Group $y = 2$				Total $= 32$
3	I	3	2:1:0	24
Group $y = 3$				Total $= 24$
4	I	4	2:2:2:0	24
4	I	5	3:2:1:0	24
Group $y = 4$				Total $= 48$
5	I	6	2:2:3:3:0	24
5	I	7	2:3:3:2:0	24
5	I	8	3:2:2:3:0	24
5	I	9	3:3:2:2:0	24
5	I	10	3:3:3:1:0	24
5	I	11	4:2:2:2:0	8
5	I	12	4:3:2:1:0	24
Group $y = 5$				Total $= 152$

Category I = 5 groups
        12 families .... Members total $= 320$

y	Category	Family	Option pattern	No. of members
3	II	1	1:1:1...1	24
Group $y = 3$				Total $= 24$
4	II	2	1:1:2:2...1	24
4	II	3	1:2:2:1...1	24
4	II	4	2:1:1:2...2	24
4	II	5	2:2:1:1...2	24
Group $y = 4$				Total $= 96$
5	II	6	1:1:2:3:3...1	24
5	II	7	1:1:3:3:2...1	24
5	II	8	1:2:2:2:3...1 (1:2:2:3:2...1)	24

TABLE 3

CLASSIFICATION OF COMBINATORIAL SUMS

$n = 5$

y	Category	Family	Option pattern	No. of members
5	II	9	1:2:3:2:2...1	24
5	II	10	1:2:3:3:1...1	24
5	II	11	1:3:2:2:2...1	8
5	II	12	1:3:3:2:1...1	24
5	II	13	2:1:1:3:3...1	24
5	II	14	2:1:2:3:2...2	24
5	II	15	2:1:3:2:2...2	24
5	II	16	2:2:1:2:3...2	24
5	II	17	2:2:2:2:2...2	24
5	II	18	2:2:3:1:2...2	24
5	II	19	2:2:3:2:1...2	24
5	II	20	2:3:2:1:2...2	24
5	II	21	2:3:2:2:1...2	24
			(2:3:1:2:2...2)	
5	II	22	2:3:3:1:1...2	24
5	II	23	3:1:1:2:3...3	24
5	II	24	3:1:2:2:2...3	24
			(3:2:1:2:2...3)	
5	II	25	3:2:1:1:3...3	24
5	II	26	3:2:2:1:2...3	24
5	II	27	3:2:2:2:1...3	8
5	II	28	3:3:1:1:2...3	24
5	II	29	3:3:2:1:1...3	24

Group y = 5 .... Total = 544

Category II = 3 groups
        29 families .... Members Total = 664

4	III	1	3:1:1:1...1	8

Group y = 4 .... Total = 8

5	III	2	4:2:2:1:1...2	24
			(4:1:1:2:2...1)	
			(4:1:2:2:1...1)	
5	III	3	4:3:1:1:1...1	8

Group y = 5 .... Total = 32

Category III = 2 groups
        3 families .... Members Total = 40

TABLE 3
CLASSIFICATION OF COMBINATORIAL SUMS

n = 5

n = 5 includes:	1,024	individually unique states
	44	families
	10	groups
	3	categories
Category I includes:	320	individually unique states
	12	families
	5	groups
Category II includes:	664	individually unique states
	29	families
	3	groups
Category III includes:	40	individually unique states
	3	families
	2	groups

Appendix B

TABLE 4
COMBINATORIAL ALGORITHMS

$$\text{Categories I} + \text{II} + \text{III} = 2^{\left[\frac{n(n-1)}{2}\right]}$$

y	Effective states (E)	Internally affective states (I)	Externally affective states (S)
1	1	1	$2^{\left[\frac{(n-1)(n-2)}{2}\right]}$
2	$(n-1)$	1	$2^{\left[\frac{(n-2)(n-3)}{2}\right]}$
3	$\dfrac{[(n-1)(n-2)]}{(y-1)!}$	4	$2^{\left[\frac{(n-3)(n-4)}{2}\right]}$
4	$\dfrac{[(n-1)(n-2)(n-3)]}{(y-1)!}$	38	$2^{\left[\frac{(n-4)(n-5)}{2}\right]}$
5	$\dfrac{[(n-1)\ldots(n-4)]}{(y-1)!}$	728	$2^{\left[\frac{(n-5)(n-6)}{2}\right]}$
6	$\dfrac{[(n-1)\ldots(n-5)]}{(y-1)!}$	$26,704$	$2^{\left[\frac{(n-6)(n-7)}{2}\right]}$
7	$\dfrac{[(n-1)\ldots(n-6)]}{(y-1)!}$	$1,866,256$	$2^{\left[\frac{(n-7)(n-8)}{2}\right]}$
8	$\dfrac{[(n-1)\ldots(n-7)]}{(y-1)!}$	$251,548,592$	$2^{\left[\frac{(n-8)(n-9)}{2}\right]}$
9	$\dfrac{[(n-1)\ldots(n-8)]}{(y-1)!}$	$66,296,291,072$	$2^{\left[\frac{(n-9)(n-10)}{2}\right]}$

Legend:

n = total number of factors
y = number of internally affective factors
x = number of environmental, externally affective factors
Note: x is implicit
y = n − x
x = n − y
The x:y ratio for any given value of n = a group

TABLE 5
COMBINATORIAL ALGORITHMS

$$\text{Category } I - \text{closed} = n\{2^{\left[\frac{(n-1)(n-2)}{2}\right]}\}$$

y	Effective states (E)	Internally affective states (I)	Externally affective states (S)
1	1	1	$2^{\left[\frac{(n-1)(n-2)}{2}\right]}$
2	$(n-1)$	1	$2^{\left[\frac{(n-2)(n-3)}{2}\right]}$
3	$\dfrac{[(n-1)(n-2)]}{(y-1)!}$	2	$2^{\left[\frac{(n-3)(n-4)}{2}\right]}$
4	$\dfrac{[(n-1)(n-2)(n-3)]}{(y-1)!}$	12	$2^{\left[\frac{(n-4)(n-5)}{2}\right]}$
5	$\dfrac{[(n-1)\ldots(n-4)]}{(y-1)!}$	152	$2^{\left[\frac{(n-5)(n-6)}{2}\right]}$
6	$\dfrac{[(n-1)\ldots(n-5)]}{(y-1)!}$	3,640	$2^{\left[\frac{(n-6)(n-7)}{2}\right]}$
7	$\dfrac{[(n-1)\ldots(n-6)]}{(y-1)!}$	160,224	$2^{\left[\frac{(n-7)(n-8)}{2}\right]}$
8	$\dfrac{[(n-1)\ldots(n-7)]}{(y-1)!}$	13,063,792	$2^{\left[\frac{(n-8)(n-9)}{2}\right]}$
9	$\dfrac{[(n-1)\ldots(n-8)]}{(y-1)!}$	2,012,388,736	$2^{\left[\frac{(n-9)(n-10)}{2}\right]}$

E = number of consequential end states for a given x:y ratio
I = number of internally affective states for a given x:y ratio
S = number of externally affective states for a given x:y ratio
$(E \times I \times S)$ = sum of all individually unique states for any given x:y ratio (i.e. group)

Every *family* (except when n = 1) contains either $(n-1)!$ or $\dfrac{(n-1)!}{3}$ members

Appendix B

TABLE 6
COMBINATORIAL ALGORITHMS

Category II – feedback to 'a'

y	Effective states (E)	Internally affective states (I)	Externally affective states (S)
1	—	—	—
2	—	—	—
3	$\dfrac{[(n-1)(n-2)]}{(y-1)!}$	2	$2^{\left[\frac{(n-3)(n-4)}{2}\right]}$
4	$\dfrac{[(n-1)(n-2)(n-3)]}{(y-1)!}$	24	$2^{\left[\frac{(n-4)(n-5)}{2}\right]}$
5	$\dfrac{[(n-1)\ldots(n-4)]}{(y-1)!}$	544	$2^{\left[\frac{(n-5)(n-6)}{2}\right]}$
6	$\dfrac{[(n-1)\ldots(n-5)]}{(y-1)!}$	22,360	$2^{\left[\frac{(n-6)(n-7)}{2}\right]}$
7	$\dfrac{[(n-1)\ldots(n-6)]}{(y-1)!}$	1,679,408	$2^{\left[\frac{(n-7)(n-8)}{2}\right]}$
8	$\dfrac{[(n-1)\ldots(n-7)]}{(y-1)!}$	236,617,024	$2^{\left[\frac{(n-8)(n-9)}{2}\right]}$
9	$\dfrac{[(n-1)\ldots(n-8)]}{(y-1)!}$	64,032,244,070	$2^{\left[\frac{(n-9)(n-10)}{2}\right]}$

Legend:

n = total number of factors
y = number of internally affective factors
x = number of environmental, externally affective factors
y = n − x
x = n − y
Note: x is implicit
The x:y ratio for any given value of n = a group

TABLE 7

COMBINATORIAL ALGORITHMS

Category III – feedback to terminals other than 'a'

y	Effective states (E)	Internally affective states (I)	Externally affective states (S)
1	—	—	—
2	—	—	—
3	—	—	—
4	$\dfrac{[(n-1)(n-2)(n-3)]}{(y-1)!}$	2	$2^{[\frac{(n-4)(n-5)}{2}]}$
5	$\dfrac{[(n-1)\ldots(n-4)]}{(y-1)!}$	32	$2^{[\frac{(n-5)(n-6)}{2}]}$
6	$\dfrac{[(n-1)\ldots(n-5)]}{(y-1)!}$	704	$2^{[\frac{(n-6)(n-7)}{2}]}$
7	$\dfrac{[(n-1)\ldots(n-6)]}{(y-1)!}$	26,784	$2^{[\frac{(n-7)(n-8)}{2}]}$
8	$\dfrac{[(n-1)\ldots(n-7)]}{(y-1)!}$	1,884,156	$2^{[\frac{(n-8)(n-9)}{2}]}$
9	$\dfrac{[(n-1)\ldots(n-8)]}{(y-1)!}$	251,518,266	$2^{[\frac{(n-9)(n-10)}{2}]}$

E = number of consequential end states for a given x:y ratio
I = number of internally affective states for a given x:y ratio
S = number of externally affective states for a given x:y ratio
$(E \times I \times S)$ = sum of all individually unique states for any given x:y ratio (i.e. group)

Every *family* (except when n = 1) contains either $(n-1)!$ or $\dfrac{(n-1)!}{3}$ members

Appendix B

TABLE 8
COMBINATORIAL SUMS

Categories I, II & III (see table 4 for algorithm & legend)

n ⇒	3	4	5	6	7	8	9
y							
1	2	8	64	1,024	32,768	2,097,152	268,435,456
2	2	6	32	320	6,144	229,376	16,777,216
3	4	12	48	320	3,840	86,016	3,670,016
4		38	152	760	6,080	85,120	2,179,072
5			728	3,640	21,840	203,840	3,261,440
6				26,704	160,224	1,121,568	11,963,392
7					1,866,256	13,063,792	104,510,336
8						251,548,592	2,012,388,736
9							66,296,291,072
total	8	64	1,024	32,768	2,097,152	268,435,456	68,719,476,736

Category I (closed) (see table 5 for algorithm & legend)

n ⇒	3	4	5	6	7	8	9
y							
1	2	8	64	1,024	32,768	2,097,152	268,435,456
2	2	6	32	320	6,144	229,376	16,777,216
3	2	6	24	160	1,920	43,008	1,835,008
4		12	48	240	1,920	26,880	688,128
5			152	760	4,560	42,560	680,960
6				3,640	21,840	152,880	1,630,720
7					160,224	1,121,568	8,972,544
8						13,063,792	104,510,336
9							2,012,388,736
total	6	32	320	6,144	229,376	16,777,216	2,415,919,104

TABLE 8
COMBINATORIAL SUMS

Category II (feedback to 'a') – (see table 6 for algorithm & legend)

n ⇒	3	4	5	6	7	8	9
y							
1	—	—	—	—	—	—	—
2	—	—	—	—	—	—	—
3	2	6	24	160	1,920	43,008	1,835,008
4		24	96	480	3,840	53,760	1,376,256
5			544	2,720	16,320	152,320	2,437,120
6				22,360	134,160	939,120	10,017,280
7					1,679,408	11,755,856	94,046,848
8						236,617,024	1,892,936,192
9							64,032,244,070
total	2	30	664	25,720	1,835,648	249,561,088	66,034,892,774

Category III (feedback to other than 'a') (see table 7 for algorithm & legend)

n ⇒	3	4	5	6	7	8	9
y							
1	—	—	—	—	—	—	—
2	—	—	—	—	—	—	—
3	—	—	—	—	—	—	—
4		2	8	40	160	4,480	114,688
5			32	160	960	8,960	143,360
6				704	4,224	29,568	315,392
7					26,784	187,488	1,499,904
8						1,884,156	15,073,248
9							251,518,266
total	—	2	40	904	32,128	2,114,652	268,664,858

TABLE 9
NUMERICAL ANALYSIS OF COMBINATORIAL SUMS

Categories I, II & III (constituent sums (E×I×S) – see table 4 for algorithms)

n⇒					3					4					5
y	E		I		S	total	E		I		S	total	E		I		S	total

y			n=3						n=4						n=5			
1	1 × 1 × 2 = 2						1 × 1 × 8 = 8						1 × 1 × 64 = 64					
2	2 × 1 × 1 = 2						3 × 1 × 2 = 6						4 × 1 × 8 = 32					
3	1 × 4 × 1 = 4						3 × 4 × 1 = 12						6 × 4 × 2 = 48					
4							1 × 38 × 1 = 38						4 × 38 × 1 = 152					
5													1 × 728 × 1 = 728					
total						8						64						1024

---

n⇒						6					7
y	E		I		S	total	E		I		S	total

n = 6

y	E		I		S		total
1	1 ×	1 ×	1,024	=	1,024
2	5 ×	1 ×	64	=	320
3	10 ×	4 ×	8	=	320
4	10 ×	38 ×	2	=	760
5	5 ×	728 ×	1	=	3,640
6	1 ×	26,704 ×	1	=	26,704
total					32,768

n = 7

y	E		I		S		total
1	1 ×	1 ×	32,768	=	32,768
2	6 ×	1 ×	1,024	=	6,144
3	15 ×	4 ×	64	=	3,840
4	20 ×	38 ×	8	=	6,080
5	15 ×	728 ×	2	=	21,840
6	6 ×	26,704 ×	1	=	160,224
7	1 ×	1,866,256 ×	1	=	1,866,256
total					2,097,152

---

n ⇒ 8

y	E		I		S		total
1	1 ×	1	×	2,097,152	=	2,097,152
2	7 ×	1	×	32,768	=	229,376
3	21 ×	4	×	1,024	=	86,016
4	35 ×	38	×	64	=	85,120
5	35 ×	728	×	8	=	203,840
6	21 ×	26,704	×	2	=	1,121,568
7	7 ×	1,866,256	×	1	=	13,063,792
8	1 ×	251,548,592	×	1	=	251,548,592
total						268,435,456

TABLE 9
NUMERICAL ANALYSIS OF COMBINATORIAL SUMS

Categories I, II & III (constituent sums (E×I×S) – see table 4 for algorithms)

n ⇒							9
y	E		I		S		total
1	1	×	1	×	268,435,456	=	268,435,456
2	8	×	1	×	2,097,152	=	16,777,216
3	28	×	4	×	32,768	=	3,670,016
4	56	×	38	×	1,024	=	2,179,072
5	70	×	728	×	64	=	3,261,440
6	56	×	26,704	×	8	=	11,963,392
7	28	×	1,866,256	×	2	=	104,510,336
8	8	×	251,548,592	×	1	=	2,012,388,736
9	1	×	66,296,291,072	×	1	=	66,296,291,072
total							68,719,476,736

Legend & notes:

E = number of consequential (effective) end states
I = number of internally affective states
S = number of externally affective (environmental) states
y = number of internally affective factors
x = number of externally affective factors (implicit: $x = n - y$)
n = total number of factors

E = 1 at y = 1, irrespective of the value of n, increases to a maximum at the middle ranges of y and decreases to 1 at y = n

I = 1 at y = 1 and y = 2, irrespective of the value of n, and increases progressively to a maximum at y = n

$S = n^{\left[\frac{(n-1)(n-2)}{2}\right]}$ at y = 1 and decreases progressively to 1 at y = (n−1)

The respective rates of increase and decrease in the values of E, I and S define the evolution of systems over periods of time and provide perfect predictive powers within any n-defined, finite analytic matrix.

Appendix C – Glossary of Terms

The words we assign to meanings are arbitrary, but it is essential that those who wish to have a useful dialogue concerning information (as distinct from literature), must agree on and share a common vocabulary and its meanings or else communications are impossible.

This partial list of defined words is the result of my geometric, causal-consequential-operational analysis of transactions and a quantification of qualitative aspects of behaviour. Obviously it must remain incomplete and perpetually subject to refinement and elaboration. Some words are left out because they are adequately defined in the text (e.g. *winning*) or in dictionaries.

Readers will find that most of the definitions given here differ from those found in standard dictionaries. These differences exist because meanings tend to become corrupted in time, even when they were correctly defined in the past. For example the word *heretic* means a *dangerous dissident* today, whereas its roots lie in classical Greek, where it meant *an individual who thinks for himself*. When meanings become corrupted to this extent we live in a value-free and essentially meaningless world – i.e. one in which causes, consequences and meanings are not understood or are reversed.

Note that all italicized words are defined either in considerable detail in the text or in this glossary. Most are found in the subject index. A certain amount of redundancy is unavoidable throughout.

Accidents – are *coincidences* of individuals, groups and events, governed by the relationship of *organic* to *inorganic* components. No *accident* involving *organic behaviour* (i.e. that of individuals or groups of human beings) ever occurs by *chance*. Chance only enters the equation as a result of 'mindless' behaviour (e.g. the shuffling of the pack of cards before playing a card-game), inattention, inorganic relationships (e.g. a rockfall where no humans are present – in which case no accident can take place) and *short-* or *intermediate-term* ignorance or irresponsibility (i.e. *relative objectivity*). In the longest run even 'mindless' and inorganic behaviours turn into relative *certainties* (thereby providing *total objectivity*). All accidents are therefore *conditionally deterministic*. Any contrary view is the result of an abrogation of responsibility. See *affect* and *analysis*.

Affect – The behaviour of *organic systems* can be *causal* and affects the *environment* and vice versa, bringing about (i.e. causing) *consequences*, *outcomes*, *results* and *end states*. The last are the *effects*. For these reasons it is crucial to make clear distinctions between affect and effect, and to assure that the sequence of *cause* and *effect* are not reversed as often occurs when it comes to *accidents*.

Algorithm – A *method* for solving problems (derived from the surname 'Algor' of an Arab mathematician). Originally a purely mathematical method (as it should be), this word has become corrupted to mean any method of problem-solving – verbal or by means of direct action (e.g. *winning*), even when this is entirely inappropriate (i.e. *unintelligent*).

Amoral – lacking all standards and *values*; without *foresight* (i.e. *imagination*) or conscience; as distinct from *immoral*, which implies making conscious *value judgements* even when doing something you know is wrong.

Analysis – A systematic and logical method of investigation that is based on clearly defined *criteria* and *value judgements* made in advance and after analysis is completed. The *algorithmic* (i.e. mathematical) is the most precise method of analysis that lends itself to the broadest possible *generalizations*.

Appropriate behaviour – The ability to adapt to all circumstances. See *intelligence* and *learning*.

Balance – The draw represents a balanced outcome between equals, one that is actually or relatively *error free* and *perfect* (i.e. a deliberate *draw*), as distinct from one achieved by *chance*, a misunderstood *stalemate* or a *victory* between an experienced and an inexperienced or unskilled player. Balanced outcomes should therefore predominate in games as they do in most processes of nature. See *error* and *error correction*.

Behaviour – is defined by movement in space over a period of time. Four categories exist: *totally objective, relatively objective, relatively subjective,* and *subjective. Inorganic* matter, unaffiliated with an organism can only behave in a *relatively objective* (i.e. mechanical, *closed, finite system*) manner. *Organic* matter can behave *relatively objectively, relatively subjectively* or *subjectively* (with extension to *infinity* and *perpetual feedback* – i.e. *learning*). See Appendices A and B.

Behaviourism – A school of psychology that subscribes to the erroneous view that *learning* depends on *operant conditioning* with reinforcement (i.e. carrot and stick training), made famous by the *theories* of Pavlov in Russia and B. F. Skinner in the US. Such conditioning is responsible for beliefs that fly in the face of factual evidence.

Brute force method – Attacking any opposing force *or* problem by trying everything without *data reduction* and when no *value judgements* are involved. The *unclassified combinatorial sum of all possibilities* represents such a method.

Categories – The highest form of *classification* in the hierarchy of systems.

Causes – It is essential to distinguish between original and immediate causes. The first lie so far back historically that they often remain unknown or are irrelevant to the present (e.g. 'The original cause of this book was the origin of life on earth'). A significant cause is one that is directly responsible for what is happening now (i.e. 'The *intentions* of the players' were the causes of the *game* being played.)

Certainty – The physicist Werner Heisenberg wrongly insisted that our universe is governed by uncertainty (i.e. the *uncertainty principle* that is a central feature of quantum theory). In *games* uncertainty is created only by attempted '*winning*' in the conventional sense and a resulting *randomization*. However, even with maximum randomization (e.g. the shuffling of a pack of playing-cards), there is absolute certainty that the *combinatorial sum of all possibilities* (and all *permutations* within them) will recur again and again in the long run, although not in its original order. Short-term *conditional* certainty can be established by systematic sorting. The same principles apply in all branches of science, including those that deal with *organic behaviour*.

Classification – according to closely defined *criteria* is the first step in the establishment of any scientific discipline. See *categories*, *groups*, *families*, *internal* and *external affect*, *effect*, *convergences*, *options*, *causes*, *consequences*, *individually unique states*, etc. These are among the criteria used for the classification of the *combinatorial sum of all possibilities*.

Classified brute force sum – See *brute force* and *classification*.

Closed system – Any system that cannot be enlarged to *infinity* except by repetition or addition, and in which *feedback*, if any, only leads to repetition. All machines are closed systems. Anyone who has a closed mind and who performs as a result of *operant conditioning* without critical thought displays machine-like (i.e. closed system) *behaviour*.

Combinatorial – Combinatorial *mathematics* is a relatively neglected field. Its origins go back to ancient China. The *I Ching* consists of a combinatorial sum (i.e. s = 64 when n = 4) as Leibnitz realized. An earlier version of the *I Ching* generated only eight patterns (s = 8 when n = 3). Early Chinese mathematicians could not consider any combinatorial sum larger than n = 4 because mechanical computing (e.g. the abacus) had not yet been invented. The original meanings of the *I Ching* were lost by the time the abacus was invented (during the Ming Dynasty).

The detailed *analyses* that led to the *classification* of combinatorial sums were first attempted by this author in 1976, confirmed by the late Dr Grey Walter, and refined ever since. The geometry itself (i.e. the direction of the *data flow*) provided the *criteria* for classification and established the *relationships* between *individual* and *group behaviours* (e.g. the many-body problem in physics) as an infinitely expandable finite series.

Combinatorial explosion – The *algorithm* (see Appendix B) that generates combinatorial sums increases them at a greater-than-exponential rate (i.e. greater than the geometric series 2, 4, 8, 16 . . .) with every increase in the value of n (i.e. when n = 2, 3, 4 . . .).

Complete information – All *games* of *strategy* (e.g. noughts and crosses and chess) and real-life situations in which all facts are known and in sight (i.e. without secrecy or random shuffling in advance of play) are complete information games.

Compromise – Conventionally a compromise is believed to be a 'fair' solution and one from which all benefit equally. The resolution of the game enigma demonstrates this to be a hypocritical fallacy. Instead, a compromise defines a situation in which the losing side in a conflict is forced to agree to less than its due and the winner loses less than he expected; i.e. the hypocrisy lies in the pretence that this is a balanced outcome – a *draw*.

Concluded system – is one without feedback, or one in which internal feedback consists of perpetual repetition. See *closed system* and Appendix B, table 2, n = 4, category I, family 2.

Conclusion – The last *node* or state in a concluded or an *open system* (i.e. prior to feedback), equivalent to a *consequence* or an *end state*. The *data flow* comes to a complete stop in a concluded system and no further *data flow* is possible (e.g. *winning* and *losing*), or it repeats itself (e.g. a *draw* played to the last turn, or a *stalemate*) in a feedback system.

Conditional branching – The human central nervous system (i.e. the organic *neural network*) and computers have conditional branching in common. The options that exist are provided by the possible directions of the *data flow* (see Appendix B, diagram 4 – the directions of the arrows) at each *node*. In human beings the actual limits to the available options are governed physically (i.e. by the internal neural network), by *free will* or by *conditioning* (i.e. habit), by systematic or random choice (both acts of will), and by the options that are available in the *external environment*.

In computers such choices are limited by the chip architecture and the programming, both man-imposed, even when *random brute force* or systematic programming methods are applied that reduce the *sum of combinatorial possibilities* to manageable proportions. One fundamental difference between the two systems is that the organic one is capable of ordering, classifying and synthesizing the options and making valuative choices autonomously, thus reducing the sum of all combinatorial possibilities to one, whereas the mechanical system can only provide a choice of options, unless it is biased in advance by the programmer. See Chapter 9 and Appendix A.

Conditional determinism – Because of the conditions described above (see *conditional branching*), and the redefinition of chance as a conditionally deterministic phenomenon in nature, all *natural laws* are governed by principles here defined as conditional (but not absolute) determinism. In other words, nature is ruled by absolute laws that do, however, offer a given but vast and ever-expanding number of choices. There is nothing random about natural phenomena in the long term, no matter how disordered or chaotic they may be or seem to us at any moment in time.

Consequences – See *conclusion*.

Context – The *subject-specific* arrangement of words according to an agreed-to vocabulary and grammar (i.e. *syntax*).

Convergence – Any *node* at which more than one arrow meets (see Appendix B, diagram 1) provides convergence (i.e. a coincidence). The sum of convergences subtracted from the value of n = the sum of *options* for the continuation of the *data flow* at that *node*, e.g. when n = 4 and convergence at any one node = 4, then the options for the continuation of the data flow = 0 and the system is *concluded*.

Cosmos – The largest, overall system we can consider. It contains many nested and possibly parallel *universes*.

Creativity – is defined by the *draw* solution with all that this implies (e.g. *individual uniqueness*, *perfectability*, etc.). It provides perpetual *learning*, *feedback* and a vast number of choices and rewards, far greater quantitatively and qualitatively in number than possible victories.

Criminality – is an extreme aspect of and equivalent to habitual *winning* (i.e. benefiting from taking advantage of, victimizing or inducing errors in others). Many forms of *insanity* are caused by the same conditions. The main difference between both depends on duration and the intensity of the *consequences*.

Criteria – Factual, *causal*, *consequential* and *operational bases* for *classification* (e.g. *concluded systems*, *feedback* to the original *node*, *feedback* to *infinity*, *convergence* and *option patterns*, etc.). See *classification* and Appendix B.

Cybernetics – A term coined by Norbert Wiener, but interpreted variously by different authors, ancient and modern. Here redefined to mean the relationship between organic and inorganic or machine behaviour.

Data base – Any related body of facts.

Data : Environment Ratio – If x = the internally affective factors and y = the *environment*, then for any value of n there is an $x : y$

ratio that describes the relationship of one to the other. See Appendix B.

Data flow – See Appendix B, diagram 4. The direction of the arrows determines the data flow, the *convergences* and the *options*, in any integrated network of related facts.

Data reduction – A form of systematic logic that enables the programmer to extract a minimal number of options after the computer has considered one or more classifications of the *sum of all combinatorial possibilities* and sifted them further according to given *criteria*.

Decision making – Only organisms can make decisions. Machines can generate and reduce *the classified sum of all combinatorial possibilities* to a minimum, leaving a residual set of choices. The initial decision to play a *game* and which *category* to consider (e.g. won, drawn or stalemated games), or which *strategies* to select from those that the computer can isolate, are purely human *decisions* based on *value judgements* that no computer can make.

Deduction – Tracing a chain of events from consequences back to a cause. See *induction*.

Determinism – The erroneous belief that all things are predetermined. See *conditional determinism*.

Dimensions – Physicists and mathematicians (and notably Einstein) speak of four- and more-dimensional universes. Obviously any dimensions greater or smaller than three are invisible. However, and despite these claims, our *universe* is purely *three-dimensional*. This three-dimensionality can be extended to *infinity* (like adding or stacking blocks next to or on top of one another). But this does not change the three-dimensional characteristics of the construction.

For example, 2^3 represents a cube, each side of which is two units of measurement in length. 2^4 represents two times that same cube. By adding additional powers we can multiply the number of cubes indefinitely, but while we have changed the shape of the construction, we have not added any new dimensions. It is still a fully three-dimensional one. This principle even applies to time, contrary to what Einstein claimed (he said it represented a fourth dimension), unless he was speaking metaphorically and in non-geometric terms.

Directed graph – All *combinatorial sums* can be represented as directed graphs. The diagrams shown in Appendices A and B are directed graphs – i.e. the direction in which the arrows point direct the *data flow*. These same graphs are also *vector geometric* and *n–defined*. That is to say they depend in size, scope and extent (i.e. the number of individual *nodes* = n) on the number of *factors* that are involved. In other words n = 4 generates far fewer patterns than n = 5.

Domain – The territory that belongs by right to any individual player. See Appendix A.

Effect – *Consequence, result, outcome, goal* or *end state*. See *affect, concluded system* and *conclusion*.

Encyclopedic knowledge – Everything that is known about any subject. See also *omniscience*. It has been claimed that when computers possess encyclopedic knowledge they are then *expert systems* and on the way to *artificial intelligence*.

End state – See *effect, conclusion, consequence*.

Environment – The world (or universe) beyond any one *node*, the self or the immediate subject, individual, community, tribe or country.

Error – Any calculation, move or behaviour that results in imbalance, conflict or unresolved differences. See *balance*.

Error correction – The *classification* of the *sum of all combinatorial possibilities* provides a self-referential method of error correction or restoration of *balance* and relative or actual *perfection*. In other words any *error* that may occur can be easily found because various *criteria*, including the binary definitions (see Appendix B), provide automatic *internal* and *external* checks that make any inadvertent error stand out clearly. See *pattern recognition*.

Ethics – As demonstrated by the game metaphor, ethics are governed by *natural* and *mathematical laws of cause and effect*. Like any other *rules* and *laws* they are defined by and define absolute limits to the *classified sum of all combinatorial possibilities*. In other words, *conditional (appropriate) value judgements* can be made about right and wrong, good and evil, within any sufficiently large, finite, but infinitely expandable, *conditionally deterministic* frame of reference.

Evolution – is any *organic process* of development, each following step arising out of the last (see *heuristic, learning*) as a consequence of interactions between the *conditionally deterministic*, *internal* processes of the system and the conditionally deterministic *environment* in which it exists.

Expert system – Every computer program is a so-called expert system in as much as it encapsulates the subject-specific expertise of three kinds of specialists – one who has practical knowledge in a particular field of application; a second who is able to analyse the method whereby the first expert applies his expertise, (such experts are systems analysts or knowledge engineers as they call themselves today – unless the first kind of expert is self-analytical); and a third who programs the computer so that it can execute the purely mechanical aspects of tasks otherwise performed by the first kind of expert.

External affect – The options that can be exercised by the *environment* to *affect* internally affective processes – i.e. the individual or the group in an *organic* or *inorganic* sense. See *affect*, *evolution* and *environment*.

Factor – The number (n) of known facts in the system, each representing a letter, word, sentence, book or subject, found or entered at each *node* on a *directed graph*.

Families – One of the *classifications* into which the *sum of all combinatorial possibilities* can be divided.

Fate – is never a product of chance but of choice, lack of choice or of options imposed from without by an individual or group. We create our own fate and one another's. There is no such thing as luck – good or bad.

Feedback – Three kinds of feedback exist: *a*) limited and recursive feedback that excludes one or more *factors* in the system; *b*) all-inclusive feedback (i.e. that includes all the factors in the system), and *c*) feedback that includes a perpetually growing number of factors (i.e. *subjective learning*). Each of these three forms of feedback is a form of conditioning, but only *a*) and *b*) define *operant conditioning* or *programming;* *c*) is self-rewarding. The specific *meanings* depend on application. Those that apply to game playing are defined in the text of this book. See *closed system* and Appendix B.

Feelings – Pleasure and pain each have a finite threshold. In one sense these feelings consist of a continuum that is finite at both extremes. An inability to feel pain also means an absence of the ability to feel pleasure (and vice versa); the conditionally absolute extremes (i.e. none or too much) of pain or pleasure lead to unconsciousness. Because of the huge and uncountable number of subtleties within the parallel spectra of pain and pleasure, I have divided feelings into three significant states for the purposes of this book – good, bad and indifferent. Each of the arrow-defined intentional states described by the numbers and diagrams in Appendices A and B can therefore be multiplied by three. In other words whether an individual feels good, bad or indifferent about *winning*, *losing*, achieving a *draw* or a *stalemate* depends on his *intentions* and their fulfilment (i.e. whether a chosen *goal* is reached).

Finite system – All systems are finite and infinitely expandable in one way or another. As demonstrated in Appendices A and B, all smaller finite systems are part of an infinite continuum of larger ones (i.e. $n = 3$ is part of and incorporated in $n = 4, 5, 6 \ldots$).

Flow chart – The *classified sum of all combinatorial possibilities* and the geometry that generates it includes every possible flow chart as used today in conventional systems analysis. This demonstrates that there is always more than one way for solving any particular problem, though some are better than others. Even more significant is that there are far fewer wrong ways (i.e. those that contain *errors*) than correct or perfect ones from which to choose in any application.

Forecasting – A *systematic*, *mathematically* based method of *predicting* the consequences of a chain of events. *Causes* must be known in order to make any kind of accurate forecast, and they can be extracted by identical means. Today forecasting is most often attempted by *stochastic*, *probabilistic* means. The methods on which the findings in this book are based are *geometric*, *linear* and *conditionally deterministic*, similar to those used by the British Meteorological Office.

Foresight – The intuitive method of predicting the *causes* and *consequences* of a chain of events. *Imagination*, an awareness of *consequences*, and a conscience are the characteristics that enable people to make accurate predictions on the basis of a limited amount of information. In the absence of these characteristics or a reliable *mathematical method* (see *forecasting*) the *future* seems *random* and unpredictable.

Future – The future, like the past, has *geometric* characteristics, relative to the *evolution* of all systems, depending on the available knowledge of the moment, the method of analysis and synthesis that is employed and the understanding of natural laws of cause and effect. See *forecasting*, *foresight* and Appendix B.

Game – Defines any *consequential* relationship between a player and him- or herself or between individuals or groups: the outcome results in a balance among equals (i.e. a perfect or near-perfect one that is consciously and systematically achieved), in victory by default for one and defeat as a result of inattention or inexperience by the other, or one of four kinds of stalemates achieved by chance (i.e. tactical or psychological randomization), or a conscious draw played to the last or last but one turn. All outcomes, except consciously achieved *draws*, create *imbalances*. See *balance*.

Generalization – An algebraic expression [e.g. $(n-1)(n+1)$] is a generalization about calculations. The given example holds true for a infinite series of numbers, the consecutive difference between each of which is the odd number series 5, 7, 9, 11 ... This differential equation is therefore an absolute generalization. Similar generalizations can be made about other matters in non-mathematical terms, despite the claim of some philosophers and logicians that this is impossible. The generalizations that can be inferred from portions of this book (as much as from the algebra given in Appendix B) are of this nature.

Geometric analysis – As Euclid and Pythagoras knew, and Descartes attempted to elaborate, geometry is the basis of all mathematical logic. In the context of this book, the analytic geometry given in Appendices A and B generates the *criteria of classification*, the mathematics and the logic that permit subject-specific, applicable *generalizations* to be extracted. An appropriate geometric method therefore allows analyses to be made of various forms of inorganic and organic behaviour.

Global data consideration – Alternative term for *holistic* or *all-inclusive*. This means 'considering everything' either in principle, mathematically or intuitively. The latter is the highest form of logic, for it is impossible to know everything even about the simplest thing, like the game of noughts and crosses.

Goals – Alternative term for *outcomes*, *end states* or *consequences*.

Group – Second order (after *category*) of *classification of the sum of all combinatorial possibilities*. See *classification*, *criteria* and Appendix B.

Heuristic method – Step-by-step, *iterative* trial and error method of *analysis* and *learning*. A useful method, provided the trial is limited (i.e. does not consist of an attempted *brute force* approach) and that the user learns from his or her mistakes.

Hierarchy – All systems are *qualitatively hierarchical*, whether this is admitted or not. For example there is a first order of *classification*, a second and so on (see *classification*, *categories*, *criteria*, *groups* and *families*, etc.). Each higher and lower self-referential order establishes its own place in the hierarchy of systems. However, the individually unique state (e.g. the individual human being) and the system as a whole – the largest, all-inclusive set – (e.g. the human race) enjoy an equal, *conditionally determined* place in the hierarchy. The *classified sum of all combinatorial possibilities* demonstrates this principle that is common to all systems.

Hindsight – The *classified sum of all combinatorial possibilities* provides perfect hindsight for any game from the first move onwards. This increases up to the last turn, at which point all possibilities concern only the past. This is now true, for example, for the game of noughts and crosses for which no further future predictions can be made, for all that can be known is known within practical limits of time and paper. Any future game played to be won and lost is limited to a repetition of the past, except that some games may differ in insignificant respects as far as the feelings and intentions of the players are concerned, although they are included in the theoretical model (see Appendix A, diagram 2).

Any *future error* on the part of either player will be a repetition of the past. The same, of course, is true for war or any other game played by 'us' against 'them' (you can only win or lose in a limited number of ways). The same is not true for love and friendship, art, craft, science and humour, etc., for it is their very subjective subtleties, possibilities and variety that assure that in these respects we will never run out of options in any foreseeable future. In theory at least, if not in practice, life on earth has the potential to offer us nothing but happy surprises. However this, like everything else, is conditional on appropriate behaviour on everyone's part – an unlikely prospect in any foreseeable future.

Holistic – See *global data consideration*. In practical terms, this does not mean either *encyclopedic knowledge* or pretended omniscience. The latter is impossible in any event, even in simple matters like noughts and crosses. However, with the future development of holography as a scientific tool, it will eventually be possible to consider all complex problems (like the weather) in terms of a moving hologram (by means other than stop-frame animation), enhancing our predictive powers to an extent limited only by our knowledge of the facts.

Holographic – An optical/mechanical process that simulates *global data consideration* functions of the human brain. See *holistic*.

Illogic – Any *totally objective, conditionally deterministic system of logic* must also contain all the illogic there is, for both logic and illogic always depend on circumstances. For example, killing (or leg-breaking) is illogical (and therefore *criminal* or *insane*) in peace-time, but it may be the only logical alternative in special circumstances such as an effective last-ditch defence against a ruthless attacker who relentlessly pursues an otherwise peaceful human being or group with an unswerving intent to do psychological or bodily harm. This should not be seen as a licence to kill in any except the rarest circumstances, nor should it be misread as an endorsement of capital punishment for, by the time the latter becomes possible, a criminal is already rendered relatively harmless by imprisonment.

Imagination – Foresight and hindsight depend entirely on the imagination (i.e. the creation of images in the mind's eye or on paper) and an awareness of *consequences*. There is of course a difference in these respects between fact and fiction, but in both cases the same mental processes are involved. See *forecasting, foresight, pattern* and *pattern recognition*.

Incomplete information – Any body of facts, except numerical or purely quantitative information, is always incomplete. While incomplete encyclopedic information storage (by means of books, computer discs, tapes or in the human memory) is possible, *omniscience* is impossible, even in simple matters. We must therefore always act on less-than-complete knowledge of the facts, and the highest form of logic is therefore *intuition*, irrespective of how much is known.

Indeterminacy – See *accident, chance, coincidence; Gödel, Heisenberg.*

Individual uniqueness – One of the *criteria* for the *classification of the sum of all combinatorial possibilities.* See Appendix B and *redundancy.*

Induction – Tracing a chain of events from *cause* to *consequences;* part of the process required to establish *meanings.* See *deduction.*

Inorganic – Any finite system; one that is incapable of autonomous growth and development in a genetic, evolutionary sense (i.e. a rock or a machine); also any relatively objective processes or judgements (e.g. treating other people like objects), for these exclude all subjective criteria (e.g. no *feedback* or *learning*).

Insanity – See *criminality, illogic.*

Intelligence – All *organic* species are *intelligent* (i.e. adaptive and autonomous) in varying degrees. The exercise of their intelligence depends on the *internal/organic* and *external/environmental* options any one species or organism is able to exercise autonomously in any environment, subject to *learning.* Intelligence, therefore, is always *conditionally deterministic,* like everything else. It finds expression only in appropriate *behaviour* in all circumstances and *environments* and the speed of adaptation (i.e. *learning*) to unfamiliar ones, relative to *value judgements.* Therefore no *machine,* object or *inorganic* material can ever be *intelligent,* although computers (or other machines) can and do mimic the mechanical aspects of organic behaviour – a fine, but crucial distinction related to *pattern recognition.*

All human beings (i.e. those who possess the same, intact and undamaged central nervous system as far as thought processes are concerned) are therefore potentially equally *intelligent,* with relatively minor differences subject only to energy, health, sensory/motor strengths or weaknesses, frame of reference, expression and application. Appropriate behaviour, subject to given conditions, is the only intelligence test worthy of the name.

Intentions – The desire to reach a certain *goal, consequence, end state* or *outcome.* This of course includes not knowing or caring what the outcome will be, in which case the *intention* is to *randomize* (i.e. to try winning by disconcerting other players tactically or psycho-logically). Intentions are therefore always *causal* in human behav-iour. It is possible to tell what anyone's intentions are by matching what they say to what they do.

Internal affect – How the internal workings of the mind or body affect the individual – *organic black-box behaviours* (e.g. *intentions, winning* and *losing, operant conditioning*, etc.). The same principle applies to *inorganic*, machine or machine-like behaviours or to aspects of the external environment that are otherwise invisible and can only be modelled.

Intuition – See *incomplete information, jump to conclusion*.

Iterative method – See *heuristic method, learning, stochastic method*.

Jump to conclusion – Every *intuition* is a jump to a conclusion. It is the best we are ever able to do. The problem is to distinguish between the right and the wrong jumps, based either on under-stood principles or a causal/consequential analysis. See *proof, theory* and Appendix B.

Laws – A distinction must be made between *natural laws* and man-made ones. *Rules* are related to natural law (see Chapter 7). They differ from laws only in so far as they apply in more limited environments and universes of discourse (e.g. in *games*). True justice, for example, only exists where natural law and man-made laws coincide (e.g. *ethics*). The *classified sum of all combinatorial possibilities* defines limits and therefore defines and is defined by natural law.

Learning – See *feedback* and Appendix B, diagram 2.

Limited feedback – *Feedback* to any *node* other than the originating one; or to the originating one only in any *less than all-inclusive* system of data consideration and/or one that cannot be extended to infinity. See *feedback* and Appendix A, diagrams 3–6 (i.e. *stalemates*).

Logic – See *illogic*.

Logistics – The discipline of ensuring that the required means are available at the right place and time. A military term that is equally applicable to inventory control as well as to the transport of people and materiel in peacetime for ecological, employment or other reasons.

Long-term consequences – All futures can be divided into *short-*, *intermediate-* and *long-term consequences*. All consequences should be the same (i.e. a *draw*) in the short-, intermediate- and longest-term when it comes to *organic, systematic behaviour*.

Machine – A *closed system* that can only be expanded by linkages in parallel or in series, but not by autonomous, evolutionary growth.

Materialism – deals exclusively with material existence (e.g. food, clothing, housing, earnings, savings and material possessions). These are essential to *short-term* survival, always depending on conditions and circumstances. Exclusive preoccupation with these tangible and material aspects of existence, except in cases of dire necessity, poverty or starvation, can lead to selfishness, greed and alienation. The 'invisible' aspects of existence (e.g. *intentions, feelings, goals, insight into the self and into others, learning,* and *subjective, qualitative success* – without sole regard for the self, earnings, profit or cash in the bank) are far more important, once the material ones are adequately provided for.

This has, in the past, been the concern of formal and informal religions and belief systems (with exceptions like Taoism, an essentially agnostic one), that have sought to teach and call attention to the non-material aspects of life and existence. As this book shows, while many religious cults, political and ethical systems share common ground, hardly any, except Taoism, certain Sufi and Hindu sects and some aspects of Buddhism, have based their teachings on totally objective logic and reason. In other words, the metaphysic of all other religions is based on *winning* and *losing, operant conditioning* and acceptance of tenets that, even when they violate common sense, are blindly accepted as articles of faith.

Mathematical method – Based on and derived from the *geometry* (see Appendices A and B and *n-defined, vector geometric, directed graphs*), combinatorial sums can be calculated for any value of n as can the various *classifications* into which the *brute force sum of all combinatorial possibilities* can be divided as a result of the analyses of the *data flow* (see Appendix B diagram 4 and table 2). Further analysis shows that common *factors* run through all systems and can be expressed *algebraically*. These steps define a *mathematical method*.

Meanings – The meanings of *informational words and phrases* can only
be extracted by a *causal-operational-consequential analysis* of the *data
flow* i.e. the direction of the arrows on the diagrams in Appendices
A and B, and the informational content of the *nodes* (e.g. words,
sentences, paragraphs or whole subjects) relative to time, place,
circumstances and *behaviour* (i.e. *context*). See *natural law*.

Memory – Two types of memory exist – mechanical and *organic*.
Mechanical memory is found, for example, in a rubber band that
snaps back to its original form when it is stretched; a mould made
from an object; or a computer tape or disc on which information
has been recorded magnetically. Organic memory consists of
genetic memories embedded in chromosomal chains, synapses
and neurons, and associations established in the human brain via
sensory/motor neural networks – combinatorial principles
dependent on interactions between portions of the organism and
its environment.

Modelling – A model is equivalent to a map. A map is not the
terrain, but it allows the user to orient himself on the actual
terrain, once he traverses it. The model, like the map, is an
analogue. The game metaphor provides a useful analogue for
modelling human competitive and co-operative behaviours.

Natural law – See *meanings*, *laws*, *limits* and *rules*. Natural laws and
meanings are synonymous, for each defines the other. Both are
extracted by the same process. This is indeed a tautology, but it
is one that describes the circularity of nature (e.g. the Yin and
the Yang). The result is an understanding of the *balances* and
imbalances in nature, including *human nature*.

n-defined graph – See Appendix B, diagram 4.

Nodes – Each of the four points, corners or terminals of every
square (see Appendix B, diagram 4) is marked with an arrow-
head of its own. Each is a node containing any amount of
information that may or may not be related to any other node in
the system, depending entirely on the *data flow* (i.e. the direction
of the arrows). Each such node can be expanded (like zooming in
with a camera), exposing its informational content that may be
arranged in a representation consisting of additional nodes,
depending on how that information is broken down into domains
and individual components. In this manner a vast information

system can be represented in a compact modular fashion without getting into too much detail and avoiding irrelevancies, and analysed in terms of its inter-connectedness – just like a *neural network*.

Objective – See *end state, conclusion, consequence, goal.*

Objectivity – See *relative objectivity* and *total objectivity.*

Omniscience – See *encyclopedic information, expert system, global data consideration* and *incomplete information.*

Open systems – See *infinity, feedback, learning.*

Operant conditioning – Carrot and stick training; equivalent to training and programming. All forms of learning involve conditioning of one sort or another. However, true learning is self-rewarding and creates perpetual feedback. See *behaviourism.*

Operational research – A game theoretical approach to general problem solving used in industry, government and by the military. It deals essentially with probabilities (e.g. winning and losing) and, like conventional game theory from which it is derived, can help minimize losses, but is unable to predict or guarantee winnings. See *statistical analysis, stochastic method.*

Operations – See *meanings.* Operations are the steps leading from the *causes* to *consequences* and vice versa.

Organic – All *organic (evolutionary, infinite, learning)* systems can evolve autonomously and include and are made up of *inorganic (finite)* components, whereas *inorganic systems* lack the ability to grow and learn. The difference is not merely one of quantitative complexity, but of qualitative differences in combinatorial organization and relationships (e.g. *perpetual feedback*). See *evolution.*

Outcome – See *conclusion, consequences, effect* and *end state.*

Paradox – A self-contradiction or an unfinished sentence – e.g. 'All generalizations are false, including this one' . . . unless it happens to be the correct one.

Past, present and future – See Appendix B. The *classified combinatorial sum analysis* suggests that the causal origin of anything includes the potential for the future. The present does not exist, except as a moving point that travels from the past into the future. The time it takes for the future to be realized depends on *conditionally determined* relationships between the *inorganic* and *organic* potential in the system, the *relatively objective* and *subjective* criteria for *evolution* in a *genetic* (i.e. innate) and a *behavioural* (adaptive) sense related to *environmental* and cultural conditions. All of the foregoing is *conditionally deterministic* and not random, stochastic or indeterminate, except for random or artificially shuffled components and those only in the short run.

Pattern – According to Grey Walter (see *The Living Brain*, London : Duckworth 1953, p. 40 and personal communication), pattern is one of the most important words in the English language. As he also stated, English is among the few languages that includes this word in its vocabulary without circumlocution. Because of Walter's deep understanding of the term and its importance, it is worth quoting him, although the following partial quote hardly does him justice : 'Pattern, then, may be defined as any sequence of events in time, or any set of objects in space, distinguishable from or comparable with another sequence or set . . . This is what distinguishes it from random events or chaos . . . you cannot remember chaos or compare one chaos to another; there is no plural for the word . . .'

Pattern recognition – *Organically* this is based on a *global* or *holistic* form of perception – i.e. seeing something as a whole in a *conditionally deterministic* manner (the way in which the game of noughts and crosses is modelled in Appendix A). Mechanically an analogous form of pattern recognition can be achieved that is wholly reflexive (e.g. Grey Walter's *Machina Speculatrix*) and that mimics certain *conditioned*, interactive aspects of the central nervous system. Another electronic type of vision simulator can be *stochastic*, like WISARD, a computer that mimics more complex, but equally mechanical aspects of pseudo-vision.

Neither machine is 'intelligent' in a human way. However *Machina Speculatrix* did simulate the mechanical aspects of the human central nervous system, whereas WISARD has more in common with a fruit machine (one-arm bandit). The latter does, none the less, have useful applications in the assembly of parts on a robot-controlled production line, provided the parts are placed in a manner that enables the machine to 'guess' what they are on a pre-programmed, probabilistic basis. Walter's machine (which can be seen in London's Science Museum) interacts with the environment in a relatively unpredictable manner (like an animal or a human being taken out of its usual environment), while WISARD makes probabilistic guesses on the basis of its stochastic program. The latter does not simulate in any fashion how normal, undamaged human beings see or think.

Walter's machine simulates relative autonomy as far as this can be done by a machine; WISARD is a control mechanism that is itself controlled statistically (i.e. solely on the basis of past probabilities), rather than one that controls itself and reacts with certainty in the future. It is indeed true that some human beings operate like either machine, but they do so only when they cannot apply their *intelligence* because they are physically or mentally damaged or fail to use innate *and* acquired autonomous, interpretative, critical and *valuative pattern recognition* abilities. In such states they are equivalent to machines.

Perfection – See *balance*, *error*, *error correction*. Mechanical perfection always contains some *error* (see *precision*).

Permutational relationships – See Appendix B for a definition of *permutations*. The *relationships* that give them meaning are defined under *criteria*, *geometry* and *mathematical method*.

Perpetual feedback – See *feedback* and Appendix B, diagram 2, *learning*.

Plans – See *strategies*.

Precision – Human intelligence is potentially the most precise measure we have. The human brain is a perfect measuring instrument. In health, the second law of thermodynamics does not apply to its processing or learning abilities within any one lifetime. All mechanical measuring instruments suffer from second law of thermodynamics imperfections and are precise only to +/−0.5 of the smallest unit of measurement that is employed – e.g. time, relative to any external reference point or any measure made with an instrument.

Prediction – The ostensible goal of science. See *forecasting*, *foresight*, *statistical analysis*, *stochastic method*.

Principle – A *principle*, based on natural laws of cause and effect, is the yardstick of any ideal and of actual or relative perfection. See *precision*.

Probabilities – used when no better yardstick exists. They are based on past performances projected into the future with the assumption that no change can ever take place within whatever universe is under consideration. See also *accident, chance, forecasting, prediction, statistical analysis, stochastic method, uncertainty*.

Problem solving – Before any problem can be solved or programmed in the expectation that a solution can be found, a precise *systems analysis* is required, based on a sufficiently inclusive set of *criteria* and information and with a clearly defined *goal, end state, conclusion* or *consequence* in mind.

Programming – is equivalent to *operant conditioning*. Computer programming achieves the same result (i.e. it limits the possibilities severely), except that in the latter case this is essential and does not involve carrot or stick, for the computer needs neither incentive nor fear of punishment in order to do its job.

Proof – A term that evokes controversy whenever it is mentioned. It is impossible to prove anything, unless theory matches practice (hence the saying : 'The proof of the pudding is in the eating'). However *theoretical* scientists do not feel called upon to provide proofs. That is the beauty of theorizing. Braithwaite, the British moral philosopher, defined the word proof when he stated that it required internal and external consistency, for that defines the relationship between theory and practice. See *jump to conclusion, theory, total freedom*.

Psychiatry – One or another of the many different *theories* of human behaviour applied, without *proof*, to the treatment of what are considered problems in mental health. In practice (but not in theory) psychiatrists, with rare exceptions, treat symptoms rather than *causes*, like much of medicine, and, as a result, cure nothing. Additionally, psychiatry, since it deals with behaviour outside a framework of practically demonstrable rules of *cause and effect* (i.e. *meanings*), tends to suffer from being *value free* and therefore *amoral* and unethical.

Psychology – The theory of *behaviour* and *learning*. See *theory* and *proof*.

Puzzles – Puzzles differ from *games* in so far as they always have a single *perfect* solution, although that, like everything else, can be achieved in a variety of ways. The outcome must therefore always be a *draw* (i.e. an agreement to agree that the perfect solution has been reached). The only time *winning* and *losing* are involved is when players are pitted against one another to see whether one or the other can solve a given puzzle faster. This then turns puzzle solving (like any *problem solving* in science or in game playing) into a *game of chance*.

Qualitative criteria – Good and bad, right and wrong, for example, are *qualitative value judgements*. Thanks to the *classification of the sum of combinatorial possibilities*, they can now be *quantified* up to a very fine point of resolution. We therefore have a totally objective yardstick for making value judgements, as explained throughout this book. Such a yardstick has always existed in everyone's mind, but this, evidently, seems to be the first time it has been calibrated and quantified.

Quantitative criteria – Heretofore only quantities could be measured. Now, however, both *quantities* and *qualities* can be quantified. See Appendices A and B.

Radical data reduction – Achieved mechanically as a result of the *classification of the sum of all combinatorial possibilities*. See Appendix B.

Randomness – is always brought about organically as a result of a mindless shuffling of the facts, and inorganically as a process in nature that precedes the evolution of lifeforms. In evolutionary and genetic terms, as in everything else, all systems, including the most random ones, tend towards dynamic order in the longest run. In organic systems the time it takes to achieve this state depends entirely on aware and *appropriate behaviour*. See *accident* and *chance*.

Reasoning – See *illogic*.

Recursion – See *feedback*.

Redundancy – The recurrence of identical permutations in combinatorial sums. Each is, however, *individually unique* in terms of option patterns – i.e. *data flow* within the *externally affective states*, relative to the internally affective ones. See Appendix B. Or, to put this in another way, at any stage of the game, many permutationally redundant drawn, won, lost or stalemated games can be isolated. None the less each is *individually unique* in terms of the players' intentions, as shown in Appendix A.

Relationships – See *permutational relationships*.

Relative objectivity – Regarding another organism as if it were an object; greed; selfishness; alienation; seeing things only from one point of view; the perspective of the would-be *winner* to the exclusion of other possibilities.

Rules – Man-made or natural limitations on the *classified sum of all combinatorial possibilities*.

Semantics – See *meanings*.

Sequence – See *permutations* and *pattern*.

Short-term consequences – See *conclusion, long-term consequences*.

Solutions – See *problem solving*.

Statistical analysis – A conclusion based on the averaging (even when weighted according to Bayesian methods) of a limited number of past events. Such methods can only be predictive in any finite environment about which all the facts are known (i.e. absolute encyclopedic *or* at least *theoretical* (e.g. *mathematical*) total knowledge or with *global* or *holistic awareness*), as for example that which now exists for prisoner's dilemma, noughts and crosses and a number of other games (i.e. where *perfect foresight* and *hindsight* exist). In all other instances (even in opinion polls, held prior to elections, with the possible exception of those taken on the election day itself, if the sample is representative), statistical analyses only concern hindsight (i.e. the past) and are absolutely non-predictive except when the future is a repetition of the past. See *forecasting, foresight* and *intuition*.

Step-by-step method – See *iterative* and *heuristic* method.

Stochastic method – Any method that is based on uncertainty and chance (e.g. *statistical analysis*).

Subjectivity – See *feedback*.

Subject-specific – See *context*.

Sum of all combinatorial possibilities – See *brute force method, classification, combinatorial explosion, data reduction, decision making, flow chart* and Appendices A and B.

Superiority – See *qualitative criteria*.

Theory – An untested and unproven *jump to a conclusion*. See *jump to conclusion* and *proof*. Many academics tend to produce unproven theories in order to ensure publication, promotion and research support (e.g. conventional game, learning and economic theories, artificial intelligence, the survival of the fittest and the definitions of the causes of human violence and aggression as conventionally perceived). This is, however, not true for all theorizing, for, if it were, science and the development of knowledge would have come to a halt long ago.

Perhaps the most dangerous theories are those that are incomplete but can be shown to work – like behaviourist theory, operant conditioning with reinforcement and nuclear fission. They work with a vengeance: for they exist only because their consequences are ignored or not understood. The general use of operant conditioning has caused people to become progressively more stupid and to believe what are palpable fictions, presented as truths. That way most turn into losers or willing victims.

Thermodynamics, the three laws of – The three laws of thermodynamics (there is a fourth that is not relevant in this context) can be defined in a number of ways, depending on context (e.g. open and closed systems, electrical, magnetic, radiation, or nuclear energy). No matter what the context may be, they concern the conservation, transformation and dissipation of energy. Simply stated, the three laws are:

1. The change in internal energy of a system is equal to the heat absorbed by the system less the work done by the system. This means, for example, that energy is neither created nor destroyed, but merely changes form, or that energy and matter are interchangeable and in equilibrium in the universe (cf. Einstein's conservation of energy principle).

2. Because heat flows from a higher to a lower temperature – and never vice versa – molecular and atomic disorder (i.e. entropy) tends to increase perpetually (e.g. when work is done).

3. At zero temperature no disorder can occur and all systems are restored to an absolute equilibrium. However at zero temperature there can be no motion (e.g. work), even at molecular, atomic and sub-atomic levels. Hence time would have to stand still.

Viewed in terms of the game metaphor relative to behaviour, the first law is equivalent to a draw, the second to winning and losing, and the third to a non-game.

Total freedom – (as shown in Appendix B, diagram 4, coordinates A8 and D1 in which the data flow emanates and the arrows point from 'a' in all possible directions) leads directly to total conditioning (e.g. the closed feedback loop b: c: d . . . b) from which there is no escape except by a reversal of the arrow leading from 'a' to 'd'.

Total objectivity – To view a system in its totality from outside it, but visualizing yourself within it (i.e. *relatively objectively* and *subjectively*). See *behaviour*.

Traffic flow – See *affect*, *directed graph*, *domain* and *effect*.

Training – See *operant conditioning*.

Trial and error – See *heuristic method* and *learning*.

Understanding – See *pattern* and *pattern recognition*.

Uniqueness – See *classification* and *redundancy*.

Universe – A closed system nested within a finite continuum of other, larger ones (of infinite size) and containing a finite sum of smaller ones within it. Other, parallel universes of an unknown number may exist that share similar or identical characteristics with our own, linked in parallel or in series. These in sum constitute the *cosmos*, the limits of which may always remain unknown.

Universe of discourse – See *context*.

Value judgement – See *qualitative criteria*.

Variations – *Individually unique states*, each of which consists of a different option pattern containing the same nodes or facts. See *classified sum of all combinatorial possibilities* and Appendix B.

x : y ratio – See *group* and *data : environment ratio*.

Annotated References

Chapter 1: *Play The Game*

1. Snyder, E. E. & Spreitzer, E. A., *Social Aspects of Sports*, Englewood Cliffs, Prentice Hall, 1983
2. Gray, H. B., *The Public Schools and the Empire*, 1913, quoted in Schostak, J., *Schooling and the Violent Imagination*, London, Routledge & Kegan Paul, 1986
3. von Neumann, J. & Morgenstern, O., *The Theory of Games and Economic Behaviour*, Princeton, Princeton Univ. Press, 1947 (originally developed in 1928 and revised in 1944)
4. Miller, D., *Gods and Games: Toward a Theology of Play*, New York, Harper Colophon Books, 1973
5. The following representative quotes illustrate the widely accepted tenet that life and games are analogous:

   Michie, D., *On Machine Intelligence*, Edinburgh, Edinburgh University Press, 1974: 'Real life has the structure of a game ... Mechanized game-playing is studied ... for its value as a model for decision-taking in real life ... Games of mental skill devised by humans for amusement provide the research worker in machine intelligence with ideal material ... all the intellectual faculties in which we pride ourselves are brought into play.'

   Roszak, T., *The Cult of Information*, New York, Pantheon Books, 1986 : '... chess, poker, business investments, thermonuclear war came to be seen as "games" – in the sense that certain general strategies could be applied to all of them. This was a valuable insight into many forms of competition and negotiation, but it was gained at great cost. Around the theory of games, a literature and discourse of military strategy grew up whose authors felt licensed to discuss the annihilation of the human race as casually as one might discuss a hand of cards.'

   Abt. C. C., *Serious Games*, New York, Viking, 1970 : '... wars are very complex processes whose outcomes are usually very uncertain ... In these circumstances no sensible general can afford to plan strategies and tactics, without considering what his adversary might do ... Thus a working [game] model of these reciprocal processes is an essential element in military planning and training.' *Note*: the author is founder and president of a US company that creates 'educational' games for schools and universities and is consultant to the Pentagon on war-gaming.

6. von Clausewitz, C., *On War*, (first published 1832) transl. by Col. F. Maude, London, Routledge & Kegan Paul, 3 vols., 1966; also edited and with an introduction by A. Rapoport, Harmondsworth, Penguin, 1968. The introduction is worth reading, since it shows Rapoport's developing viewpoint.

7. Dawkins, R., *The Selfish Gene*, Oxford, Oxford University Press, 1976

8. Arnold, A., *Violence and Your Child*, New York, Award Books, 1969

9. Benedict, R., *Patterns of Culture*, Boston, Houghton Mifflin Co., 1959 (first published 1934)

10. Asimov, I., *Guide to Science*, vol. 2, Harmondsworth, Penguin, 1975

11. von Neumann & Morgenstern op. cit.

12. Berne, E., *Games People Play*, Harmondsworth, Penguin, 1967

13. Shubik, M., 'Towards a Theory of Threats'; in *Theory of Games – Techniques and Applications*, Proceedings of a conference under the aegis of NATO Scientific Affairs Committee, A. Mensch, ed., Toulon, 1964; London, English University Press, 1966

14. Braithwaite, R. B., *Theory of Games as a Tool for the Moral Philosopher*, Cambridge, Cambridge University Press, 1955

15. von Neumann & Morgenstern op. cit.

Chapter 2: *A Brief History of Games*

1. Green, J. & Atyeo, D., *The Book of Sports Quotes*, London, Omnibus Press, 1979

2. Murray, H. J. R., *A History of Board Games*, Oxford, Clarendon Press, 1952

3. Culin, S., *Games of the Orient*, Tokyo, Charles Tuttle & Co. 1958 (first published 1895). See also by the same author *Korean Games, with notes on the corresponding games in China and Japan*, Philadelphia, University of Pennsylvania, 1895. And see below.

4. Groos, K., *The Play of Man*, transl. by E. L. Baldwin, 1901

5. Huizinga, J., *Homo Ludens*, London, Routledge & Kegan Paul, 1949

6. Plato, *Laws*; vii, 803

7. Temple, R. C., *China*, Wellingborough, Patrick Stephens Press, 1986

8. Culin, S., *The Gambling Games of the Chinese in America*, Philadelphia, University of Pennsylvania, 1891

9. Hone, W., *The Every-Day Book and Table Book or Everlasting Calendar of Popular Amusements, Sports, Pastimes, Ceremonies, Manners, Customs, and Events*, 2 vols., London, Thomas Tegg, 1830, vol. II, p. 1440

10. ibid.

11. ibid.

12. Strutt, J., *The Sports and Pastimes of the People of England*, London, Thomas Tegg & Sons, 1801

13. ibid.
14. ibid.
15. Yerkey, G., 'Dutch Roulette : Scheveningen Casino', Paris, *International Herald Tribune*, 10 Nov 1978. See also Bautell, E., Davenport, H., Robinson, D. & Robinson, J., 'The Casino Whirl in Europe', Paris, *International Herald Tribune*, 31 Aug 1979
16. Lowe, B., 'Social origins of sport predating the first recording of the Olympic games, 776 B.C.' in *The History and Diffusion of Sports and Games in Different Cultures*, Proceedings of the 4th International HISPA Seminar, Leuven, Belgium, 1–5 Apr 1975, Brussels, B.L.O.S.O. 1976
17. Atyeo, D., *Blood and Guts*, London, Paddington Press, 1979
18. ibid.
19. Catlin, G., *Letters and Notes on the North American Indians*, vols. I & II, New York, Dover
20. Atyeo, op. cit.
21. Mangan, J. A., *Athleticism in the Victorian and Edwardian Public School*, Cambridge, Cambridge University Press, 1981
22. Wilson, A., *War-Gaming*, Harmondsworth, Penguin, 1970
23. Allen, T. B., *War-Games*, London, Heinemann, 1987
24. Wilson, op. cit.
25. Rapoport, A., *Strategy and Conscience*, New York, Harper & Row, 1964. See also by the same author together with Chammah, A. M., & Orwant, C. J., *Prisoner's Dilemma – A Study in Conflict and Co-operation*, Ann Arbor, University of Michigan Press, 1965. See also by the same author *Two-Person Game Theory – Essential Ideas*, Ann Arbor, University of Michigan Press, 1966. See also von Clausewitz, op. cit.
26. Cardano, G., *The Book of My Life*, transl. J. Stoner, New York, Dover, 1962. See also Oystein, O., *Cardano, The Gambling Scholar* (includes translation of Cardano's *The Book on Games of Chance*, 1663), New York, Dover, 1965. See also David, F. N., *Games, Gods, and Gambling – The Origins and History of Probability and Statistical Ideas from the Earliest Times to the Newtonian Era*, New York, Hafner, 1962
27. von Neumann & Morgenstern op. cit.
28. Guetzow, H. (ed.), *Simulation in Social Science: Readings*, Englewood Cliffs, Prentice-Hall, 1962
29. Dresher, M., Tucker, A. W. & Wolfe, P. (eds.), *Contributions to the Theory of Games*, vol. IV., Princeton, Princeton University Press, 1957; contains 1,009 entries. For additional refs., see *Index of Selected Publications of The Rand Corporation* and the computer index of the Library of Congress. See also Chapter 9, note 15.
30. Klaus, G. & Liebscher, H., (eds.), *Wörterbuch der Kybernetik*, 2 vols., pp. 741–8, Frankfurt, Fischer Taschenbuch Verlag, 1976 (first published in East Berlin, Dietz Verlag, 1967)

Chapter 3: *Meanings*

1. Green & Atyeo, op. cit.
2. Korzybski, A., *Science and Sanity*, Lakeville, The Institute of General

Semantics, 1973. The author was the founder of the School of General Semantics on the basis of which a form of psychoanalysis – neurolinguistics – was founded.

3. Chuang Tzu, *The Works of Chuang Tzu*, transl. A. Giles, London, Allen & Unwin, 1961 (first published 1889)
4. Toynbee, A., *A Study of History*, London, Thames & Hudson, 1972
5. Mead, M., *Co-operation and Competition Among Primitive Peoples*, New York, McGraw Hill Book Co., 1937
6. Wittgenstein, L., *Philosophical Investigations*, Oxford, Blackwell, 1958
7. Skinner, B. F., *Walden II*, New York, Macmillan, 1962
8. Lorenz, K., *On Aggression*, New York, Bantam Books, 1967
9. Storr, A., *Human Aggression*, London, Allen Lane, 1968

Chapter 4: *Games People Play*

1. Berne, op. cit.
2. Mathews, J., 'It's "War" on L. A.'s Overheated Freeways', Paris, *International Herald Tribune*, 29 July 1978
3. Gunston, J., 'The Closet Commandos Come Out To Play', London, *The Mail on Sunday, You Magazine*, 17 Jan 1988
4. Searle, J., *Minds, Brains and Science*, Reith Lecture, London, BBC Publications, 1984
5. Berne, op. cit.
6. Harris, T. A., *I'm OK – You're OK*, London, Pan Books, 1973
7. Fromm, E., *The Anatomy of Human Destructiveness*, Harmondsworth, Penguin, 1977
8. Barash, D. P., *Sociology and Behavior*, with a foreword by E. O. Wilson, New York, Elsevier, 1977
9. ibid.
10. ibid.
11. See note 20, chapter 8.
12. Barash, op. cit.
13. Hardin, G., *Stalking the Wild Taboo*, Los Altos, California, William Kaufman, 1973
14. Berger, P. L. & Berger, B., *Sociology*, New York, Basic Books, 1972
15. Hardin, op. cit.
16. Huxley, T. H., *Evolution and Ethics*, New York, D. Appleton & Co., 1894
17. Freud, S., *Jokes and their Relation to the Unconscious*, Harmondsworth, Penguin, 1976 (first published 1905)
18. Szasz, T., *Ideology and Insanity*, London, Calder & Boyars, 1973
19. Fromm, op. cit.
20. ibid.
21. Watson, J. D., *The Double Helix*, Harmondsworth, Penguin, 1970
22. Storr, op. cit.
23. ibid.
24. Kraft, I., *NEA Journal*, Washington, DC, National Education Association, Jan 1976, pp. 71–2

25. Chuang Tzu, op. cit.
26. Gee, H., 'Who's for drinks? – Science Reports', London, *The Times*, 2 Feb 1988

Chapter 5: *The Savage Mind*

1. Mangan, op. cit.
2. Lévi-Strauss, C., *The Savage Mind*, London, Weidenfeld & Nicolson, 1966
3. Mead, op. cit.
4. Benedict, op. cit.
5. ibid.
6. Gorer, G., *The Americans*, London, Cresset Press, 1948
7. *Proceedings of the First Colloquium on Personality Investigation*, held under the auspices of the American Psychological Association Committee on Relations of Psychology and the Social Sciences; First: 1–2 Dec 1927, Maryland, Lord Baltimore Press, 1928; Second: 29–30 Nov 1929; publ. ibid, 1930. See also mimeographed report on the same subject by the same organization, Sept 1934
8. Maller, J. B., *Cooperation and Competition: An Experimental Study in Motivation*, New York, Teachers' College Press, 1972 (orig. PhD thesis, published in 1929)
9. Mead, op. cit.
10. ibid.
11. Mirsky, J., 'The Eskimo of Greenland', in Mead, M., op. cit.
12. Goldman, I., 'The Kwakiutl of Vancouver Island', in Mead, M., op.cit.
13. Worsley, P., *The Trumpet Shall Sound; A Study of 'Cargo' Cults in Melanesia*, New York, Schocken Books, 1968
14. Benedict, R., 'Primitive Freedom', *Atlantic Monthly*, CLXIX, No 6, 1942, pp. 756–63
15. ibid.
16. Catlin, op. cit.
17. Lorenz, K., in *Discussions on Child Development*, London, 1955; New York, International University Press, 1958
18. Benedict, R., 'Anthropology and the Abnormal', *Journal of General Psychology*, X : 2 : 59–62, 1934

Chapter 6: *The Random Universe*

1. Pliny, *Natural History*
2. Mumford, L., *The Condition of Man: Prelude to an Era*, London, Secker & Warburg, 1954
3. Bateson, G., *Steps to an Ecology of Mind*, London, Paladin, 1973
4. Mauthner, F., *Wörterbuch der Philosophie*, 2 vols., Zürich, Diogenes Verlag, 1980
5. Bell, E. T., *Men of Mathematics*, London, Victor Gollancz Ltd, 1937

6. Eddington, A. S., *The Nature Of The Physical World*, Cambridge, Cambridge University Press, 1932

7. Leggett, A. J., 'The "Arrow of Time" and Quantum Mechanics' in *The Encyclopaedia of Ignorance*, ed. R. Duncan and M. Weston-Smith, vol. 1, Physical Sciences, Oxford, Pergamon Press, 1977

8. see Appendices B and C

9. Rhine, J. B. & Pratt, J. G., *Parapsychology: Frontier Science of the Mind*, Springfield, Charles C. Thomas, 1957

10. Haken, H. (ed.) *Cooperative Effects – Progress in Synergetics*, lectures given at a summer school at Erice, Sicily, May 1974, New York, American Elsevier Publishing Co. Inc., 1974

11. Einstein, A., *Relativity – The Special and The General Theory*, transl. R. W. Lawson, London, Methuen & Co. Ltd, 1922

12. Lighthill, J., *Artificial Intelligence: A Paper Symposium*, London, The Scientific Research Council, April 1973

13. Lehman, M. M., 'Human Thought and Action as an Ingredient of System Behaviour', in *The Encyclopaedia of Ignorance*, ed. R. Duncan and M. Weston-Smith, vol. 2, Life and Earth Sciences, Oxford, Pergamon Press, 1977

Chapter 7: *Games of So-Called Chance*

1. von Neumann & Morgenstern, op. cit.

2. Wykes, A., *Gambling*, London, Aldus Books, 1964

3. 'Catch-22', New York, *Time Magazine*, Time-Life Publications, 12 Feb. 1979, p. 39

4. Lycett, A., 'Econometric crystal balls', London, *The Times*, 30 Dec. 1986. The remark quoted in the text is taken from this year-end article about forecasts for 1987. Another forecasting expert, James Bellini, former Associate of The Hudson Institute, one of the Pentagon's think-tanks, is also quoted as stating that '[in 1987 there will be a] ... breakthrough in artificial intelligence'. To date no such breakthrough has taken place.

5. Dickinson, A. & Tempterton, C., 'The Operational Numerical Weather Prediction Model, Met. Office 11 Technical Note No. 183, Bracknell: Forecasting Research, Meteorological Office, Jan 1984 (unpubl.)

6. Bramer, M. A. (ed.), *Computer Game Playing; theory and practice*, Ellis Horwood Series in Artificial Intelligence, Chichester, Ellis Horwood, 1983. See chapter 17, pp. 229–255. This chapter deals specifically with poker and is typical of its genre. The editor of this book and its various authors are firmly committed to the idea that 'superior' intelligence and strategies (and not dirty tricks) win games of strategy and chance. Even Scrabble and Othello are considered here and 'artificially intelligent' programs written in attempts to win them. None of the authors seem aware of the fact that any game – even a purely strategic one – turns into a game of chance as soon as conventional winning becomes the criterion of success.

Chapter 8: *Nature Red in Tooth and Claw*

1. Dawkins, R., *The Blind Watchmaker*, Harlow, Longman Scientific & Technical, 1986

2. Monod, J., *Chance and Necessity*, London, Fontana, 1974

3. Tucker, A., Private communication, 1984

4. Tinbergen, N., *Social Behaviour in Animals*, London, Methuen & Co. Ltd, 1953

5. ibid.

6. Altner, G. (ed.), *The Nature of Human Behaviour*, London, George Allen & Unwin, 1976; quoted by Baitch, H., *Future Aspects of Human Genetics*, p. 77

7. Hagberg, K., *Carl Linnaeus*, transl. A. Blair, London, Jonathan Cape, 1952

8. Gruber, H. E., *Darwin on Man – Darwin's Early and Unpublished Notebooks*, annotated by P. H. Barrett, with a foreword by J. Piaget, London, Wildwood House, 1974

9. Galton, F., *Hereditary Genius*, London, The Fontana Library, 1962

10. Eysenck, H. J. & Kamin, L., *Intelligence: The Battle for the Mind*, London, Pan Books, 1981

11. Darwin, C., *Origin of Species*, compiled by I. Manton, with a foreword by his son Major L. Darwin, and with a table of differences between the first, second and sixth final, revised edition, London, 1929. Includes note by Thomas Huxley : '[Darwin] had the noble weakness of thinking too much of other people's doings and too little of his own.' Darwin's son writes: 'Where changes of opinion appear in later editions, they were probably often due to the criticisms of other scientific men.'

12. Spencer, H., *A System of Synthetic Philosophy – The Principles of Ethics*, London, Williams & Norgate, 1900

13. Morris, D., *The Naked Ape*, London, Jonathan Cape, 1967

14. Gorer, G., *Ardrey on Human Nature: Animals, Nations, Imperatives*, New York, Encounter, June 1967

15. Ardrey, R., *African Genesis*, London, Collins/Fontana, 1967

16. ibid.

17. ibid.

18. Marx, K. & Engels, F., *Selected Correspondence 1846–1895*, Engels' letter to F. A. Lange, 29 March 1865, London, Martin Lawrence, 1934

19. Montagu, A. (ed.), *Man and Aggression*, London, Oxford University Press, 1973

20. Lorenz, K., *On Aggression*, op. cit. See Lorenz, K., 'Durch Domestikation verursachte Störungen arteigenen Verhaltens' (Disorders of species-specific behaviour caused by domestication) in *Zeitschrift für angewandte Psychologie und Charakterkunde*, 59, 2–81, 1940. See also 'Die angeboren Formen möglicher Erfahrung (The innate forms of possible experience) by K. Lorenz, in *Zeitschrift für Tierphysiologie*, 5, 235–409, 1943. See also Eisenberg, L., 'The Human Nature of Human Nature'

in *Science*, 176, 123–28, 14 April 1972, and Nisbett, A., *Konrad Lorenz*, London, J. M. Dent & Sons Ltd., 1976, for discussions about Lorenz's 'scientific' support of Nazi doctrine before and during World War II. Lorenz is quoted in Eisenberg:

> The only resistance which mankind of healthy stock can offer . . . against being penetrated by symptoms of degeneracy is based on the existence of certain innate schemata . . . . . . Decadent art provides many examples of such a change of signs . . . The selection for toughness, heroism, social utility . . . must be accomplished by some human institution if mankind, in default of selective factors, is not to be ruined . . . The racial idea as the basis of our state has already accomplished much in this respect . . .

It is noteworthy that Lorenz borrowed Jean Piaget's term 'innate schemata', one that recurs in his post-war writing. The passage cited above was written in 1940 during the Nazi regime in Austria, with concentration camp internment and 'the final solution' for Jews and other *Untermenschen* (sub-humans, according to the Nazi philosophy to which Lorenz lent his 'intellectual' support) well under way with public knowledge within and outside Germany. The 'decadent art' to which Lorenz refers included not only 'Jewish' art, but all of the late Impressionists, including Munch (a Norwegian), whose works Hitler banned.

21. Eibl-Eibesfeld, I., *The Biology of Peace & War, Men, Animals and Aggression*, transl. E. Mosbacher, London, Thames and Hudson, 1979
22. Dawkins, R., *The Selfish Gene*, op.cit.
23. ibid.
24. ibid.
25. Morris, D., & Marsh, P., *Tribes*, Pyramid Books. Excerpted in London, *The Times*, 18 Sept 1988

Chapter 9: *Games of Pure Strategy*

1. Aleksander, I. & Burnett, P., *Reinventing Man – The Robot Becomes Reality*, Harmondsworth, Penguin, 1984
2. Waltz, D., 'Artificial Intelligence', New York, *Scientific American*, Oct 1982
3. Menabrea, L. F., *Taylor's Scientific Memoirs*, vol. III, pp. 666–731, transl. by the Countess of Lovelace, Bibliothèque Universelle, No 82, 10, 1842; reprinted in Bowden, B. V., *Faster Than Thought*, London, Pitman & Sons, 1953
4. Babbage, C., *Passages from the Life of a Philosopher*, London, Longman, Green, 1864
5. 'Tit-tat-to by machinery', *The Builder*, London, George Goodwin, vol. XXXVI, 23 Nov 1887, p. 1224
6. The most celebrated automaton of the eighteenth century was The

Great Turk Chess Player, invented in 1769 by a Baron von Kempelen. A great many legends have grown up around this machine. Only two hundred years later it is claimed that when computers can defeat every chess-master, the concept of artificial intelligence will have been proven.

One of the earliest descriptions of this automaton appeared in a letter to *The Gentleman's Magazine*, vol. 41, 1771, pp. 26–7. It is remarkably like more recent claims made for chess-playing, intelligent computers.

Von Kempelen, alias Kempett, eventually sold his chess-playing automaton to M. M. Maelzl who continued to exhibit it throughout Europe as late as 1820, at which time its mechanism still remained a mystery. Napoleon is said to have played against The Great Turk and lost. The Rev. Cartwright was inspired to persevere in his invention of the power loom by accounts of the chess-playing automaton that had reached him. The Great Turk kept on winning until the day someone shouted 'fire' while a game was in progress, or so the legend goes.

A panel opened on one side of the cabinet on which the chessboard rested, supposedly containing the secret mechanism. It certainly did contain it, for the latest in a succession of cramped, human chess champions emerged and ran out of doors. He and his predecessors had been hunched inside the base, making their moves by inserting one arm into the hollow one of the dummy. Sir David Brewster described and illustrated how this may have been achieved in his *Letters to Sir Walter Scott on Natural Magic*, London, John Murray, 1832. Edgar Allen Poe insisted that Maelzl's automaton could not be a true chess machine because: '. . . it sometimes lost a game . . . Were the machine a pure machine . . . it would always win.' (Cf. notes 18 and 21 below.)

7. de Latil, P., *Thinking Machine*, transl. Y. M. Golla, with a foreword by I. Asimov, Boston, Houghton Mifflin, 1957. Contains an account of a game between Quevedo's chess-playing machine and Norbert Wiener at the 1951 Cybernetic Congress in Paris. The machine won, as it must, given the limited end game for which it was designed. As Turing wrote (note 8.): '. . . with a rook and a king [Quevedo's chess automaton] can checkmate an opponent with a single king. This machine avoids stalemates very cleverly and always wins its games.'

8. Turing, A. M., 'Digital Computers Applied to Games', pp. 263–310 in *Faster Than Thought*, B. V. Bowden (ed.), Pitman & Sons, 1953

9. Michie, D., *On Machine Intelligence*, Edinburgh, Edinburgh University Press, 1974

10. Trackman, I., *The Computer Programme – Program 2*, London, BBC Micro-soft cassette/booklet, 1982. This booklet claims to explain how a computer can 'learn to win' at best and, at worst, not to lose: 'It is not particularly difficult to design a program so that the computer can play noughts and crosses without losing.' The author continues: 'One of the ways in which we learn is by experience – we remember events, recall

them (more or less accurately) at a later date and act accordingly to our memorized experience. Our program does the same . . . what might happen if instead of random moves, we gave the opponent program the best winning strategy that we could discover? If the learning program then found a way to win, should we say that it had become cleverer than us [sic] ? . . . Using the same "learning" strategy, you might like to tackle other simple positional games, such as the traditional English game of nine men's morris or fox and geese.'

11. George, F., *Man The Machine*, London, Granada, 1979
12. Rapoport, A., *Fights, Games and Debates*, Ann Arbor, University of Michigan Press, 1960. See also titles listed under note 25, chapter 2.
13. Zaslavsky, C., *Tic-Tac-Toe*, New York, Thomas Y. Crowell, 1982. Other statements in this book include: '. . . Helping an opponent to improve his or her skills makes the game more interesting for both players. Each player should have an equal chance of winning. In some games the first player to move is more likely to win . . . A smart computer will never lose a game of tic-tac-toe . . . Psychologists have found that some young people set out to win, while the more timid children only play for a draw.' Cf. Sutton-Smith below.
14. Rice, P. M., 'Local Strategies and Equilibria with an Application to the Committee Decision Process', *Journal of Game Theory*, vol. 8 : 1, pp. 1–12, Vienna, Physica Verlag, 1979
15. Sutton-Smith, B. & Avedon, E. M., 'Achievement and Strategic Competence' in *The Study of Games*, B. Sutton-Smith (ed.), New York, Wiley, 1971
16. Turkle, S., *The Second Self*, London, Granada, 1984
17. Packard, V., *The People Shapers*, London, MacDonald & Jane's, 1978
18. The following citations concern different views – and historical facts – concerning the value of 'winning', achieving a draw or a stalemate in chess as a sign of human or machine 'intelligence':

     Newell, A., Shaw, J. C., & Simon, H. A., 'Chess Playing Programs and the Problem of Complexity' in *Computers and Thought*, E. A. Feigenbaum & J. Feldman (eds), New York, McGraw-Hill, 1963, p. 39. The authors cite Shannon, C., 'Automatic Chess Player', *Scientific American*, Feb 1950: 182: 48, and 'Programming a Digital Computer for Playing Chess', *Philosophy Magazine*, March 1950, 41 : 356–375. They state: 'As Shannon observed, chess is a finite game . . . Thus chess can be described as a branching tree. It is intuitively clear, and easily proven, that for a player who can view the entire tree and see all ultimate consequences of each alternative, chess becomes a simple game'.

     Brule, J. F., in *Artificial Intelligence: Theory, Logic and Application*, Blue Ridge Summit, Pa., 1986 (pp. 82–3), maintains that there are 20 possible moves in chess at each player's first turn; 400 at the second and 8,000 at the third. According to him, by the 20th turn the number of options will have increased to 2×10^{26}. In go the 20th turn generates 4 million times as many options as in chess.

Bremermann, H. J., in an article 'Complexity And Transcomputability', *Encyclopedia of Ignorance*, vol. 1, op. cit. writes: 'In . . . artificial intelligence, the excessive computational cost [in terms of time] of known algorithms has been the main obstacle to having, for example, computers play perfect games of chess (or checkers or go).' The author does not define what he means by 'perfect'. One can only assume that he is referring to a computer program that can defeat every chess-master. See Hofstadter below.

Murray, H. J. R., *A Short History of Chess*; with chapters by B. Goulding Brown & H. Golombek, Oxford, Clarendon Press, 1964. According to these authors certain (unspecified) conditions of play 'increased the probability of the draw, the theoretical ending of any well-played game . . .' This game ending that we know as the 'draw' was referred to as *tabula* (Latin) in medieval central Europe and as *tavola* in Italy (no connection with backgammon) but not in any other dialect or language (see Chapter 3). By 1450 a stalemate counted as a draw in Italy and Germany, and as a half-win in Spain (as today, according to FIDE rules). Before 1600 a stalemate was counted as a full win in England.

19. Aleksander & Burnett, op.cit.
20. Newell, A., Shaw, J. C. & Simon, H. A., 'Chess-playing Programs and the Problem of Complexity', in *Computers and Thought*, E. A. Feigenbaum & J. Feldman (eds.), New York, McGraw-Hill, 1963
21. Hofstadter, D. R., *Gödel, Escher, Bach: An Eternal Golden Braid*, Harmondsworth, Penguin, 1980. On p. 573 Hofstadter writes : '. . . is intelligence the ability to play chess well ? If so, then AI [artificial intelligence] is well on its way, since chess-playing programs can defeat most good amateurs; and the level of artificial chess will probably continue to improve slowly.' On p. 678 the author declares: 'Question: Will there be chess programs that can beat anyone ? Speculation: No. There may be programs which can beat anyone at chess, but they will not be exclusively chess players. They will be programs of general intelligence . . .'
22. Levy, D., quoted in Bolter, D., *Turing's Man : Western Culture in the Computer Age*, London, Duckworth, 1984
23. Bramer, M. A. (ed.), *Computer Game-Playing : theory and practice*, Chichester, Ellis Horwood, 1983
24. Michie, D. & Johnston, R., *The Creative Computer*, New York, Viking, 1984
25. Michie, D., *On Machine Intelligence*, op. cit.
26. Spanier, D., *Total Chess*, London, Secker and Warburg, 1984
27. Hofstadter, op. cit.
28. Spanier, op.cit.
29. Samuel, A. L., 'Some Studies In Machine Learning Using The Game of Checkers', in *Computers and Thought*, E. Feigenbaum and J. Feldman (eds.), New York, McGraw-Hill, 1963

30. McCorduck, P., *Machines Who Think*, San Francisco, W. H. Freeman & Co., 1979

31. Feigenbaum, E. & McCorduck, P., *The Fifth Generation*, London, Michael Joseph, 1984

32. Dreyfus, H. L. & Dreyfus, S. E., *Mind Over Machine*, Oxford, Basil Blackwell, 1986

33. Rapoport, A., see titles listed under note 25, chapter 2. See also Meek, R. L., *Figuring Out Society*, London, Fontana, 1971; Brams, S. J., *Superpower Games*, New Haven, Yale University Press, 1985

34. Axelrod, R., *The Evolution of Cooperation*, New York, Basic Books, 1981

35. Personal communication.

36. Bennett, P. G. & Dando, M. R., 'The Arms Race: is it just a mistake?' London, *New Scientist*, 17 Feb 1983

37. Smith, J. M., *Evolution and the Theory of Games*, Cambridge, Cambridge University Press, 1982. The author believes that while co-operation plays a role in evolution, relationships are primarily governed by conflicts of interest. In a chapter called 'The evolution of co-operation', Smith seems to share Axelrod's view (see note 34) that co-operation is not innate and requires special education in human and other species.

38. Brams, S. J., *Biblical Games: A Strategic Analysis of Stories in The Old Testament*, Cambridge, MIT Press, 1980. Starting with the Book of Genesis, the author, a well-known game theorist, analyses the Bible in terms of zero-sum gaming. He discusses, for example: '. . . the creation game (*player : God*) . . . the constraint game (*players : God vs Adam and Eve*) . . . the temptation game (*players : serpent vs Eve*) . . . the sharing game (*players : Eve vs Adam*) . . .' Note that according to this author ALL games, except the creation game, are played *vs* (i.e. against) and never *with* one another by the players, thus pitting Eve 'against' Adam, even in a 'sharing' game, as well as God against his own creations – Hobbes' war of 'all against all' carried to its ultimate conclusion.

39. Bennett & Dando, op. cit.

Chapter 10: *The Sporting Life*

1. Atyeo, op. cit.

2. Zohar, D., 'McEnroe : match point against Freud', London, *Sunday Times*, 11 July 1982

3. Evans, R., *McEnroe : A Rage for Perfection*, London, Sidgwick & Jackson, 1982

4. Zohar, op. cit.

5. Freeman, S., 'One mouth-fault and McEnroe will be out, says Wimbledon', London, *Sunday Times*, 29 May 1983

6. 'Four Big Names of Tennis Turn Gambling Racketeers', Paris, *International Herald Tribune*, 26 Nov 1987

7. Eitzen, D. S. & Sage, G. H., *Sociology of American Sport*, Dubuque, Wm C. Brown Co., 1978

8. Gaier, E. L., 'The Self-Concept of the Winner : What if the Dream Comes True?' in *The Winning Edge*; Proceedings of the First National Sports Psychology Conference, 18–20 May 1973, Buffalo, NY; W. C. Schwank (ed.), Washington, DC, The National Education Association, 1974

9. Korzybski, op. cit.

10. Green & Atyeo, op. cit.

11. Snyder & Spreitzer, op. cit.

12. Snyder & Spreitzer, op. cit.

13. The effect on children and young people of these sports attitudes over a period of time are reflected in the following typical stories:

   Hopkins, J., 'How to destroy a great game', London, *Sunday Times*, 18 Nov 1978 : 'Since 1974 there has been an average of one [case of paralysis as a result of rugby injuries] each season, and this season there have already been two . . . Clearly the dirty practices of senior rugby have seeped down to schoolboy games . . . Ron Tennick, secretary of the Rugby Football School's Union : ". . . Before the game, sir [the football coach] is banging the table in the changing-room shouting, 'Come on boys, you've got to win.' Now winning has become the most important thing in schools." ' Five years later this situation had clearly worsened:

   Deely, P., 'Alarm raised over injuries in mini-rugby', London, *Observer*, 5 Aug 1983 : 'Indoctrinating eight-year-old rugby players with a "win-at-all-costs", spirit poses the danger of serious accidents on the field, according to a leading junior rugby coach . . . In the last 18 months the school committee of the Rugby Football Union has reports of two deaths and seven cases of serious paralysis during games.'

14. Atyeo, op. cit.

15. Gaskell, G. & Pearton, R., 'Aggression and Sport', in *Sports, Games and Play – Social and Psychological Viewpoints*, J. H. Goldstein (ed.), Hillsdale, Lawrence Erlbaum Associates, 1979

   A typical excuse was made by a former soccer hooligan – Taylor, E., 'I was a soccer hooligan – Class of '64', London, *Guardian*, 28 March 1984 : 'Football hooliganism is simply a contemporary way in which many of today's youngsters go through the process known as growing up; and so far from being "anti-social idiocy" it is a way of learning about those bonds of loyalty, commitment, friendship, rivalry, and group identity that tie society together.'

16. Arnold, op. cit.

17. Green & Atyeo, op. cit.

18. Eitzen & Sage, op. cit.

19. Jenkins, I., 'If you go down in the woods today . . .', London, *Observer*, 18 Nov 1984

Chapter 11: *Winning and Losing and The Dismal Science*

1. von Neumann & Morgenstern, op.cit. The following is typical of the conventional appraisal of von Neumann & Morgenstern's work:

Morton, G., 'Electronic Machines and Economics', in B. V. Bowden (ed.), *Faster Than Thought*, Pitman & Sons, London, 1953: 'When J. von Neumann and O. Morgenstern published the Theory of Games and Economic Behaviour in 1944, economics took a long stride forward. For electronic machines provide simplified models of economic behaviour. The inter-relation between man and machine is strengthened by the fact that machines can be made to play games and that economic life can be thought of as "solving" highly complicated computational problems.'

However, W. C. Fields, the film comedian, although hardly a professional economist and probably quite unaware of these authors and their work, put all of this more succinctly : 'Business [seen in the von Neumann and Morgenstern context] is an establishment that gives you the legal, even though unethical, right to screw the naïve – right, left and in the middle.'

2. Arrow, K. J., 'Mathematical Models in the Social Sciences' in *Journal of General Systems*, Yearbook of the Society for the Advancement of General Systems Theory, Ludwig von Bertalanffy & Anatol Rapoport (eds.), Ann Arbor, Society for the Advancement of General Systems, vol. 1, 1956

3. Von Neumann & Morgenstern, op. cit.

4. Arrow, op. cit. See footnote 5. 'Credit for the first significant use of mathematics in economics, is due to the great French economist Augustin Cournot, who published in 1838 his *Recherches sur les Principes mathématiques de la théorie des richesses*. His work was largely neglected. It was the contribution of W. Stanley Jevons in *The Theory of Political Economy* (1871) and especially the contribution of Leon Walras in *Elements d'economie politique pure* (1874), which brought the power of the mathematical methods to the attention of the economists . . .'

However, because these mathematical techniques were basically statistical, they merely looked back into the past (it is all statistical methods can do) and offered no predictive options for the future. The methods given in Appendices A and B of this book provide both hindsight and foresight within any finite system.

5. Weintraub, E. R., *Conflict and Cooperation in Economics*, London, Macmillan, 1975

6. Smith, A., *The Wealth of Nations*, A. Skinner (ed.), Harmondsworth, Penguin, 1970 (first published 1776)

7. Friedman, M., *Free to Choose*, London, Secker & Warburg, 1980. The author, deeply committed to total freedom (see Chapter 3 – the MIT student game example), complains because: 'As consumers, we are not even free to choose how to spend the part of our income that is left after taxes . . . to buy cyclamates or laetrile, and soon, perhaps, saccharine . . . We are not free to buy an automobile without seat belts . . .'

We are also not free to drive while drunk, go through red lights or run people down with our cars and leave them in the road to suffer and die. It is clear that Friedman, like others who admire him, does not understand the conditional nature of freedom. US Chief Justice Holmes was very clear on the subject when he stated that you are not allowed (i.e. you are not free) to shout 'fire' in a crowded theatre. This is not a limitation on freedom but one of its essential characteristics. You have total conditioning and a shrinking of options – as now – when these rules and conditions are lacking, are not agreed to, and are not understood.

8. Galbraith, J. K., *The New Industrial State*, London, Hamish Hamilton, 1967
9. ibid.
10. Manchester, W., *The Arms of Krupp*, New York, Bantam Books, 1970
11. Thurow, L. C., *The Zero-Sum Society*, Harmondsworth, Penguin, 1982
12. Thurow, L. C., *The Zero-Sum Solution*, Harmondsworth, Penguin, 1987
13. Von Neumann & Morgenstern, op. cit.
14. Wiener, N., *Cybernetics*, New York, Wiley, 1948. In this book the author had unkind words to say about von Neumann and Morgenstern's principles of rational behaviour. He objected to zero-sum gaming and realized, like Thurow (op. cit.), that a co-operative principle was the only certain guide to a sane society. However, Wiener is also a typical example of conditioning, for after castigating von Neumann for his competitive principles, he devoted a sizeable appendix of this book to an attempted winning computer chess program. See also de Latil, op. cit.

Chapter 12: *Peace or War – The Biggest Game of All*

1. von Clausewitz, op.cit.
2. Spencer, op. cit.
3. George, F., *Man The Machine*, Granada, 1979
4. Hayes, P. J., 'The Frame Problem and Related Problems in Artificial Intelligence', in *Artificial and Human Thinking*: Proceedings of a Nato Symposium entitled 'Human Thinking: Computer Techniques for its Evaluation', A. Elithorn & D. Jones (eds), Amsterdam, Elsevier, 1973
5. Atyeo, op. cit.
6. ibid.
7. Evans, C., *The Mighty Micro*, London, Gollancz, 1979
8. Holmes, R., *Firing Line*, London, Cape, 1985. Quotes Joost van Meerlo, p. 273, Glenn J. Gray, p. 394 and from the US My-Lai hearings.
9. ibid.
10. Just, W., *Military Men*, New York, Avon Books, 1970
11. Vagts, A., *A History of Militarism – Civilian and Military*, London, Hollis & Carter, 1959
12. James, W., 'The Moral Equivalent of War', in *Memories and Studies*, New York, Longmans, Green & Co., 1911
13. Wells, H. G., *First and Last Things*, New York, G. P. Putnam's Sons, 1908

14. Lucas, J., *Kommando – German Special Forces in World War II*, Chap. 2, 'Pretext for War', London, Arms & Armour Press, 1985

15. Eibl-Eibesfeld, op. cit.

16. ibid.

17. Freud, S., 'Why War?' in *Sigmund Freud, Collected Papers* transl. Stuart Gilbert, New York, Basic Books, 1959. This exchange of letters between Einstein and Freud was initiated in 1932 by the International Institute of Intellectual Co-operation, a branch of the League of Nations, who asked Einstein to correspond with anyone he chose on the issue of prevention of war. Einstein chose Freud whom he admired. Freud's views are clearly social Darwinist and authoritarian. Cited without identification of the author of this letter, it might have been written by any despot:

    'Thus we see that, even within the group itself, the exercise of violence cannot be avoided when conflicting interests are at stake . . .'

    Freud recognized no society other than his own, no instincts other than sex (seen as materialistic gratification only), self-hate (i.e. the death wish), and could not conceive of the actual meanings of love, play, creativity and peace – the draw state in any frame of reference. According to him the human psyche is composed of competing and conflicting interests – sexual surrender and possession, losing and winning made complex by the introduction of irrelevant or secondary causes (past, real and fantasized trauma).

18. ibid.

19. ibid.

20. Rosenberg, M., *Occupations and Values*, Glencoe, III, Free Press, 1957, quoted in Dixon, N. F., *On the Psychology of Military Incompetence*, London, Cape, 1976

21. Asprey, R. B., *War in the Shadows*, London, MacDonald & Jane's, 1975

22. Zuckerman, S., *Nuclear Illusion and Reality*, London, Collins, 1982

23. Teller, E., *The Pursuit of Simplicity*, Los Angeles, Pepperdine University Press, 1980

24. Wilson, op. cit.

25. Allen, op. cit.

26. ibid.

27. von Clausewitz, op. cit.

28. Feigenbaum & McCorduck, op. cit.

29. Sun Tzu, *The Art of War*, transl. and with an introduction by S. B. Griffith; foreword by B. H. Liddell Hart, London, Oxford University Press, 1971

30. ibid.

31. Machiavelli, N., *The Discourses*, B. Crick (ed.); transl. by L. J. Walker with revisions by B. Richardson, Harmondsworth, Penguin, 1981

32. Dixon, N. F., *On the Psychology of Military Incompetence*, London, Cape, 1976

33. Asprey, op. cit.

34. Arnold, op. cit.
35. Gunston, J., 'The Closet Commando Come Out To Play', London, *The Mail On Sunday : You Magazine*, 17 Jan 1988
36. Malone, P. (ed.), 'Playtime for Gunman Pat', London, *Observer Magazine*, 13 Dec 1987

Conclusions

1. Rapoport, A., L., *Uses and Limitations of Mathematical Models in Social Sciences*, Symposium on Sociological Theory, L. Gross (ed.), Evanston, Illinois, Row, Peterson, 1959
2. von Bertalanffy, L. *General Systems Theory*, Harmondsworth, Penguin, 1971
3. Beer, S., *Platform for Change*, London, Wiley, 1975
4. Ashby, W. R., *An Introduction to Cybernetics*, London, Chapman & Hall, 1956

Appendix B: *Combinatorial Neural-Networks*

1. Khachian, L. G., *A Polynomial Algorithm in Linear Programming*, Moscow, Soviet Math., Dokl., vol. 20, 1, 1979
2. Karmarkar, N., in *Combinatorica*, 4 : 4, 373–92, 1984. See also 'Linear Programming made simpler than Simplex', *New Scientist*, 6 Dec 1984 and Devlin, K., *Mathematics: The New Golden Age*, Harmondsworth, Penguin, 1988

Index of Names

Subject Index

Notes

1. Bold numerals refer to the Glossary of Terms.
2. Individual games and sports are listed under 'games' and 'sports' respectively.
3. Combinatorial (neural-network) classification criteria are listed under 'classification, combinatorial sum'.

accident, 66, 70, 120, 169, 176–7, 181, 196, 235, **374**

advantage, 71–2, 103, 159, 181, 202, 216, 298, 327
first turn –, 204, 334–6; *see also* chess, noughts and crosses, prisoner's dilemma

Afghanistan, 39, 117, 285, 293, 304

Africa, 33, 40, 64, 105, 116, 293

aggression, 29, 41, 53–60, 65–6, 71, 82–7, 106, 109, 117, 167–9, 192, 199, 204, 208, 236, 288, 306

agreement-to-agree; *see* draw
– to disagree, 60, 198, 322, 336; *see also* stalemates

algorithm, **375**

alliances, 63, 172, 254, 271, 298, 301–2

altruism, 17, 21, 28, 48, 74–7, 84, 86, 181, 189, 193, 199, 205, 220, 257, 286, 288

America, North; *see* Canada, Indian, United States

America, Central, 144, 293, 304

amoral, **375**

analysis, 45, 49, 52, 67–8, 72, 91, 107, 156, 271, 314–15, 319, 346, 337–73, **375**; *see also* classification, combinatorial
behavioural –, 68–97, 316, 320
causal/consequential/operational –, 49, 51–2, 54, 66–8, 72, 81, 92, 198, 253, 276, 286, 315, 324; *see also* causes, consequences, meanings

shortest path –, 337–73

systematic –, 145, 176; *see also* cards, order

systems –, 45, 296, 309, 346

Arabia, 33, 116

arrangement, systematic, 143, 167, 299; *see also* cards, order

art, 18, 67, 74, 81–2, 84, 113, 184, 227, 279, 289, 302, 309, 334

artificial intelligence, 21, 137, 194, 200–201, 205, 215, 221, 279, 281, 289–90, 293, 295–7, 304, 307, 337, 340

Ashanti, 117

Assyria, 33

Athens, 33

attack, 65, 87, 181, 286, 298, 302–3, 343; *see also* aggression, first strike
counter –, 71

attention, 20, 71, 128, 130, 145–6, 153, 176, 178, 204, 239, 270, 333, 335
in –, 147, 151

Australia, 33, 105, 186

Austria, 37, 80

automation, 260–65; *see also* robots

balance, 89, 116–17, 136, 143, 165, 178, 180–81, 183, 324, **375**

battle, 70, 103, 293; *see also* military, war

behaviour, 13, 28, 56, 70, 72, 81, 87, 115, 119, 123, 138, 173, 180, 191,